COMBINATORIAL LOTTERY SYSTEMS (WHEELS) with GUARANTEED WINS

Iliya Bluskov, Ph. D.

LOTBOOK

All inquires should be addressed to:

Lotbook Publishing
1557 4th Avenue, Suite 1088
Prince George, B.C.
V2L 3K1 Canada

National Library of Canada Cataloguing in Publication Data

Bluskov, Iliya, 1957-
Combinatorial lottery systems (wheels) with guaranteed wins

ISBN 0-9689502-0-5

1. Lotteries--Statistical methods. 2. Gambling systems. I. Title.
HG6111.B58 2001 795.3'8 C2001-911298-X

Printed in Canada

Contents

Introduction

Lotteries

> Life is finite. Time is infinite. The probability that I am alive today is zero. In spite of this, I am now alive. Now, how is that?
>
> Albert Einstein

Unlike the curious example of Einstein, the lottery is finite and the probability of winning the jackpot is greater than zero, approximately $1/14,000,000$ in a $6/49$ lottery. The chances of winning smaller prizes are much better. That is why, in the quest for the elusive Jackpot, many players prefer to play with a well-organized group of tickets, so that they can win guaranteed smaller prizes. This book presents an interesting and precise strategy for playing the lottery, called a lottery system. Although lottery systems have been created using advanced mathematics, they are very easy to use. In fact, you do need not have ANY mathematical knowledge aside from counting... The lottery systems will be thoroughly explained in what follows. First, let us briefly discuss what a lottery is. A **lottery** is a game where one has to correctly guess several numbers (usually 3 or more) drawn from a larger set (currently there are lotteries with 25,26,27, etc., up to 69 numbers) in order to win a prize. This book discusses lotteries where 6 numbers are drawn out of a larger set of numbers (anywhere between 25 and 69). However, you can use the lottery systems in this book for ANY such lottery in the world. You can even use the systems for playing 7-numbers-drawn lotteries, by adding a power number (a number that is present in all of your tickets).

Let us concentrate on 6-numbers-drawn lotteries. Players fill out **slips** containing one or more **tables** with all of the numbers of the lottery. We also refer to these tables as **tickets**. (Other sources use terms such as games, plays, or boards.) A **combination** is the set of 6 numbers filled in a particular table. When the draw comes, 6 numbers are drawn arbitrarily from the set of all numbers in the lottery. Players win whenever they correctly guess 3 or more of the numbers drawn in one of their tickets. The number of tables on a slip does not matter for the application of our lottery systems.

Lottery Systems

Players from all over the world have been using lottery systems for many years. Lottery systems are **the most entertaining and well-organized way** to play lotteries. This book introduces the best-known lottery systems (also called trapping systems, or wheeling systems, or **wheels**, or coverings).

Suppose for example, you want to play with 10 numbers instead of just 6. Naturally, you are willing to play more than one ticket. However, you want a certain guarantee. Let us say that you want a 4-win whenever 4 of the numbers drawn are in your set of 10 numbers. This means you want a set of combinations (tickets) that covers every possible quadruple out of your 10 numbers. Such a set of combinations is what we call a lottery system. In this example, the lottery system has the property that any quadruple out of your set of 10 numbers is contained in at least one of your combinations, so you get a guaranteed 4-win whenever 4 of your 10 numbers are drawn. You can find a lottery system with this property under # 20 in the book.

In a sense, a lottery system expands the guarantee that you have on playing just 6 numbers (one ticket). If you correctly guess 4 numbers, you are guaranteed a 4-win. The lottery system in our example guarantees a 4-win on 4 numbers guessed correctly, playing with 10 numbers. (In this book we present systems with 4 on 4 guarantee for playing anywhere between 7 and 19 numbers.)

Guarantees

All of the lottery systems presented in this book have certain guarantees. Let me explain what the advantages of using a lottery system are and what exactly a **guarantee** is in terms of a lottery system. Using a lottery system assumes that you are playing with more than six numbers, and you want to organize your numbers in such a way that a certain minimum win is guaranteed. If you play with just one ticket and you correctly guess 4 numbers, then you are guaranteed exactly one 4-win. A possible question is how to build a system that will guarantee a 4-win on 4 guessed numbers, if you play with not 6 but say, 10 numbers. Let us look at our previous example from the book, System # 20. Using System # 20 you get a 4-win whenever 4 of your 10 numbers are among the 6 numbers drawn. The system shows that you only need 20 combinations (or 20 tickets) to do so. Out of 10 numbers, one can form 210 distinct sextuples (the non-mathematicians can take my word for it; those with some math preparation could apply the formula $\binom{10}{6} = 210$). Therefore, you only need to play 20 of these 210 combinations to achieve the 4 if 4 guarantee. What are the advantages of playing for such a guaranteed win? Let us compare playing with 20 random tickets against 20 tickets chosen according to our lottery system. We should mention that the probability of a 6-win ("hitting the jackpot") is the same for each ticket. However, if any 4 of the numbers drawn are among the 10 numbers chosen by you, then the 20 tickets of the lottery system guarantee at least one 4-win, while 20 random tickets (on the same 10 numbers) guarantee nothing!

Minimality

Now we take the opportunity to mention one important quality of all lottery systems in the book. It concerns the following question: How many tickets have to be played in order to have a certain guarantee? Clearly, you want to achieve this guarantee in the minimum number of tickets possible. Well, you have bought the right book: **All of our systems use the minimum known number of tickets**. These systems are combinatorial objects that have been extensively studied, and most of the systems in this book are not likely to ever be improved. Some of the systems represent classical results in combinatorics; others originate from recent research. Many of the systems have been obtained by the author and described in depth in a series of scientific papers. Others have been obtained via hundreds of hours of programming and computations. As a result, all of the systems are currently the best (in the minimum number of tickets) known. For some of the systems we can say even more: They are **mathematically minimal**, meaning that no further improvement (that is, reducing the number of tickets while preserving the guarantee) can ever be done.

Let us look once more at our example, System # 20. It has been proven that the minimum number of tickets is 20 for the given guarantee. In other words, if you want to play 10 numbers and you want a guaranteed 4-win if 4 of your 10 numbers are drawn, then you need to play at least 20 tickets. System # 20 achieves this guarantee in exactly 20 tickets, and this is the minimum possible number of tickets. That is why we call such a system mathematically minimal.

Tables Of Wins

A new feature and a very important quality of this book is the full table of possible wins for each of the systems presented. The tables give the distribution of wins in all possible draws and are excellent tools for determining which system to choose and what could the expected win be once you hit some (usually at least three) of the numbers drawn. Let us take a look at the table of possible wins for System # 20. Each line represents a possible distribution of wins. The last column shows the probability of the corresponding distribution of wins.

Winning possibilities

Guessed	**6**	**5**	**4**	**3**	%
6	1	-	12	4	2.38
	1	-	10	8	7.14
	-	3	8	7	28.57
	-	3	7	9	28.57
	-	2	9	8	28.57
	-	-	15	2	4.77
5	-	1	4	10	23.81
	-	1	3	11	23.81
	-	-	7	6	23.81
	-	-	5	11	23.81
	-	-	5	10	4.76
4	-	-	3	4	2.38
	-	-	3	2	4.76
	-	-	2	7	28.57
	-	-	1	9	28.57
	-	-	1	8	35.72
3	-	-	-	5	8.33
	-	-	-	4	16.67
	-	-	-	3	75.00

If you play System # 20 and 4 of your 10 numbers are drawn, then the system guarantees you at least one 4-win. However, you will actually win more than the guaranteed one 4-win: There are five possibilities that are clearly seen from the table. You can either get one 4-win and either 8 or 9 3-wins with probabilities 35.72% or 28.57%, correspondingly, or you can get two 4-wins and seven 3-wins (probability 28.57%), or three 4-wins and either two or four 3-wins with probabilities 4.76% or 2.38% correspondingly. Similarly, if you correctly guess only three numbers, you get at least three 3-wins, or more precisely, three 3-wins with probability 75%, four 3-wins with probability 16.67%, or five 3-wins (probability 8.33%). For those of you who are not familiar with probabilities we include a brief explanation: Suppose you have played long enough with the same system and hit 3 of the numbers many times. Then, in approximately 75 out of 100 cases, you will have three 3-wins, in 17(16.67, to be precise) out of 100 cases, you will have four 3-wins, and in 8(8.33, to be precise) out of 100 cases, you will get five 3-wins.

Presenting individually every line in the full table is not always physically possible; in many cases the full table would contain up to several thousands entries. In such cases I have presented an abbreviated table. An abbreviated table still comprises all possible distributions of wins, but most of the lines in such a table actually represent several lines from the full table. I have chosen to keep distinction between the highest prizes. For example, had the table for System # 20 been much longer, we could have written the abbreviated 6-wins section as

Guessed	**6**	**5**	**4**	**3**	%
6	1	-	10-12	4-8	9.52
	-	3	7-8	7-9	57.14
	-	2	9	8	28.57
	-	-	15	2	4.77

instead of

Guessed	**6**	**5**	**4**	**3**	%
6	1	-	12	4	2.38
	1	-	10	8	7.14
	-	3	8	7	28.57
	-	3	7	9	28.57
	-	2	9	8	28.57
	-	-	15	2	4.77

We can justify such abbreviations by observing that what matters most are the highest-ranked prizes (those in the leftmost non-empty column of the corresponding part of the table). What you get in lower-ranked prizes is usually just a small percentage of the entire win.

Playing With The Systems

Playing with the systems is very easy: In our example (System # 20), where you play with 10 numbers, you just **(1)** write the numbers from 1 to 10 in a line (these are the numbers in the original system), then **(2)** write your 10 numbers in a line below the first one, and finally, **(3)** substitute each number in the original system with the corresponding number from the second line to obtain your set of tickets. Now, it only remains to **(4)** fill your combinations in the playing slips. For example, if you choose your 10 numbers to be 3,7,12,14,18,22,29,33,40, and 46, then you will write

Numbers in the original system:	1	2	3	4	5	6	7	8	9	10
Your numbers:	3	7	12	14	18	22	29	33	40	46

Original system:							**Your set of tickets:**						
1.	1	2	3	4	8	9	1.	3	7	12	14	33	40
2.	1	2	3	5	6	7	2.	3	7	12	18	22	29
3.	1	2	3	5	9	10	3.	3	7	12	18	40	46
4.	1	2	4	5	8	10	4.	3	7	14	18	33	46
5.	1	2	4	6	7	8	5.	3	7	14	22	29	33
6.	1	2	6	7	9	10	6.	3	7	22	29	40	46
7.	1	3	4	5	6	10	7.	3	12	14	18	22	46
8.	1	3	4	5	7	8	8.	3	12	14	18	29	33
9.	1	3	5	6	8	9	9.	3	12	18	22	33	40
10.	1	3	7	8	9	10	10.	3	12	29	33	40	46
11.	1	4	5	7	9	10	11.	3	14	18	29	40	46
12.	1	4	6	8	9	10	12.	3	14	22	33	40	46
13.	2	3	4	5	7	9	13.	7	12	14	18	29	40
14.	2	3	4	6	9	10	14.	7	12	14	22	40	46
15.	2	3	5	7	8	10	15.	7	12	18	29	33	46
16.	2	3	6	7	8	9	16.	7	12	22	29	33	40
17.	2	4	5	6	7	10	17.	7	14	18	22	29	46
18.	2	5	6	8	9	10	18.	7	18	22	33	40	46
19.	3	4	6	7	8	10	19.	12	14	22	29	33	46
20.	4	5	6	7	8	9	20.	14	18	22	29	33	40

The order in which you write your numbers on the second line does not matter. That is, you cannot change the main guarantee of the system if you write your numbers in any possible order. Usually the systems are balanced, in the sense that all numbers are almost equally represented. That is why I recommend arranging your numbers in increasing order; then the substitution can be done in the easiest possible way. Of course, if the system is not well balanced, then you might choose to put your favorite numbers under the system numbers with the highest number of occurrences.

Let us illustrate once more the guarantee of the system in our example (a 4-win if four of your numbers are drawn): Suppose the numbers 7,12,29, and 40 are drawn, then the system must bring you at least one 4-win. Indeed, it is easy to check that this is so. In fact, you will get two 4-wins (in tickets 13 and 16), and according to the table of wins, you will also get seven 3-wins (in tickets 1,2,3,6,10,14, and 15).

The book also contains systems with other types of guarantees, for example, a guaranteed 4-win if 5 of the numbers drawn are guessed correctly. The use of such systems is the same as in the example above. We also introduce a type of systems that has never appeared in the lottery literature or software: Systems where the main guarantee is multiple prizes, for example, a guarantee of two 4-wins if 4 of the numbers drawn are guessed correctly. Again, these systems can be used in the same way as explained above.

Why Is This Book The Best One On The Market?

A comparison of the wheels (systems) in this book with any other published book or software product shows that **our systems are better than the existing ones in almost all applications**. For example, below is a table which gives a comparison with the popular book, Gail Howard's Lotto: How To Win A Fortune. We have listed only those systems for which we offer the same guarantee in fewer tickets.

We should mention though that this table shows just a fraction of the advantages of our book in comparison with Gail Howard's book and any other book on the market. Other improvements include the organization of the material, and many systems that are not included in Howard's book. One of the best qualities of my book is the newly introduced complete table of possible wins. Each table is generated by complete experiment over ALL theoretically possible draws. A computer program has performed the experiment for every system in the book. The tables have been additionally abbreviated and customly designed "by hand".

The complete tables appear for the first time in a lottery publication. The systems with multiple guarantees also appear for the first time ever.

Guarantee	**Numbers played**	**Gail Howard's book:**		**Iliya's Book:**	
		System (wheel) #	**Number of tickets**	System (wheel) #	**Number of tickets**
5 if 5	11	205	**101**	4	**100**
4 if 4	11	305	**37**	21	**32**
4 if 4	12	306	**42**	22	**41**
4 if 4	13	307	**76**	23	**66**
4 if 4	14	308	**99**	24	**80**
4 if 4	15	309	**130**	25	**118**
4 if 4	16	310	**162**	26	**152**
4 if 4	18	312	**258**	28	**236**
5 if 6	10	403	**16**	10	**14**
5 if 6	11	404	**26**	11	**22**
5 if 6	12	405	**42**	12	**38**
5 if 6	13	406	**77**	13	**61**
5 if 6	14	407	**123**	14	**98**
5 if 6	15	408	**190**	15	**142**
5 if 6	16	409	**280**	16	**224**
4 if 5	11	504	**12**	32	**10**
4 if 5	12	505	**18**	33	**14**
4 if 5	13	506	**28**	34	**21**
4 if 5	14	507	**40**	35	**31**
4 if 5	15	508	**46**	36	**41**
4 if 5	16	509	**65**	37	**54**
4 if 5	17	510	**88**	38	**70**
4 if 5	18	511	**118**	39	**81**
4 if 5	19	512	**164**	40	**115**
4 if 5	20	513	**216**	41	**145**
4 if 6	13	604	**12**	49	**10**
4 if 6	14	605	**15**	50	**14**
4 if 6	15	606	**22**	51	**19**
4 if 6	16	607	**38**	52	**25**
4 if 6	19	609	**64**	55	**54**
4 if 6	20	610	**100**	56	**66**
4 if 6	21	611	**124**	57	**80**
4 if 6	22	612	**140**	58	**102**
4 if 6	23	613	**153**	59	**127**
4 if 6	24	614	**169**	60	**154**
4 if 6	25	615	**238**	61	**175**

Can You Win The Jackpot By Playing With A Lottery System?

Of course, you can! In fact, every ticket of your system can win the jackpot. The advantage of using a lottery system is that even if you do not win the jackpot, you will still get your guaranteed wins. That is why lottery players and groups of players prefer to use systems. The number of tickets purchased by individual players and groups increases with the increase of the jackpot. A lottery system gives you the opportunity to chase the jackpot in the most organized and entertaining way, and also guarantees some smaller prizes if less than 6 of your numbers are drawn. Of course, if you hit the jackpot, using a lottery system, then you will also win a number of smaller prizes.

A system that guarantees the jackpot (that is, a 6-win if 6 of your numbers have been drawn) is expensive. Below is a table that gives you the number of combinations you need to play in order to get every possible combination out of your numbers.

Numbers Played	Number Of Combinations
7	7
8	28
9	84
10	210
11	462
12	924
13	1,716
14	3,003
15	5,005
16	8,008
17	12,376

The number of tickets increases very fast. A system that contains all possible combinations is called a **complete system**. If you play with n numbers, then the number of combinations in a complete system can be computed by the formula

$$\frac{n(n-1)(n-2)(n-3)(n-4)(n-5)}{720}.$$

Complete systems are not included in this book. Most of the existing lotteries allow using such systems automatically and supply the corresponding tables of wins.

Bonus Number(s)

Some lotteries introduce one or more additional numbers and pay prizes if you hit, say, 5 of the "regular" numbers plus an additional number, which corresponds to a 5+1-win. Other winning combinations are also possible. All of our systems are valid for these lotteries. Due to the diversity in using bonus numbers, and in order to keep the book compact, I have chosen not to include information on bonus number prizes in the tables of wins. If your lottery has bonus numbers, you only need to double-check the winning tickets containing these numbers.

The Odds Of Winning

The odds (or probability, or chance) of hitting the jackpot are the same for any particular ticket. A system contains several tickets, so the chance of winning the jackpot increases with the number of tickets played, but so do the expenses. What a system really does is that it guarantees smaller wins, while just a random selection of tickets usually guarantees nothing, even if all of the 6 numbers drawn are in your set of numbers (assuming that you play with more than 9 numbers). The chance of winning any particular set of prizes is clearly seen from the tables of wins.

Attention!

A frequently asked question is: I have used a system and won, but my set of prizes can be found nowhere in the table of wins. What is wrong? There are two possible explanations: You have either produced your set of tickets incorrectly, or you have made a mistake while filling your playing slips. So, do the substitution carefully, avoid any distraction while filling the playing slips. A single mistake can cost you a huge prize...

Larger Systems

The systems in this book can be used to play any 6-numbers-drawn lottery in the world. I believe that playing the lottery with systems with exceptionally large number of tickets contradicts the idea of lottery itself and is a risky investment. Therefore, most of the systems presented in this book have less than 300 combinations. There are only two exceptions, systems # 7 and # 29. However, larger systems have been created and are available on request from me. Also, larger systems can be used for group playing, where one plays together with a group of people. Group playing has been successfully applied in playing for large (and not so large) jackpots. Even if the jackpot has not been hit, the participants could still win a number of lower guaranteed prizes with a lottery system.

A Word From The Author

I would like to mention that I do not promote any particular lottery and am not connected to any of the existing lotteries. The book itself does not promote playing with a (large) number of tickets. It is a book for those players (or groups of players) who have ALREADY decided to play with more than two tickets. The book came as a result of long years of experience in creating and improving lottery systems. I have worked as a freelance writer for a number of lottery publications in Europe and North America, and I have spent many years in research in Combinatorics, an area of Mathematics, that among other things deals with combinatorial lottery systems (or coverings, as they call them in Combinatorics). I hold a M.Sc. and Ph.D. in Mathematics and work as a university professor. All of my publications, including both my master's thesis and doctoral dissertation, are related to lottery systems. The objects in this book originate from the most recent research in the area, and are based on my expert knowledge of the subject. That is why this book has no match among the publications and software in existence. I hope you will appreciate the qualities of this fine book and enjoy playing with the lottery systems. I wish you the best of luck! Finally, I would appreciate letters from my successful readers and users of lottery systems. Please write about your experience with the lottery systems, especially if you hit it big! Your stories could provide useful input for further improvements of this book. You can write to the address given below or send an e-mail to `lotbook@telus.net`.

Lotbook Publishing
1557 4th Avenue, Suite 1088
Prince George, B.C.
V2L 3K1 Canada

Easy Navigating

The next two tables give you a quick and easy way to compare the systems in the book and choose the most appropriate one in terms of either how many numbers or how many combinations you want to play. The systems are listed by guarantees in the contents and numbered consecutively. The first new table lists the systems by the number of combinations in increasing order. It can be used to find a system in a preferred price range. The second table can help if you already have a clear idea on how many numbers you want to play.

The contents and both tables can be used to compare the systems in the book by various characteristics. More facts about the properties of the systems can be found by comparison of the tables of wins. Each system is presented as a separate article. The title shows the **main guarantee** of the system. Many systems have additional guarantees that are explained in the presentation. I have also included some comments featuring particular strengths of the systems, information on the balance of the system (number of appearances of each number in all combinations of the system), and information on minimality.

# of comb.	Num-bers	Syst. #	# of comb.	Num-bers	Syst. #	# of comb.	Num-bers	Syst. #
3	9	30	**26**	13	95	**80**	14	24
3	10	46	**28**	14	121	**80**	21	57
4	8	8	**30**	9	2	**81**	18	39
4	8	63	**30**	10	88	**84**	17	112
5	7	17	**30**	15	102	**88**	18	113
5	10	115	**31**	14	35	**91**	14	122
5	11	47	**31**	15	70	**96**	10	82
6	12	48	**32**	11	21	**98**	14	14
7	8	18	**34**	13	108	**100**	11	4
7	8	103	**34**	17	53	**102**	22	58
7	9	9	**38**	12	12	**104**	23	77
7	9	64	**38**	16	71	**112**	16	125
7	10	31	**39**	11	85	**115**	19	40
7	11	98	**41**	12	22	**116**	24	78
10	10	65	**41**	15	36	**118**	15	25
10	10	93	**42**	14	109	**120**	13	91
10	11	32	**42**	18	54	**127**	23	59
10	12	99	**44**	12	119	**130**	26	79
10	13	49	**44**	17	72	**132**	11	118
11	9	104	**48**	16	124	**132**	12	5
11	11	66	**48**	18	73	**136**	17	126
12	8	1	**49**	14	96	**142**	15	15
12	9	19	**50**	10	3	**145**	20	41
13	13	100	**51**	9	81	**152**	16	26
14	10	10	**52**	13	120	**154**	24	60
14	12	33	**54**	16	37	**167**	27	80
14	14	50	**54**	19	55	**169**	21	42
15	10	105	**55**	11	89	**175**	25	61
15	12	67	**55**	15	110	**176**	11	83
17	11	94	**60**	10	116	**188**	17	27
19	15	51	**61**	13	13	**189**	22	43
20	10	20	**63**	12	86	**204**	18	28
20	10	84	**63**	19	74	**224**	16	16
20	11	106	**66**	11	117	**229**	23	44
21	13	34	**66**	13	23	**236**	18	28
21	13	68	**66**	20	56	**243**	27	62
21	14	101	**68**	18	127	**245**	13	6
22	9	87	**69**	16	111	**267**	24	45
22	11	11	**70**	17	38	**273**	14	123
22	12	107	**72**	15	97	**280**	16	92
24	9	114	**72**	20	75	**325**	19	29
25	14	69	**77**	12	90	**371**	14	7
25	16	52	**77**	22	76			

Numbers	# of comb.	Syst. #	Numbers	# of comb.	Syst. #	Numbers	# of comb.	Syst. #
7	5	17	**12**	10	99	**16**	48	124
8	4	8	**12**	14	33	**16**	54	37
8	4	63	**12**	15	67	**16**	69	111
8	7	18	**12**	22	107	**16**	112	125
8	7	103	**12**	38	12	**16**	152	26
8	12	1	**12**	41	22	**16**	224	16
9	3	30	**12**	44	119	**16**	280	92
9	7	9	**12**	63	86	**17**	34	53
9	7	64	**12**	77	90	**17**	44	72
9	11	104	**12**	132	5	**17**	70	38
9	12	19	**13**	10	49	**17**	84	112
9	22	87	**13**	13	100	**17**	136	126
9	24	114	**13**	21	34	**17**	188	27
9	30	2	**13**	21	68	**18**	42	54
9	51	81	**13**	26	95	**18**	48	73
10	3	46	**13**	34	108	**18**	68	127
10	5	115	**13**	52	120	**18**	81	39
10	7	31	**13**	61	13	**18**	88	113
10	10	65	**13**	66	23	**18**	204	128
10	10	93	**13**	120	91	**18**	236	28
10	14	10	**13**	245	6	**19**	54	55
10	15	105	**14**	14	50	**19**	63	74
10	20	20	**14**	21	101	**19**	115	40
10	20	84	**14**	25	69	**19**	325	29
10	30	88	**14**	28	121	**20**	66	56
10	50	3	**14**	31	35	**20**	72	75
10	60	116	**14**	42	109	**20**	145	41
10	96	82	**14**	49	96	**21**	80	57
11	5	47	**14**	80	24	**21**	169	42
11	7	98	**14**	91	122	**22**	77	76
11	10	32	**14**	98	14	**22**	102	58
11	11	66	**14**	273	123	**22**	189	43
11	17	94	**14**	371	7	**23**	104	77
11	20	106	**15**	19	51	**23**	127	59
11	22	11	**15**	30	102	**23**	229	44
11	32	21	**15**	31	70	**24**	116	78
11	39	85	**15**	41	36	**24**	154	60
11	55	89	**15**	55	110	**24**	267	45
11	66	117	**15**	72	97	**25**	175	61
11	100	4	**15**	118	25	**26**	130	79
11	132	118	**15**	142	15	**27**	167	80
11	176	83	**16**	25	52	**27**	243	62
12	6	48	**16**	38	71			

PART I
LOTTERY SYSTEMS WITH A SINGLE GUARANTEE

LOTTERY SYSTEMS WITH A 5-WIN GUARANTEED IF 5 OF YOUR NUMBERS ARE DRAWN

SYSTEM # 1: GUARANTEED 5–WIN IF 5 OF THE NUMBERS DRAWN ARE IN YOUR SET OF 8 NUMBERS ©Copyright 2001

Winning possibilities

Guessed	**6**	**5**	**4**	**3**	%
6	1	4	7	-	42.86
	-	6	6	-	57.14
5	-	3	3	6	14.29
	-	1	7	4	85.71
4	-	-	6	-	2.86
	-	-	3	6	45.71
	-	-	2	8	51.43
3	-	-	-	6	14.29
	-	-	-	4	85.71

This is a nice small system for a 5 on 5 guarantee. Note that the complete system would require 28 combinations. The system presented here also guarantees at least two 4-wins (and a number of 3-wins) on guessing correctly 4 of the numbers drawn, and at least four 3-wins if three of the numbers drawn are guessed correctly. If all of the numbers are guessed correctly, you will either win the jackpot (plus some extra cash!) or you will get six 5-wins and six 4-wins. The system is MATHEMATICALLY MINIMAL with respect to the main guarantee and also with respect to the guarantees of two 4-wins on four numbers guessed correctly and four 3-wins on three numbers guessed correctly. It is also HIGHLY BALANCED: Each number participates in exactly 9 of the combinations of the system.

1. 1 2 3 4 5 7
2. 1 2 3 4 6 8
3. 1 2 3 5 6 7
4. 1 2 3 5 7 8
5. 1 2 4 5 6 8
6. 1 2 4 6 7 8
7. 1 3 4 5 6 7
8. 1 3 4 5 7 8
9. 1 3 5 6 7 8
10. 2 3 4 5 6 8
11. 2 3 4 6 7 8
12. 2 4 5 6 7 8

System # 2: Guaranteed 5–win if 5 of the numbers drawn are in your set of 9 numbers ©Copyright 2001

Winning possibilities

Guessed	6	5	4	3	%
6	1	7	13	9	3.57
	1	5	17	7	25.00
	1	4	19	6	7.14
	-	10	10	10	3.57
	-	8	14	8	14.29
	-	7	16	7	35.71
	-	6	18	6	10.72
5	-	4	5	18	4.76
	-	3	7	17	2.38
	-	2	9-11	12-16	23.81
	-	1	11-15	7-15	69.05
4	-	-	7	7	2.38
	-	-	5	11-12	14.29
	-	-	4	13-14	19.05
	-	-	3	15-18	64.28
3	-	-	-	10	3.57
	-	-	-	9	3.57
	-	-	-	8	14.29
	-	-	-	7	60.71
	-	-	-	6	17.86

Aside from the main guarantee, the system also guarantees at least three 4-wins (and a number of 3-wins) on guessing correctly 4 of the numbers drawn, and at least six 3-wins if three of the numbers drawn are guessed correctly. The complete system would require 84 combinations. If all of the numbers are guessed correctly, you will either win the jackpot (plus some extra cash!) or you will get anywhere between six and ten 5-wins (and a number of smaller prizes). The system is MATHEMATICALLY MINIMAL with respect to the main guarantee. It is also HIGHLY BALANCED: Each number is in exactly twenty of the combinations of the system.

1. 1 2 3 4 5 9
2. 1 2 3 4 6 9
3. 1 2 3 4 7 9
4. 1 2 3 4 8 9
5. 1 2 3 5 6 8
6. 1 2 3 5 7 8
7. 1 2 3 6 7 8
8. 1 2 4 5 6 7

16. 1 3 5 6 7 8
17. 1 3 5 7 8 9
18. 1 3 6 7 8 9
19. 1 4 5 6 7 9
20. 1 4 5 6 8 9
21. 2 3 4 5 6 7
22. 2 3 4 5 6 8
23. 2 3 4 7 8 9

9. 1 2 4 5 8 9
10. 1 2 4 6 8 9
11. 1 2 4 7 8 9
12. 1 2 5 6 7 9
13. 1 3 4 5 6 9
14. 1 3 4 5 7 8
15. 1 3 4 6 7 8

24. 2 3 5 6 7 9
25. 2 3 5 6 8 9
26. 2 4 5 6 7 8
27. 2 4 5 6 7 9
28. 2 5 6 7 8 9
29. 3 4 5 7 8 9
30. 3 4 6 7 8 9

System # 3: Guaranteed 5–win if 5 of the numbers drawn are in your set of 10 numbers ©Copyright 2001

Winning possibilities

Guessed	6	5	4	3	%
6	1	4	24	16	19.05
	1	-	30	16	4.76
	-	8	18	20	19.05
	-	6	21	20	57.14
5	-	5	-	40	0.79
	-	3	8	28	7.94
	-	1	16	16	3.97
	-	1	13	22	63.49
	-	1	10	28	23.81
4	-	-	5	16	19.05
	-	-	4	20	19.05
	-	-	3	20	57.14
	-	-	3	16	4.76
3	-	-	-	9	66.67
	-	-	-	7	33.33

Aside from the main guarantee, the system also guarantees at least three 4-wins (and a number of 3-wins) on guessing correctly 4 of the numbers drawn, and at least seven 3-wins if three of the numbers drawn are guessed correctly. The complete system would require 210 combinations. If all of the numbers are guessed correctly, you will either win the jackpot (plus some extra cash!) or you will get either six or eight 5-wins (and a number of smaller prizes). The system is MATHEMATICALLY MINIMAL with respect to the main guarantee. It is also HIGHLY BALANCED: Each number participates in exactly 30 of the combinations of the system.

1. 1 2 3 4 5 10
2. 1 2 3 4 6 9
3. 1 2 3 4 7 9
4. 1 2 3 4 8 9
5. 1 2 3 5 6 8
6. 1 2 3 5 7 8
7. 1 2 3 5 8 9
8. 1 2 3 6 7 10
9. 1 2 3 8 9 10
10. 1 2 4 5 6 7
11. 1 2 4 5 7 8
12. 1 2 4 5 7 9
13. 1 2 4 6 8 10

26. 1 4 5 6 7 10
27. 1 4 5 8 9 10
28. 1 4 6 7 8 9
29. 1 5 6 7 8 9
30. 1 6 7 8 9 10
31. 2 3 4 5 6 10
32. 2 3 4 5 7 10
33. 2 3 4 5 8 10
34. 2 3 4 5 9 10
35. 2 3 4 6 7 8
36. 2 3 5 6 7 9
37. 2 3 6 8 9 10
38. 2 3 7 8 9 10

14.	1	2	4	7	9	10	39.	2	4	5	6	8	9
15.	1	2	5	6	9	10	40.	2	4	6	7	9	10
16.	1	2	5	7	8	10	41.	2	4	7	8	9	10
17.	1	2	6	7	8	9	42.	2	5	6	7	8	10
18.	1	3	4	5	6	7	43.	2	5	7	8	9	10
19.	1	3	4	5	6	8	44.	3	4	5	7	8	9
20.	1	3	4	5	6	9	45.	3	4	6	7	9	10
21.	1	3	4	6	9	10	46.	3	4	6	8	9	10
22.	1	3	4	7	8	10	47.	3	5	6	7	8	10
23.	1	3	5	6	8	10	48.	3	5	6	8	9	10
24.	1	3	5	7	9	10	49.	4	5	6	7	8	10
25.	1	3	6	7	8	9	50.	4	5	6	7	9	10

System # 4: Guaranteed 5–win if 5 of the numbers drawn are in your set of 11 numbers ©Copyright 2001

Winning possibilities

Guessed	6	5	4	3	%
6	1	9	28	47	0.22
	1	7	29-35	37-47	0.88
	1	6	28-37	37-51	3.51
	1	5	33-37	39-45	3.04
	1	4	33-40	37-46	3.07
	1	3	36-42	32-44	3.94
	1	2	37-43	33-45	5.69
	1	1	41-44	30-40	1.53
	-	11	20-29	45-57	0.88
	-	10	24-29	44-52	0.88
	-	9	21-34	40-63	6.12
	-	8	23-35	39-56	16.28
	-	7	26-37	36-52	40.99
	-	6	30-36	37-47	12.97
5	-	6	5	58	0.22
	-	6	1	63	0.22
	-	5	7	57	0.43
	-	4	11-13	46-51	0.66
	-	3	11-15	47-54	1.54
	-	2	11-21	33-56	21.05
	-	1	15-23	30-49	75.88
4	-	-	9	23	0.30
	-	-	8	25	0.30
	-	-	7	24-31	3.02
	-	-	6	26-33	8.49
	-	-	5	24-36	25.77
	-	-	4	28-38	62.12
3	-	-	-	14-16	12.12
	-	-	-	11-13	87.88

Aside from the main guarantee, the system also guarantees at least four 4-wins (and a number of 3-wins) on guessing correctly 4 of the numbers drawn, and at least eleven 3-wins if three of the numbers drawn are guessed correctly. The complete system would require 462 combinations. If all of the numbers are guessed correctly, you will either win the jackpot (plus some extra cash!) or you will get anywhere between six and eleven 5-wins (and a number of smaller prizes). The next table contains information on the balance of the system.

Number(s)	Occurrences
2	58
8,9	56
1,6,7	55
4,5,10	54
3	52
11	51

1.	1	2	3	4	5	6
2.	1	2	3	4	5	10
3.	1	2	3	4	7	10
4.	1	2	3	4	7	11
5.	1	2	3	4	8	9
6.	1	2	3	5	6	7
7.	1	2	3	5	8	9
8.	1	2	3	5	10	11
9.	1	2	3	6	8	9
10.	1	2	3	6	10	11
11.	1	2	3	7	8	9
12.	1	2	3	8	9	10
13.	1	2	3	8	9	11
14.	1	2	4	5	6	8
15.	1	2	4	5	7	8
16.	1	2	4	5	9	10
17.	1	2	4	5	9	11
18.	1	2	4	6	7	9
19.	1	2	4	6	7	10
20.	1	2	4	6	8	11
21.	1	2	4	8	10	11
22.	1	2	5	6	7	9
23.	1	2	5	6	7	10
24.	1	2	5	6	7	11
25.	1	2	5	7	8	10
26.	1	2	5	7	8	11
27.	1	2	6	7	8	9
28.	1	2	6	8	9	10
29.	1	2	6	8	9	11
30.	1	2	7	9	10	11
31.	1	3	4	5	7	9
32.	1	3	4	5	8	11
33.	1	3	4	6	7	8
34.	1	3	4	6	8	10
35.	1	3	4	6	9	11
36.	1	3	4	9	10	11
37.	1	3	5	6	8	11
38.	1	3	5	6	9	10
51.	1	5	6	7	8	10
52.	1	5	6	9	10	11
53.	1	5	7	8	9	10
54.	1	5	8	9	10	11
55.	1	6	7	8	10	11
56.	2	3	4	5	6	9
57.	2	3	4	5	7	8
58.	2	3	4	5	7	11
59.	2	3	4	6	7	9
60.	2	3	4	6	8	9
61.	2	3	4	6	9	10
62.	2	3	4	6	9	11
63.	2	3	4	8	10	11
64.	2	3	5	6	8	10
65.	2	3	5	6	9	11
66.	2	3	5	7	9	10
67.	2	3	5	8	9	11
68.	2	3	6	7	8	10
69.	2	3	6	7	8	11
70.	2	3	7	9	10	11
71.	2	4	5	6	7	8
72.	2	4	5	6	10	11
73.	2	4	5	7	8	9
74.	2	4	5	7	8	10
75.	2	4	5	8	9	11
76.	2	4	6	7	8	11
77.	2	4	6	8	9	10
78.	2	4	7	9	10	11
79.	2	5	6	8	9	10
80.	2	5	6	8	10	11
81.	2	5	7	9	10	11
82.	2	6	7	9	10	11
83.	2	7	8	9	10	11
84.	3	4	5	6	7	10
85.	3	4	5	6	8	11
86.	3	4	5	8	9	10
87.	3	4	5	9	10	11
88.	3	4	6	7	10	11

39.	1	3	5	7	8	10
40.	1	3	5	7	9	11
41.	1	3	6	7	9	10
42.	1	3	6	7	9	11
43.	1	3	7	8	10	11
44.	1	4	5	6	7	11
45.	1	4	5	6	8	9
46.	1	4	5	6	8	10
47.	1	4	5	7	10	11
48.	1	4	6	9	10	11
49.	1	4	7	8	9	10
50.	1	4	7	8	9	11

89.	3	4	7	8	9	10
90.	3	4	7	8	9	11
91.	3	5	6	7	8	9
92.	3	5	6	7	10	11
93.	3	5	7	8	10	11
94.	3	6	8	9	10	11
95.	4	5	6	7	9	10
96.	4	5	6	7	9	11
97.	4	5	7	8	10	11
98.	4	6	7	8	9	10
99.	4	6	8	9	10	11
100.	5	6	7	8	9	11

SYSTEM # 5: GUARANTEED 5–WIN IF 5 OF THE NUMBERS DRAWN ARE IN YOUR SET OF 12 NUMBERS ©Copyright 2001

Winning possibilities

Guessed	6	5	4	3	%
6	1	-	45	40	14.29
	-	6	30	60	85.71
5	-	1	15	50	100.00
4	-	-	4	32	100.00
3	-	-	-	12	100.00

This system is EXCEPTIONALLY HIGHLY BALANCED: Each number is in exactly 66 combinations; each pair of numbers is in exactly 30 combinations; each triple of numbers is in exactly 12 combinations; each quadruple is in 4 combinations, and each quintuple of numbers is in exactly one combination! The system is also MATHEMATICALLY MINIMAL in the entire range of guarantees! It also has an additional nice property: Every two combinations differ in at least two numbers, that is, the combinations are as 'apart' as possible. The complete system would require 924 combinations.

1. 1 2 3 4 5 7
2. 1 2 3 4 6 10
3. 1 2 3 4 8 11
4. 1 2 3 4 9 12
5. 1 2 3 5 6 11
6. 1 2 3 5 8 12
7. 1 2 3 5 9 10
8. 1 2 3 6 7 12
9. 1 2 3 6 8 9
10. 1 2 3 7 8 10
11. 1 2 3 7 9 11
12. 1 2 3 10 11 12
13. 1 2 4 5 6 8
14. 1 2 4 5 9 11
15. 1 2 4 5 10 12
16. 1 2 4 6 7 9
17. 1 2 4 6 11 12
18. 1 2 4 7 8 12
19. 1 2 4 7 10 11
20. 1 2 4 8 9 10
21. 1 2 5 6 7 10
22. 1 2 5 6 9 12
23. 1 2 5 7 8 9

67. 2 3 4 5 6 9
68. 2 3 4 5 8 10
69. 2 3 4 5 11 12
70. 2 3 4 6 7 11
71. 2 3 4 6 8 12
72. 2 3 4 7 8 9
73. 2 3 4 7 10 12
74. 2 3 4 9 10 11
75. 2 3 5 6 7 8
76. 2 3 5 6 10 12
77. 2 3 5 7 9 12
78. 2 3 5 7 10 11
79. 2 3 5 8 9 11
80. 2 3 6 7 9 10
81. 2 3 6 8 10 11
82. 2 3 6 9 11 12
83. 2 3 7 8 11 12
84. 2 3 8 9 10 12
85. 2 4 5 6 7 12
86. 2 4 5 6 10 11
87. 2 4 5 7 8 11
88. 2 4 5 7 9 10
89. 2 4 5 8 9 12

24.	1	2	5	7	11	12
25.	1	2	5	8	10	11
26.	1	2	6	7	8	11
27.	1	2	6	8	10	12
28.	1	2	6	9	10	11
29.	1	2	7	9	10	12
30.	1	2	8	9	11	12
31.	1	3	4	5	6	12
32.	1	3	4	5	8	9
33.	1	3	4	5	10	11
34.	1	3	4	6	7	8
35.	1	3	4	6	9	11
36.	1	3	4	7	9	10
37.	1	3	4	7	11	12
38.	1	3	4	8	10	12
39.	1	3	5	6	7	9
40.	1	3	5	6	8	10
41.	1	3	5	7	8	11
42.	1	3	5	7	10	12
43.	1	3	5	9	11	12
44.	1	3	6	7	10	11
45.	1	3	6	8	11	12
46.	1	3	6	9	10	12
47.	1	3	7	8	9	12
48.	1	3	8	9	10	11
49.	1	4	5	6	7	11
50.	1	4	5	6	9	10
51.	1	4	5	7	8	10
52.	1	4	5	7	9	12
53.	1	4	5	8	11	12
54.	1	4	6	7	10	12
55.	1	4	6	8	9	12
56.	1	4	6	8	10	11
57.	1	4	7	8	9	11
58.	1	4	9	10	11	12
59.	1	5	6	7	8	12
60.	1	5	6	8	9	11
61.	1	5	6	10	11	12
62.	1	5	7	9	10	11
63.	1	5	8	9	10	12
64.	1	6	7	8	9	10
65.	1	6	7	9	11	12
66.	1	7	8	10	11	12
90.	2	4	6	7	8	10
91.	2	4	6	8	9	11
92.	2	4	6	9	10	12
93.	2	4	7	9	11	12
94.	2	4	8	10	11	12
95.	2	5	6	7	9	11
96.	2	5	6	8	9	10
97.	2	5	6	8	11	12
98.	2	5	7	8	10	12
99.	2	5	9	10	11	12
100.	2	6	7	8	9	12
101.	2	6	7	10	11	12
102.	2	7	8	9	10	11
103.	3	4	5	6	7	10
104.	3	4	5	6	8	11
105.	3	4	5	7	8	12
106.	3	4	5	7	9	11
107.	3	4	5	9	10	12
108.	3	4	6	7	9	12
109.	3	4	6	8	9	10
110.	3	4	6	10	11	12
111.	3	4	7	8	10	11
112.	3	4	8	9	11	12
113.	3	5	6	7	11	12
114.	3	5	6	8	9	12
115.	3	5	6	9	10	11
116.	3	5	7	8	9	10
117.	3	5	8	10	11	12
118.	3	6	7	8	9	11
119.	3	6	7	8	10	12
120.	3	7	9	10	11	12
121.	4	5	6	7	8	9
122.	4	5	6	8	10	12
123.	4	5	6	9	11	12
124.	4	5	7	10	11	12
125.	4	5	8	9	10	11
126.	4	6	7	8	11	12
127.	4	6	7	9	10	11
128.	4	7	8	9	10	12
129.	5	6	7	8	10	11
130.	5	6	7	9	10	12
131.	5	7	8	9	11	12
132.	6	8	9	10	11	12

System # 6: Guaranteed 5–win if 5 of the numbers drawn are in your set of 13 numbers ©Copyright 2001

Winning possibilities

Guessed	**6**	**5**	**4**	**3**	%
6	1	5	45	100	0.12
	1	4	46-47	99-100	0.52
	1	3	48-50	94-99	1.52
	1	2	51-55	86-97	3.96
	1	1	55-59	80-91	6.18
	1	-	60-63	71-81	1.98
	-	9	35-37	109-116	0.23
	-	8	36-42	103-116	3.96
	-	7	40-44	99-111	55.36
	-	6	45-49	90-101	26.17
5	-	2	15-19	80-93	14.22
	-	1	20-23	72-83	85.78
4	-	-	6	44-47	13.99
	-	-	5	48-50	86.01
3	-	-	-	18	13.29
	-	-	-	17	86.71

Aside from the main guarantee, the system also guarantees at least five 4-wins (and a number of 3-wins) on guessing correctly 4 of the numbers drawn, and at least seventeen 3-wins if three of the numbers drawn are guessed correctly. The complete system would require 1,716 combinations. If all of the numbers are guessed correctly, you will either win the jackpot (plus some extra cash!) or you will get anywhere between six and nine 5-wins (and a number of smaller prizes). The system is MATHEMATICALLY MINIMAL with respect to the main guarantee. It is well balanced: The number 3 is in 114 combinations; the remaining 12 numbers are each in 113 combinations.

1. 1 2 3 4 5 13
2. 1 2 3 4 6 11
3. 1 2 3 4 6 12
4. 1 2 3 4 7 8
5. 1 2 3 4 9 10
6. 1 2 3 4 11 12
7. 1 2 3 5 6 13
8. 1 2 3 5 7 9
9. 1 2 3 5 8 12
10. 1 2 3 5 10 11
11. 1 2 3 6 7 10

123. 2 3 4 8 12 13
124. 2 3 4 9 11 13
125. 2 3 5 6 7 8
126. 2 3 5 6 8 12
127. 2 3 5 6 9 11
128. 2 3 5 7 8 10
129. 2 3 5 7 12 13
130. 2 3 5 8 11 13
131. 2 3 5 9 10 13
132. 2 3 5 9 11 12
133. 2 3 6 7 10 12

12.	1	2	3	6	8	9	134.	2	3	6	7	11	13
13.	1	2	3	7	10	12	135.	2	3	6	8	9	12
14.	1	2	3	7	11	13	136.	2	3	6	8	10	11
15.	1	2	3	8	9	11	137.	2	3	6	9	10	13
16.	1	2	3	8	10	13	138.	2	3	6	11	12	13
17.	1	2	3	9	12	13	139.	2	3	7	8	9	13
18.	1	2	4	5	6	9	140.	2	3	7	8	11	12
19.	1	2	4	5	7	12	141.	2	3	7	9	10	11
20.	1	2	4	5	8	10	142.	2	3	8	9	10	12
21.	1	2	4	5	9	11	143.	2	3	10	11	12	13
22.	1	2	4	6	7	8	144.	2	4	5	6	7	13
23.	1	2	4	6	10	13	145.	2	4	5	6	8	11
24.	1	2	4	7	9	13	146.	2	4	5	6	11	12
25.	1	2	4	7	10	11	147.	2	4	5	7	8	13
26.	1	2	4	8	9	12	148.	2	4	5	7	9	10
27.	1	2	4	8	11	13	149.	2	4	5	8	11	12
28.	1	2	4	10	12	13	150.	2	4	5	9	12	13
29.	1	2	5	6	7	11	151.	2	4	5	10	11	13
30.	1	2	5	6	8	10	152.	2	4	6	7	10	11
31.	1	2	5	6	12	13	153.	2	4	6	7	12	13
32.	1	2	5	7	8	11	154.	2	4	6	8	9	10
33.	1	2	5	7	10	13	155.	2	4	6	8	11	12
34.	1	2	5	8	9	13	156.	2	4	6	9	10	12
35.	1	2	5	9	10	12	157.	2	4	6	9	11	13
36.	1	2	5	11	12	13	158.	2	4	7	8	9	11
37.	1	2	6	7	8	12	159.	2	4	7	8	10	12
38.	1	2	6	7	9	13	160.	2	4	7	11	12	13
39.	1	2	6	8	11	13	161.	2	4	8	9	10	13
40.	1	2	6	9	10	11	162.	2	4	9	10	11	12
41.	1	2	6	9	12	13	163.	2	5	6	7	9	10
42.	1	2	6	10	11	12	164.	2	5	6	7	9	12
43.	1	2	7	8	9	10	165.	2	5	6	8	9	13
44.	1	2	7	8	12	13	166.	2	5	6	8	10	12
45.	1	2	7	9	11	12	167.	2	5	6	10	11	13
46.	1	2	8	10	11	12	168.	2	5	7	8	9	12
47.	1	2	9	10	11	13	169.	2	5	7	9	11	13
48.	1	3	4	5	6	7	170.	2	5	7	10	11	12
49.	1	3	4	5	7	10	171.	2	5	8	9	10	11
50.	1	3	4	5	8	11	172.	2	5	8	10	12	13
51.	1	3	4	5	9	12	173.	2	6	7	8	9	11
52.	1	3	4	6	8	10	174.	2	6	7	8	10	13
53.	1	3	4	6	9	13	175.	2	6	7	9	11	12
54.	1	3	4	7	9	11	176.	2	6	8	10	12	13
55.	1	3	4	7	12	13	177.	2	7	8	10	11	13
56.	1	3	4	8	9	13	178.	2	7	9	10	12	13
57.	1	3	4	8	10	12	179.	2	8	9	11	12	13

58. 1 3 4 10 11 13
59. 1 3 5 6 7 12
60. 1 3 5 6 8 11
61. 1 3 5 6 9 10
62. 1 3 5 6 10 12
63. 1 3 5 7 8 13
64. 1 3 5 7 11 12
65. 1 3 5 8 9 10
66. 1 3 5 9 11 13
67. 1 3 5 10 12 13
68. 1 3 6 7 8 13
69. 1 3 6 7 9 11
70. 1 3 6 7 9 12
71. 1 3 6 8 11 12
72. 1 3 6 10 11 13
73. 1 3 6 10 12 13
74. 1 3 7 8 9 12
75. 1 3 7 8 10 11
76. 1 3 7 9 10 13
77. 1 3 8 11 12 13
78. 1 3 9 10 11 12
79. 1 4 5 6 8 13
80. 1 4 5 6 9 12
81. 1 4 5 6 10 11
82. 1 4 5 7 8 9
83. 1 4 5 7 11 13
84. 1 4 5 8 12 13
85. 1 4 5 9 10 13
86. 1 4 5 10 11 12
87. 1 4 6 7 9 10
88. 1 4 6 7 10 12
89. 1 4 6 7 11 13
90. 1 4 6 8 9 11
91. 1 4 6 8 12 13
92. 1 4 6 9 11 12
93. 1 4 7 8 10 13
94. 1 4 7 8 11 12
95. 1 4 7 9 10 12
96. 1 4 8 9 10 11
97. 1 4 9 11 12 13
98. 1 5 6 7 8 9
99. 1 5 6 7 10 13
100. 1 5 6 8 11 12
101. 1 5 6 9 11 13
102. 1 5 7 8 10 12
103. 1 5 7 9 10 11

180. 3 4 5 6 8 9
181. 3 4 5 6 11 13
182. 3 4 5 6 12 13
183. 3 4 5 7 8 12
184. 3 4 5 7 9 13
185. 3 4 5 8 10 13
186. 3 4 5 9 10 11
187. 3 4 5 11 12 13
188. 3 4 6 7 8 11
189. 3 4 6 7 10 13
190. 3 4 6 7 11 12
191. 3 4 6 8 10 12
192. 3 4 6 9 10 11
193. 3 4 6 9 12 13
194. 3 4 7 8 9 10
195. 3 4 7 8 11 13
196. 3 4 7 10 11 12
197. 3 4 8 9 11 12
198. 3 4 9 10 12 13
199. 3 5 6 7 9 13
200. 3 5 6 7 10 11
201. 3 5 6 8 10 13
202. 3 5 6 9 11 12
203. 3 5 6 10 11 12
204. 3 5 7 8 9 11
205. 3 5 7 9 10 12
206. 3 5 7 10 11 13
207. 3 5 8 9 12 13
208. 3 5 8 10 11 12
209. 3 6 7 8 9 10
210. 3 6 7 8 12 13
211. 3 6 8 9 11 13
212. 3 6 9 10 11 12
213. 3 7 8 10 12 13
214. 3 7 9 11 12 13
215. 3 8 9 10 11 13
216. 4 5 6 7 8 10
217. 4 5 6 7 8 12
218. 4 5 6 7 9 11
219. 4 5 6 7 10 12
220. 4 5 6 9 10 13
221. 4 5 7 8 10 11
222. 4 5 7 9 11 12
223. 4 5 7 10 12 13
224. 4 5 8 9 10 12
225. 4 5 8 9 11 13

104.	1	5	7	9	12	13
105.	1	5	8	9	11	12
106.	1	5	8	10	11	13
107.	1	6	7	8	10	11
108.	1	6	7	11	12	13
109.	1	6	8	9	10	12
110.	1	6	8	9	10	13
111.	1	7	8	9	11	13
112.	1	7	10	11	12	13
113.	1	8	9	10	12	13
114.	2	3	4	5	6	10
115.	2	3	4	5	7	11
116.	2	3	4	5	8	9
117.	2	3	4	5	10	12
118.	2	3	4	6	7	9
119.	2	3	4	6	8	13
120.	2	3	4	7	9	12
121.	2	3	4	7	10	13
122.	2	3	4	8	10	11

226.	4	6	7	8	9	12
227.	4	6	7	8	9	13
228.	4	6	8	10	11	13
229.	4	6	10	11	12	13
230.	4	7	8	9	12	13
231.	4	7	9	10	11	13
232.	4	8	10	11	12	13
233.	5	6	7	8	11	13
234.	5	6	7	11	12	13
235.	5	6	8	9	10	11
236.	5	6	8	9	12	13
237.	5	6	9	10	12	13
238.	5	7	8	9	10	13
239.	5	7	8	11	12	13
240.	5	9	10	11	12	13
241.	6	7	8	10	11	12
242.	6	7	9	10	11	13
243.	6	7	9	10	12	13
244.	6	8	9	11	12	13
245.	7	8	9	10	11	12

System # 7: Guaranteed 5–win if 5 of the numbers drawn are in your set of 14 numbers ©Copyright 2001

Winning possibilities

Guessed	6	5	4	3	%
6	1	4	52-58	128-144	2.80
	1	2	59-61	126-132	5.59
	1	-	62-72	108-132	3.96
	-	8	43-49	142-152	22.38
	-	6	45-57	128-152	65.27
5	-	3	15-18	108-116	5.59
	-	1	20-25	98-112	94.41
4	-	-	7	56	8.39
	-	-	6	56-60	39.16
	-	-	5	56-64	52.45
3	-	-	-	21	69.23
	-	-	-	19	30.77

Aside from the main guarantee, the system also guarantees at least five 4-wins (and a number of 3-wins) on guessing correctly 4 of the numbers drawn, and at least nineteen 3-wins if three of the numbers drawn are guessed correctly. The complete system would require 3,003 combinations. If all of the numbers are guessed correctly, you will either win the jackpot (plus some extra cash!) or you will get either six or eight 5-wins (and a number of smaller prizes). The system is HIGHLY BALANCED: Every number is in exactly 159 combinations.

1.	1	2	3	4	5	8
2.	1	2	3	4	6	9
3.	1	2	3	4	7	12
4.	1	2	3	4	10	13
5.	1	2	3	4	11	14
6.	1	2	3	5	6	7
7.	1	2	3	5	7	9
8.	1	2	3	5	7	13
9.	1	2	3	5	10	14
10.	1	2	3	5	11	12
11.	1	2	3	6	8	14
12.	1	2	3	6	9	10
13.	1	2	3	6	9	13
14.	1	2	3	6	11	12
15.	1	2	3	7	8	14
16.	1	2	3	7	10	11
17.	1	2	3	8	9	14

186.	2	3	6	7	9	14
187.	2	3	6	7	10	13
188.	2	3	6	8	9	12
189.	2	3	6	8	10	11
190.	2	3	6	11	13	14
191.	2	3	7	8	9	11
192.	2	3	7	8	9	12
193.	2	3	7	8	9	13
194.	2	3	7	10	12	14
195.	2	3	7	11	12	13
196.	2	3	8	10	13	14
197.	2	3	8	11	12	14
198.	2	3	9	10	11	14
199.	2	3	9	10	12	13
200.	2	4	5	6	8	12
201.	2	4	5	6	9	13
202.	2	4	5	6	10	13

18.	1	2	3	8	10	12	203.	2	4	5	6	11	13
19.	1	2	3	8	11	13	204.	2	4	5	7	8	9
20.	1	2	3	9	11	12	205.	2	4	5	7	10	13
21.	1	2	3	12	13	14	206.	2	4	5	7	11	12
22.	1	2	4	5	6	14	207.	2	4	5	8	10	13
23.	1	2	4	5	7	14	208.	2	4	5	9	11	14
24.	1	2	4	5	9	12	209.	2	4	5	10	12	14
25.	1	2	4	5	10	11	210.	2	4	6	7	8	10
26.	1	2	4	5	13	14	211.	2	4	6	7	8	14
27.	1	2	4	6	7	13	212.	2	4	6	7	9	12
28.	1	2	4	6	8	11	213.	2	4	6	8	9	14
29.	1	2	4	6	10	12	214.	2	4	6	8	13	14
30.	1	2	4	7	8	10	215.	2	4	6	9	10	11
31.	1	2	4	7	9	11	216.	2	4	6	11	12	14
32.	1	2	4	8	9	13	217.	2	4	7	8	10	12
33.	1	2	4	8	12	14	218.	2	4	7	8	11	13
34.	1	2	4	9	10	14	219.	2	4	7	9	13	14
35.	1	2	4	11	12	13	220.	2	4	7	10	11	14
36.	1	2	5	6	8	10	221.	2	4	7	12	13	14
37.	1	2	5	6	9	11	222.	2	4	8	9	11	12
38.	1	2	5	6	12	13	223.	2	4	8	10	11	14
39.	1	2	5	7	8	13	224.	2	4	9	10	12	13
40.	1	2	5	7	10	12	225.	2	4	10	11	13	14
41.	1	2	5	7	11	13	226.	2	5	6	7	8	11
42.	1	2	5	8	9	12	227.	2	5	6	7	9	10
43.	1	2	5	8	11	14	228.	2	5	6	7	13	14
44.	1	2	5	9	10	13	229.	2	5	6	8	9	14
45.	1	2	5	9	12	14	230.	2	5	6	9	11	12
46.	1	2	6	7	8	9	231.	2	5	6	10	11	14
47.	1	2	6	7	10	14	232.	2	5	7	8	12	14
48.	1	2	6	7	11	14	233.	2	5	7	9	10	11
49.	1	2	6	7	12	14	234.	2	5	7	9	10	14
50.	1	2	6	8	12	13	235.	2	5	7	9	12	13
51.	1	2	6	9	12	13	236.	2	5	8	9	10	12
52.	1	2	6	9	13	14	237.	2	5	8	9	11	13
53.	1	2	6	10	11	13	238.	2	5	8	10	11	12
54.	1	2	7	8	11	12	239.	2	5	8	10	12	13
55.	1	2	7	9	10	12	240.	2	5	8	10	13	14
56.	1	2	7	9	13	14	241.	2	5	11	12	13	14
57.	1	2	7	10	12	13	242.	2	6	7	8	12	13
58.	1	2	8	9	10	11	243.	2	6	7	9	11	13
59.	1	2	8	10	13	14	244.	2	6	7	10	11	12
60.	1	2	9	11	13	14	245.	2	6	8	9	10	13
61.	1	2	10	11	12	14	246.	2	6	8	9	11	14
62.	1	3	4	5	6	10	247.	2	6	8	10	12	14
63.	1	3	4	5	7	11	248.	2	6	8	11	12	13

64.	1	3	4	5	9	13
65.	1	3	4	5	12	14
66.	1	3	4	6	7	10
67.	1	3	4	6	8	12
68.	1	3	4	6	10	11
69.	1	3	4	6	13	14
70.	1	3	4	7	8	13
71.	1	3	4	7	9	14
72.	1	3	4	8	9	11
73.	1	3	4	8	10	14
74.	1	3	4	9	10	12
75.	1	3	4	11	12	13
76.	1	3	5	6	8	11
77.	1	3	5	6	9	12
78.	1	3	5	6	11	13
79.	1	3	5	6	11	14
80.	1	3	5	7	8	12
81.	1	3	5	7	9	10
82.	1	3	5	7	9	14
83.	1	3	5	8	9	10
84.	1	3	5	8	13	14
85.	1	3	5	9	10	11
86.	1	3	5	10	12	13
87.	1	3	6	7	8	9
88.	1	3	6	7	11	14
89.	1	3	6	7	12	13
90.	1	3	6	8	10	13
91.	1	3	6	9	11	14
92.	1	3	6	10	12	14
93.	1	3	7	8	10	11
94.	1	3	7	9	11	13
95.	1	3	7	9	12	14
96.	1	3	7	10	11	12
97.	1	3	7	10	13	14
98.	1	3	8	9	12	13
99.	1	3	8	11	12	14
100.	1	3	9	10	13	14
101.	1	3	10	11	13	14
102.	1	4	5	6	7	8
103.	1	4	5	6	7	9
104.	1	4	5	6	7	12
105.	1	4	5	6	11	12
106.	1	4	5	6	12	13
107.	1	4	5	7	10	13
108.	1	4	5	8	9	14
109.	1	4	5	8	10	12

249.	2	6	9	10	12	14
250.	2	6	10	12	13	14
251.	2	7	8	9	10	14
252.	2	7	8	10	11	13
253.	2	7	8	11	13	14
254.	2	7	9	10	13	14
255.	2	7	9	11	12	14
256.	2	8	9	12	13	14
257.	2	9	10	11	12	13
258.	3	4	5	6	8	13
259.	3	4	5	6	9	14
260.	3	4	5	6	11	12
261.	3	4	5	7	8	9
262.	3	4	5	7	10	12
263.	3	4	5	7	10	13
264.	3	4	5	7	10	14
265.	3	4	5	8	10	11
266.	3	4	5	8	11	12
267.	3	4	5	9	11	12
268.	3	4	5	11	13	14
269.	3	4	6	7	9	11
270.	3	4	6	7	11	13
271.	3	4	6	7	12	14
272.	3	4	6	8	9	12
273.	3	4	6	8	10	12
274.	3	4	6	8	11	14
275.	3	4	6	9	10	13
276.	3	4	7	8	10	11
277.	3	4	7	8	12	14
278.	3	4	7	9	12	13
279.	3	4	7	11	12	14
280.	3	4	8	9	13	14
281.	3	4	8	10	11	13
282.	3	4	9	10	11	14
283.	3	4	10	12	13	14
284.	3	5	6	7	8	14
285.	3	5	6	7	9	13
286.	3	5	6	7	10	11
287.	3	5	6	8	9	10
288.	3	5	6	8	12	13
289.	3	5	6	10	13	14
290.	3	5	7	8	11	13
291.	3	5	7	9	11	12
292.	3	5	7	12	13	14
293.	3	5	8	9	10	13
294.	3	5	8	9	11	14

110.	1	4	5	8	11	13
111.	1	4	5	9	10	11
112.	1	4	5	10	11	14
113.	1	4	6	7	11	14
114.	1	4	6	8	9	10
115.	1	4	6	8	13	14
116.	1	4	6	9	11	13
117.	1	4	6	9	12	14
118.	1	4	6	10	13	14
119.	1	4	7	8	9	12
120.	1	4	7	8	11	14
121.	1	4	7	9	10	13
122.	1	4	7	10	11	13
123.	1	4	7	10	12	14
124.	1	4	7	11	12	13
125.	1	4	7	11	13	14
126.	1	4	8	10	11	12
127.	1	4	8	10	12	13
128.	1	4	9	11	12	14
129.	1	4	9	12	13	14
130.	1	5	6	7	10	11
131.	1	5	6	7	13	14
132.	1	5	6	8	9	13
133.	1	5	6	8	12	14
134.	1	5	6	9	10	14
135.	1	5	6	10	12	13
136.	1	5	7	8	9	11
137.	1	5	7	8	10	14
138.	1	5	7	9	12	13
139.	1	5	7	11	12	14
140.	1	5	8	10	11	13
141.	1	5	8	11	12	13
142.	1	5	9	10	11	12
143.	1	5	9	11	13	14
144.	1	5	10	12	13	14
145.	1	6	7	8	9	14
146.	1	6	7	8	10	12
147.	1	6	7	8	11	13
148.	1	6	7	9	10	13
149.	1	6	7	9	11	12
150.	1	6	8	9	11	12
151.	1	6	8	10	11	14
152.	1	6	9	10	11	12
153.	1	6	11	12	13	14
154.	1	7	8	9	10	13
155.	1	7	8	12	13	14

295.	3	5	8	10	12	14
296.	3	5	9	10	12	14
297.	3	5	9	11	12	13
298.	3	5	10	11	12	14
299.	3	6	7	8	10	14
300.	3	6	7	8	11	12
301.	3	6	7	8	13	14
302.	3	6	7	9	10	12
303.	3	6	8	9	11	13
304.	3	6	8	9	12	14
305.	3	6	9	10	11	14
306.	3	6	9	11	12	14
307.	3	6	9	12	13	14
308.	3	6	10	11	12	13
309.	3	7	8	9	10	14
310.	3	7	8	10	11	14
311.	3	7	8	10	12	13
312.	3	7	9	10	11	13
313.	3	7	9	11	13	14
314.	3	8	9	10	11	12
315.	3	8	11	12	13	14
316.	4	5	6	7	10	11
317.	4	5	6	7	13	14
318.	4	5	6	8	9	11
319.	4	5	6	8	10	14
320.	4	5	6	9	10	12
321.	4	5	6	11	12	14
322.	4	5	7	8	9	10
323.	4	5	7	8	11	14
324.	4	5	7	8	12	13
325.	4	5	7	9	11	13
326.	4	5	7	9	12	14
327.	4	5	8	9	12	13
328.	4	5	8	12	13	14
329.	4	5	9	10	13	14
330.	4	5	10	11	12	13
331.	4	6	7	8	9	13
332.	4	6	7	8	11	12
333.	4	6	7	9	10	14
334.	4	6	7	10	12	13
335.	4	6	8	10	11	13
336.	4	6	8	12	13	14
337.	4	6	9	11	12	13
338.	4	6	9	11	13	14
339.	4	6	10	11	12	14
340.	4	7	8	9	11	14

156. 1 7 9 10 11 14
157. 1 8 9 10 12 14
158. 1 8 9 11 13 14
159. 1 9 10 11 12 13
160. 2 3 4 5 6 7
161. 2 3 4 5 8 11
162. 2 3 4 5 8 14
163. 2 3 4 5 9 10
164. 2 3 4 5 12 13
165. 2 3 4 6 7 8
166. 2 3 4 6 7 11
167. 2 3 4 6 10 14
168. 2 3 4 6 12 13
169. 2 3 4 7 9 10
170. 2 3 4 7 13 14
171. 2 3 4 8 9 10
172. 2 3 4 8 12 13
173. 2 3 4 9 11 13
174. 2 3 4 9 12 14
175. 2 3 4 10 11 12
176. 2 3 5 6 7 12
177. 2 3 5 6 8 13
178. 2 3 5 6 9 11
179. 2 3 5 6 10 12
180. 2 3 5 6 12 14
181. 2 3 5 7 8 10
182. 2 3 5 7 11 14
183. 2 3 5 8 9 12
184. 2 3 5 9 13 14
185. 2 3 5 10 11 13

341. 4 7 8 10 13 14
342. 4 7 9 10 11 12
343. 4 8 9 10 11 13
344. 4 8 9 10 12 14
345. 4 8 11 12 13 14
346. 5 6 7 8 9 12
347. 5 6 7 8 10 13
348. 5 6 7 9 11 14
349. 5 6 7 10 12 14
350. 5 6 7 11 12 13
351. 5 6 8 10 11 12
352. 5 6 8 11 13 14
353. 5 6 9 10 11 13
354. 5 6 9 12 13 14
355. 5 7 8 9 13 14
356. 5 7 8 10 11 12
357. 5 7 9 10 12 13
358. 5 7 10 11 13 14
359. 5 8 9 10 11 14
360. 5 8 9 11 12 14
361. 6 7 8 9 10 11
362. 6 7 8 11 12 14
363. 6 7 9 12 13 14
364. 6 7 10 11 13 14
365. 6 8 9 10 12 13
366. 6 8 9 10 13 14
367. 7 8 9 10 12 14
368. 7 8 9 11 12 13
369. 7 10 11 12 13 14
370. 8 10 11 12 13 14
371. 9 10 11 12 13 14

LOTTERY SYSTEMS WITH A 5-WIN GUARANTEED IF 6 OF YOUR NUMBERS ARE DRAWN

SYSTEM # 8: GUARANTEED 5–WIN IF 6 OF THE NUMBERS DRAWN ARE IN YOUR SET OF 8 NUMBERS

Winning possibilities

Guessed	6	5	4	3	%
6	1	-	3	-	14.29
	-	2	2	-	85.71
5	-	1	1	2	42.86
	-	-	3	1	57.14
4	-	-	2	-	8.57
	-	-	1	2	68.57
	-	-	-	4	22.86
3	-	-	-	2	42.86
	-	-	-	1	57.14

Note that this system guarantees not one but two 5-wins if six numbers are guessed correctly. Also, the system is MATHEMATICALLY MINIMAL with respect to each of the following guarantees: Two 5-wins on six numbers guessed correctly; three 4-wins on five numbers guessed correctly; and a 3-win on three numbers guessed correctly. The complete system would require 28 combinations. If all of the numbers are guessed correctly, you will either win the jackpot (plus some extra cash!), or you will get two 5-wins plus two 4-wins. The system is HIGHLY BALANCED: Each number participates in exactly 3 of the combinations of the system. In addition, every two combination differ in at least two numbers, that is, the combinations are as 'apart' as possible.

1. 1 2 3 5 6 7
2. 1 2 4 5 6 8
3. 1 3 4 5 7 8
4. 2 3 4 6 7 8

SYSTEM # 9: GUARANTEED 5–WIN IF 6 OF THE NUMBERS DRAWN ARE IN YOUR SET OF 9 NUMBERS ©Copyright 2001

Winning possibilities

Guessed	**6**	**5**	**4**	**3**	%
6	1	2	0-1	3-4	7.14
	1	-	3	3	1.19
	-	3	0-3	1-4	13.10
	-	2	3-4	1-2	17.86
	-	1	4-6	0-2	60.71
5	-	3	-	-	0.79
	-	2	2	-	2.38
	-	1	3	-	1.59
	-	1	2	2-4	21.43
	-	1	-	5-6	3.17
	-	-	5	1	2.38
	-	-	4	2	2.38
	-	-	3	2-4	44.44
	-	-	2	4-5	21.44
4	-	-	4	-	0.79
	-	-	3	-	3.97
	-	-	2	2	9.52
	-	-	1	1-5	49.21
	-	-	-	4-6	36.51
3	-	-	-	4	4.76
	-	-	-	3	11.90
	-	-	-	2	35.71
	-	-	-	1	40.48
	-	-	-	-	7.15

Aside from the main guarantee, the system also guarantees at least two 4-wins (and a number of 3-wins) on guessing correctly 5 of the numbers drawn. The complete system would require 84 combinations. If all of the numbers are guessed correctly, you will either win the jackpot (plus some extra cash!), or you will get anywhere between one and three 5-wins (and a number of smaller prizes). The system is well balanced: The numbers 5,8 and 9 are each in 4 combinations; the remaining six numbers are each in 5 combinations.

1. 1 2 3 4 6 8
2. 1 2 3 5 7 9
3. 1 2 4 6 7 8
4. 1 3 4 5 7 9
5. 1 3 5 6 7 9
6. 2 3 4 6 7 8
7. 2 4 5 6 8 9

System # 10: Guaranteed 5–win if 6 of the numbers drawn are in your set of 10 numbers ©Copyright 2001

Winning possibilities

Guessed	6	5	4	3	%
6	1	1	4	8	2.86
	1	-	3-6	7-10	3.81
	-	3	3-5	5-8	10.48
	-	2	3-7	3-9	42.86
	-	1	6-10	1-6	39.99
5	-	2	-	8	1.19
	-	1	1-4	4-9	30.94
	-	-	5	4-7	14.28
	-	-	4	5-8	36.90
	-	-	3	7-9	16.69
4	-	-	2	1-5	22.86
	-	-	1	4-7	54.29
	-	-	-	7-10	22.85
3	-	-	-	4	3.33
	-	-	-	3	37.50
	-	-	-	2	48.33
	-	-	-	1	10.84

Aside from the main guarantee, the system also guarantees at least three 4-wins (and a number of 3-wins) on guessing correctly 5 of the numbers drawn, and at least one 3-win (89.16% chances for two or more 3-wins) if three of the numbers drawn are guessed correctly. The complete system would require 210 combinations. If all of the numbers are guessed correctly, you will either win the jackpot (plus some extra cash!), or you will get anywhere between one and three 5-wins (and a number of smaller prizes). The system is well balanced: The numbers 1,5,9 and 10 are each in 9 combinations; the remaining six numbers are each in 8 combinations.

1. 1 2 3 5 6 9
2. 1 2 4 5 7 9
3. 1 2 4 5 7 10
4. 1 2 6 8 9 10
5. 1 3 4 5 8 10
6. 1 3 4 6 7 10
7. 1 3 5 7 8 9
8. 1 3 7 8 9 10
9. 1 4 5 6 8 9
10. 2 3 4 6 7 8
11. 2 3 4 8 9 10
12. 2 3 5 6 9 10
13. 2 5 6 7 8 10
14. 4 5 6 7 9 10

SYSTEM # 11: GUARANTEED 5–WIN IF 6 OF THE NUMBERS DRAWN ARE IN YOUR SET OF 11 NUMBERS ©Copyright 2001

Winning possibilities

Guessed	**6**	**5**	**4**	**3**	%
6	1	-	5	15	4.76
	-	2	6	10	47.62
	-	1	9	7	23.81
	-	1	8	10	23.81
5	-	1	2	10	23.81
	-	1	-	15	4.76
	-	-	5	7	23.81
	-	-	4	10	47.62
4	-	-	2	4	16.67
	-	-	1	7	33.33
	-	-	1	6	33.33
	-	-	-	10	16.67
3	-	-	-	3	66.67
	-	-	-	2	33.33

Aside from the main guarantee, the system also guarantees at least four 4-wins (and a number of 3-wins) on guessing correctly 5 of the numbers drawn, and at least two 3-wins if three of the numbers drawn are guessed correctly. The complete system would require 462 combinations. If all of the numbers are guessed correctly, you will either win the jackpot (plus some extra cash!), or you will get either one or two 5-wins (and a number of smaller prizes). The system is EXCEPTIONALLY HIGHLY BALANCED: Each number is in exactly 12 combinations; each pair of numbers is in exactly 6 combinations. It also has an additional nice property: Every two combinations differ in at least two numbers, that is, the combinations are as 'apart' as possible.

1.	1	2	3	5	6	8
2.	1	2	3	7	9	11
3.	1	2	4	5	7	9
4.	1	2	4	6	10	11
5.	1	2	4	8	9	10
6.	1	2	5	6	7	10
7.	1	3	4	5	10	11
8.	1	3	4	6	7	8
9.	1	3	4	8	9	11
10.	1	3	6	7	9	10
11.	1	5	6	8	9	11
12.	1	5	7	8	10	11
13.	2	3	4	5	6	9
14.	2	3	4	7	8	10
15.	2	3	5	9	10	11
16.	2	3	6	8	10	11
17.	2	4	5	7	8	11
18.	2	6	7	8	9	11
19.	3	4	5	6	7	11
20.	3	5	7	8	9	10
21.	4	5	6	8	9	10
22.	4	6	7	9	10	11

SYSTEM # 12: GUARANTEED 5–WIN IF 6 OF THE NUMBERS DRAWN ARE IN YOUR SET OF 12 NUMBERS

Winning possibilities

Guessed	6	5	4	3	%
6	1	2	-	32	0.22
	1	1	9	16	0.43
	1	1	4	26	1.73
	1	-	6	24	1.73
	-	3	5-8	16-22	5.63
	-	2	6-17	0-22	38.31
	-	1	8-13	10-20	51.95
5	-	2	1	16	1.01
	-	2	-	17	0.51
	-	1	6	12	0.51
	-	1	4	14	2.02
	-	1	3	15	8.08
	-	1	2	16	12.12
	-	1	1	17	3.03
	-	-	8	11	1.01
	-	-	7	12	1.52
	-	-	6	13	15.66
	-	-	5	14	37.37
	-	-	4	15	17.16
4	-	-	3	5-8	1.21
	-	-	2	4-10	28.28
	-	-	1	8-13	54.95
	-	-	-	12-16	15.56
3	-	-	-	5	7.27
	-	-	-	4	30.91
	-	-	-	3	61.82

Aside from the main guarantee, the system also guarantees at least four 4-wins (and a number of 3-wins) on guessing correctly 5 of the numbers drawn, and at least three 3-wins if three of the numbers drawn are guessed correctly. The complete system would require 924 combinations. If all of the numbers are guessed correctly, you will either win the jackpot (plus some extra cash!), or you will get anywhere between one and three 5-wins (and a number of smaller prizes). The system is HIGHLY BALANCED: Each number participates in exactly 19 combinations.

1. 1 2 3 4 9 12
2. 1 2 3 4 10 11
3. 1 2 3 5 7 10

20. 2 3 4 5 10 12
21. 2 3 4 6 7 8
22. 2 3 5 6 11 12

4. 1 2 3 8 9 11
5. 1 2 4 5 6 8
6. 1 2 4 7 11 12
7. 1 2 5 7 10 11
8. 1 2 6 8 10 12
9. 1 2 6 9 10 12
10. 1 3 4 6 10 11
11. 1 3 5 6 7 9
12. 1 3 5 8 11 12
13. 1 3 6 10 11 12
14. 1 3 7 8 10 12
15. 1 4 5 6 7 12
16. 1 4 5 8 9 10
17. 1 4 7 8 9 10
18. 1 5 9 10 11 12
19. 1 6 7 8 9 11

23. 2 3 6 7 11 12
24. 2 3 8 9 10 11
25. 2 4 5 6 9 11
26. 2 4 5 7 8 9
27. 2 4 6 7 9 10
28. 2 4 8 10 11 12
29. 2 5 7 8 9 12
30. 3 4 5 7 8 11
31. 3 4 5 7 9 11
32. 3 4 6 8 9 12
33. 3 5 6 8 9 10
34. 3 7 9 10 11 12
35. 4 5 6 7 10 12
36. 4 6 8 9 11 12
37. 5 6 7 8 9 12
38. 5 6 7 8 10 11

System # 13: Guaranteed 5–win if 6 of the numbers drawn are in your set of 13 numbers ©Copyright 2001

Winning possibilities

Guessed	6	5	4	3	%
6	1	3	6	32	0.06
	1	2	8	30	0.12
	1	1	6-13	23-33	0.52
	1	-	5-13	25-41	0.06
	-	5	7	24	0.12
	-	4	5-9	22-32	0.82
	-	3	14-13	19-36	10.14
	-	2	7-16	15-33	28.73
	-	1	9-18	14-31	56.63
5	-	2	1-5	12-27	0.62
	-	1	0-9	9-31	27.20
	-	-	10-11	4-10	0.64
	-	-	8-9	11-18	2.80
	-	-	6-7	11-23	34.95
	-	-	4	17-23	33.79
4	-	-	4	0-9	0.56
	-	-	3	1-13	5.31
	-	-	2	6-14	22.52
	-	-	1	9-16	64.76
	-	-	-	14-19	6.85
3	-	-	-	7	1.75
	-	-	-	6	5.59
	-	-	-	5	24.48
	-	-	-	4	53.85
	-	-	-	3	14.33

Aside from the main guarantee, the system also guarantees at least four 4-wins (and a number of 3-wins) on guessing correctly 5 of the numbers drawn, and at least three 3-wins if three of the numbers drawn are guessed correctly. The complete system would require 1,716 combinations. If all of the numbers are guessed correctly, you will either win the jackpot (plus some extra cash!), or you will get anywhere between one and five 5-wins (and a number of smaller prizes). The next table contains information on the balance of the system.

Number(s)	Occurrences
1, 8, 9	29
2, 3, 4, 5, 6, 7,10,12,13	28
11	27

1.	1	2	3	4	6	11
2.	1	2	3	4	7	8
3.	1	2	3	4	7	13
4.	1	2	3	4	8	9
5.	1	2	3	7	8	13
6.	1	2	5	6	10	12
7.	1	2	5	7	9	10
8.	1	2	5	7	12	13
9.	1	2	5	8	9	12
10.	1	2	5	8	10	13
11.	1	2	6	7	11	13
12.	1	2	6	8	9	11
13.	1	2	7	8	10	12
14.	1	2	9	10	12	13
15.	1	3	4	5	10	12
16.	1	3	5	6	9	13
17.	1	3	5	7	10	11
18.	1	3	5	8	11	12
19.	1	3	6	7	9	12
20.	1	3	6	8	9	10
21.	1	3	10	11	12	13
22.	1	4	5	6	7	8
23.	1	4	5	9	11	13
24.	1	4	6	7	10	13
25.	1	4	6	8	12	13
26.	1	4	7	9	11	12
27.	1	4	8	9	10	11
28.	1	5	6	9	10	12
29.	1	7	8	9	11	13
30.	2	3	5	6	7	10
31.	2	3	5	6	8	12
32.	2	3	5	9	11	13
33.	2	3	6	10	12	13
34.	2	3	7	9	11	12
35.	2	3	8	9	10	11
36.	2	4	5	6	9	13
37.	2	4	5	7	8	11
38.	2	4	5	10	11	12
39.	2	4	6	7	9	12
40.	2	4	6	8	9	10
41.	2	4	7	10	11	13
42.	2	4	8	11	12	13
43.	2	6	7	8	9	13
44.	3	4	5	7	8	9
45.	3	4	5	7	12	13
46.	3	4	5	8	10	13
47.	3	4	5	9	10	12
48.	3	4	6	7	9	11
49.	3	4	6	8	11	13
50.	3	4	7	8	10	12
51.	3	4	7	9	10	13
52.	3	4	8	9	12	13
53.	3	6	7	8	11	13
54.	4	5	6	10	11	12
55.	5	6	7	9	10	11
56.	5	6	7	11	12	13
57.	5	6	8	9	11	12
58.	5	6	8	10	11	13
59.	5	8	9	10	12	13
60.	6	7	8	10	11	12
61.	6	9	10	11	12	13

System # 14: Guaranteed 5–win if 6 of the numbers drawn are in your set of 14 numbers ©Copyright 2001

Winning possibilities

Guessed	6	5	4	3	%
6	1	2	5-14	35-50	0.37
	1	1	6-13	36-51	0.87
	1	-	4-16	34-60	2.03
	-	6	6	37	0.03
	-	5	7-10	32-41	0.37
	-	4	4-13	31-53	2.36
	-	3	6-18	26-47	9.36
	-	2	8-18	23-46	30.87
	-	1	12-30	3-44	53.74
5	-	2	1-7	18-34	1.20
	-	1	0-10	16-45	26.97
	-	-	10-12	14-22	1.15
	-	-	8-9	17-31	12.49
	-	-	6-7	19-35	50.75
	-	-	5	26-34	7.44
4	-	-	5	0-6	0.30
	-	-	4	5-13	1.20
	-	-	3	3-18	7.09
	-	-	2	10-21	31.57
	-	-	1	14-23	56.14
	-	-	-	17-22	3.70
3	-	-	-	8	2.47
	-	-	-	7	7.97
	-	-	-	6	32.14
	-	-	-	5	40.93
	-	-	-	4	15.93
	-	-	-	3	0.56

Aside from the main guarantee, the system also guarantees at least five 4-wins (and a number of 3-wins) on guessing correctly 5 of the numbers drawn, and at least three 3-wins (99.44% chances for four or more 3-wins) if three of the numbers drawn are guessed correctly. The complete system would require 3,003 combinations. If all of the numbers are guessed correctly, you will either win the jackpot (plus some extra cash!), or you will get anywhere between one and six 5-wins (and a number of smaller prizes). Information on the balance of the system is given in the next table.

Number(s)	Occurrences
1,11	44
12,14	43
2, 3, 5, 7, 9,10	42
6,13	41
4, 8	40

1.	1	2	3	4	5	12
2.	1	2	3	4	7	10
3.	1	2	3	6	9	14
4.	1	2	3	7	9	11
5.	1	2	3	8	10	13
6.	1	2	4	6	10	14
7.	1	2	4	7	10	12
8.	1	2	4	8	9	13
9.	1	2	5	6	7	14
10.	1	2	5	6	8	11
11.	1	2	5	7	8	13
12.	1	2	5	9	10	14
13.	1	2	5	11	13	14
14.	1	2	6	9	12	13
15.	1	2	7	10	11	12
16.	1	2	8	9	12	14
17.	1	3	4	5	7	9
18.	1	3	4	6	8	11
19.	1	3	4	9	10	12
20.	1	3	4	11	13	14
21.	1	3	5	6	10	14
22.	1	3	5	7	10	11
23.	1	3	5	8	9	13
24.	1	3	6	7	8	14
25.	1	3	6	7	12	13
26.	1	3	6	11	12	13
27.	1	3	7	8	12	14
28.	1	3	7	11	12	13
29.	1	3	8	11	12	14
30.	1	4	5	6	9	14
31.	1	4	5	7	9	12
32.	1	4	5	8	10	13
33.	1	4	6	7	11	13
34.	1	4	6	8	11	12
35.	1	4	7	8	11	14
36.	1	4	11	12	13	14
37.	1	5	6	10	12	13
38.	1	5	7	9	11	12
39.	1	5	8	10	12	14
50.	2	3	6	8	10	12
51.	2	3	6	10	11	14
52.	2	3	7	9	11	12
53.	2	3	7	9	13	14
54.	2	3	8	9	11	13
55.	2	3	10	12	13	14
56.	2	4	5	9	10	11
57.	2	4	6	7	8	9
58.	2	4	6	9	11	14
59.	2	4	6	10	12	14
60.	2	4	7	9	13	14
61.	2	4	8	10	11	13
62.	2	5	6	7	8	12
63.	2	5	6	11	12	14
64.	2	5	7	12	13	14
65.	2	5	8	9	10	12
66.	2	5	8	11	12	13
67.	2	5	9	10	12	13
68.	2	6	7	10	11	13
69.	2	6	8	10	13	14
70.	2	7	8	10	11	14
71.	3	4	5	10	11	12
72.	3	4	6	7	12	14
73.	3	4	6	9	10	13
74.	3	4	7	8	12	13
75.	3	4	7	9	10	11
76.	3	4	8	9	10	14
77.	3	5	6	8	9	12
78.	3	5	6	9	11	14
79.	3	5	7	10	11	12
80.	3	5	7	10	13	14
81.	3	5	8	10	11	13
82.	3	5	9	12	13	14
83.	3	6	7	8	11	13
84.	4	5	6	7	8	10
85.	4	5	6	9	12	14
86.	4	5	6	10	11	14
87.	4	5	7	10	13	14
88.	4	5	8	9	11	13

40.	1	6	7	8	9	10
41.	1	6	8	11	12	14
42.	1	6	9	10	11	14
43.	1	7	9	10	13	14
44.	1	8	9	10	11	13
45.	2	3	4	5	6	13
46.	2	3	4	5	7	11
47.	2	3	4	5	8	14
48.	2	3	4	9	11	12
49.	2	3	5	7	9	10

89.	4	6	7	11	12	13
90.	4	6	8	12	13	14
91.	4	7	8	11	12	14
92.	5	6	7	9	11	13
93.	5	6	8	9	13	14
94.	5	7	8	9	11	14
95.	6	7	9	10	12	14
96.	6	8	9	10	11	12
97.	7	8	9	10	12	13
98.	9	10	11	12	13	14

System # 15: Guaranteed 5–win if 6 of the numbers drawn are in your set of 15 numbers ©Copyright 2001

Winning possibilities

Guessed	6	5	4	3	%
6	1	1	5-17	46-66	0.48
	1	-	5-20	44-68	2.36
	-	6	9-11	45-52	0.08
	-	5	5-12	45-64	0.06
	-	4	5-15	42-67	1.12
	-	3	8-20	34-66	9.61
	-	2	21	35-61	32.35
	-	1	14-25	29-61	53.94
5	-	2	1-4	35-42	0.40
	-	1	0-11	23-49	27.57
	-	-	13	20-32	4.26
	-	-	6-9	22-42	67.63
	-	-	5	40-42	0.14
4	-	-	4	1-16	0.51
	-	-	3	13-20	7.18
	-	-	2	12-23	40.81
	-	-	1	17-25	50.85
	-	-	-	25-26	0.65
3	-	-	-	9	2.86
	-	-	-	5-8	96.49
	-	-	-	4	0.65

Aside from the main guarantee, the system also guarantees at least five 4-wins (and a number of 3-wins) on guessing correctly 5 of the numbers drawn, and at least four 3-wins (99.35% chances for five or more 3-wins) if three of the numbers drawn are guessed correctly. The complete system would require 5,005 combinations. If all of the numbers are guessed correctly, you will either win the jackpot (plus some extra cash!), or you will get anywhere between one and six 5-wins (and a number of smaller prizes). The next table contains information on the balance of the system.

Number(s)	Occurrences
15	63
2, 3	62
14	61
9,12	56
1, 4, 5, 7,10,11	55
6, 8,13	54

1.	1	2	3	4	6	11
2.	1	2	3	4	7	9
3.	1	2	3	4	14	15
4.	1	2	3	5	8	10
5.	1	2	3	5	12	13
6.	1	2	3	6	8	9
7.	1	2	3	7	10	13
8.	1	2	3	10	11	12
9.	1	2	4	5	8	15
10.	1	2	4	8	13	14
11.	1	2	4	9	10	15
12.	1	2	4	10	12	14
13.	1	2	5	6	10	15
14.	1	2	5	7	11	15
15.	1	2	5	9	11	14
16.	1	2	5	10	12	14
17.	1	2	6	7	13	14
18.	1	2	6	9	12	14
19.	1	2	6	11	13	15
20.	1	2	7	8	11	14
21.	1	2	7	8	12	15
22.	1	2	9	12	13	15
23.	1	3	4	5	8	14
24.	1	3	4	8	13	15
25.	1	3	4	9	10	14
26.	1	3	4	10	12	15
27.	1	3	5	6	10	14
28.	1	3	5	7	11	14
29.	1	3	5	9	11	15
30.	1	3	5	10	12	15
31.	1	3	6	7	13	15
32.	1	3	6	9	12	15
33.	1	3	6	11	13	14
34.	1	3	7	8	11	15
35.	1	3	7	8	12	14
36.	1	3	9	12	13	14
37.	1	4	5	6	7	12
38.	1	4	5	6	9	13
39.	1	4	5	10	11	13
40.	1	4	6	7	8	10
41.	1	4	6	11	14	15
42.	1	4	7	9	14	15
43.	1	4	7	11	12	13
44.	1	4	8	9	11	12
45.	1	5	6	8	11	12
46.	1	5	7	8	9	13

72.	2	3	9	10	14	15
73.	2	4	5	6	11	14
74.	2	4	5	7	10	14
75.	2	4	5	7	13	15
76.	2	4	5	11	12	15
77.	2	4	6	7	9	15
78.	2	4	6	8	12	14
79.	2	4	6	12	13	15
80.	2	4	7	9	11	14
81.	2	4	8	9	13	14
82.	2	4	8	10	11	15
83.	2	5	6	8	13	14
84.	2	5	7	12	13	14
85.	2	5	8	9	12	15
86.	2	5	9	10	13	15
87.	2	6	7	10	12	15
88.	2	6	8	9	11	15
89.	2	6	8	10	11	14
90.	2	6	9	10	13	14
91.	2	7	8	9	10	14
92.	2	7	8	10	13	15
93.	2	7	9	11	12	15
94.	2	8	11	12	13	14
95.	2	10	11	12	13	14
96.	3	4	5	6	11	15
97.	3	4	5	7	10	15
98.	3	4	5	7	13	14
99.	3	4	5	11	12	14
100.	3	4	6	7	9	14
101.	3	4	6	8	12	15
102.	3	4	6	12	13	14
103.	3	4	7	9	11	15
104.	3	4	8	9	13	15
105.	3	4	8	10	11	14
106.	3	5	6	8	13	15
107.	3	5	7	12	13	15
108.	3	5	8	9	12	14
109.	3	5	9	10	13	14
110.	3	6	7	10	12	14
111.	3	6	8	9	11	14
112.	3	6	8	10	11	15
113.	3	6	9	10	13	15
114.	3	7	8	9	10	15
115.	3	7	8	10	13	14
116.	3	7	9	11	12	14
117.	3	8	11	12	13	15

47.	1	5	7	9	10	12
48.	1	5	8	10	14	15
49.	1	5	12	13	14	15
50.	1	6	7	9	10	11
51.	1	6	8	9	14	15
52.	1	6	8	10	12	13
53.	1	7	10	13	14	15
54.	1	8	9	10	11	13
55.	1	10	11	12	14	15
56.	2	3	4	5	9	12
57.	2	3	4	6	10	13
58.	2	3	4	7	8	12
59.	2	3	4	7	10	11
60.	2	3	4	9	11	13
61.	2	3	5	6	7	8
62.	2	3	5	6	7	9
63.	2	3	5	6	10	12
64.	2	3	5	7	14	15
65.	2	3	5	8	11	13
66.	2	3	5	9	10	11
67.	2	3	6	7	11	12
68.	2	3	6	12	13	15
69.	2	3	7	9	11	13
70.	2	3	8	9	10	12
71.	2	3	8	11	14	15

118.	3	10	11	12	13	15
119.	4	5	6	8	9	10
120.	4	5	7	8	9	11
121.	4	5	8	10	12	13
122.	4	5	9	12	14	15
123.	4	6	7	8	11	13
124.	4	6	9	10	11	12
125.	4	6	10	13	14	15
126.	4	7	8	12	14	15
127.	4	7	9	10	12	13
128.	4	7	10	11	14	15
129.	4	9	11	13	14	15
130.	5	6	7	8	14	15
131.	5	6	7	9	14	15
132.	5	6	7	10	11	13
133.	5	6	9	11	12	13
134.	5	6	10	12	14	15
135.	5	7	8	10	11	12
136.	5	8	11	13	14	15
137.	5	9	10	11	14	15
138.	6	7	8	9	12	13
139.	6	7	11	12	14	15
140.	6	8	9	12	13	15
141.	7	9	11	13	14	15
142.	8	9	10	12	14	15

SYSTEM # 16: GUARANTEED 5–WIN IF 6 OF THE NUMBERS DRAWN ARE IN YOUR SET OF 16 NUMBERS ©Copyright 2001

Winning possibilities

Guessed	6	5	4	3	%
6	1	3	7-15	69-92	0.17
	1	2	7-21	59-93	0.32
	1	1	7-21	64-96	0.85
	1	-	9-24	61-98	1.45
	-	7	5-11	72-88	0.02
	-	6	8-19	56-80	0.11
	-	5	7-19	59-92	0.46
	-	4	8-25	53-85	2.11
	-	3	11-26	47-85	13.02
	-	2	13-31	44-87	33.67
	-	1	16-31	46-85	47.82
5	-	4	3-4	48-50	0.05
	-	3	2-4	49-52	0.09
	-	2	0-9	40-59	1.30
	-	1	0-12	34-68	27.70
	-	-	6-17	27-55	70.86
4	-	-	6	20	0.05
	-	-	5	1-27	0.44
	-	-	4	16-26	1.76
	-	-	3	14-29	15.66
	-	-	2	19-33	46.32
	-	-	1	23-32	35.44
	-	-	-	31-33	0.33
3	-	-	-	11-13	4.11
	-	-	-	7-10	93.21
	-	-	-	5-6	2.68

Aside from the main guarantee, the system also guarantees at least six 4-wins (and a number of 3-wins) on guessing correctly 5 of the numbers drawn, and at least five 3-wins (97.32% chances for seven or more 3-wins) if three of the numbers drawn are guessed correctly. The complete system would require 8,008 combinations. If all of the numbers are guessed correctly, you will either win the jackpot (plus some extra cash!), or you will get anywhere between one and seven 5-wins (and a number of smaller prizes). The next table contains information on the balance of the system.

Number(s)	Occurrences
15	90
10	86
6, 7,13	85
1, 2, 5, 8	84
4, 9,12	83
3,11,14,16	82

1.	1	2	3	4	5	11	113.	2	4	7	10	14	16
2.	1	2	3	5	8	15	114.	2	4	7	12	13	15
3.	1	2	3	6	10	12	115.	2	4	8	9	15	16
4.	1	2	3	7	12	13	116.	2	4	8	10	11	13
5.	1	2	3	8	11	16	117.	2	5	6	10	11	12
6.	1	2	3	9	14	16	118.	2	5	6	10	12	15
7.	1	2	3	14	15	16	119.	2	5	7	11	12	13
8.	1	2	4	6	7	12	120.	2	5	7	12	13	15
9.	1	2	4	6	10	16	121.	2	5	8	11	14	15
10.	1	2	4	6	13	15	122.	2	5	8	11	14	16
11.	1	2	4	7	10	15	123.	2	5	9	11	12	15
12.	1	2	4	7	13	16	124.	2	6	7	8	9	15
13.	1	2	4	8	9	14	125.	2	6	7	9	12	16
14.	1	2	4	8	15	16	126.	2	6	7	10	13	16
15.	1	2	4	9	11	15	127.	2	6	8	9	10	16
16.	1	2	4	10	12	13	128.	2	6	8	12	13	14
17.	1	2	5	6	8	13	129.	2	6	9	10	11	14
18.	1	2	5	6	9	13	130.	2	6	11	12	13	16
19.	1	2	5	7	8	10	131.	2	6	11	13	15	16
20.	1	2	5	7	9	10	132.	2	7	8	9	13	16
21.	1	2	5	9	15	16	133.	2	7	8	10	12	14
22.	1	2	5	12	14	16	134.	2	7	9	11	13	14
23.	1	2	6	7	11	14	135.	2	7	10	11	12	16
24.	1	2	6	7	14	15	136.	2	7	10	11	15	16
25.	1	2	8	9	11	12	137.	2	8	9	10	13	15
26.	1	2	8	11	12	15	138.	2	8	12	14	15	16
27.	1	2	9	12	14	15	139.	2	9	10	12	13	16
28.	1	2	10	11	13	14	140.	3	4	5	6	9	10
29.	1	2	10	13	14	15	141.	3	4	5	6	12	13
30.	1	3	4	5	8	15	142.	3	4	5	7	9	13
31.	1	3	4	6	7	8	143.	3	4	5	7	10	12
32.	1	3	4	6	13	14	144.	3	4	5	8	14	16
33.	1	3	4	7	10	14	145.	3	4	6	7	15	16
34.	1	3	4	8	10	13	146.	3	4	6	10	11	16
35.	1	3	4	9	12	16	147.	3	4	7	11	13	16
36.	1	3	5	6	13	16	148.	3	4	8	9	11	14
37.	1	3	5	7	10	16	149.	3	4	8	9	11	15
38.	1	3	5	8	12	14	150.	3	4	9	12	14	15

39.	1	3	5	9	11	14
40.	1	3	6	8	9	10
41.	1	3	6	9	10	15
42.	1	3	6	10	12	13
43.	1	3	6	11	12	15
44.	1	3	7	8	9	13
45.	1	3	7	9	13	15
46.	1	3	7	10	12	16
47.	1	3	7	11	12	15
48.	1	3	8	12	14	15
49.	1	3	10	11	12	15
50.	1	3	11	12	13	15
51.	1	4	5	6	10	14
52.	1	4	5	7	13	14
53.	1	4	5	8	9	16
54.	1	4	5	8	11	12
55.	1	4	5	9	15	16
56.	1	4	5	12	14	15
57.	1	4	6	9	11	13
58.	1	4	7	9	10	11
59.	1	4	8	9	12	15
60.	1	4	11	12	14	16
61.	1	4	11	14	15	16
62.	1	5	6	7	9	12
63.	1	5	6	7	11	15
64.	1	5	6	10	11	16
65.	1	5	7	11	13	16
66.	1	5	8	9	15	16
67.	1	5	9	10	12	13
68.	1	5	10	11	13	15
69.	1	6	7	8	14	16
70.	1	6	7	9	11	16
71.	1	6	7	10	11	13
72.	1	6	8	10	11	15
73.	1	6	8	10	12	16
74.	1	6	8	11	13	14
75.	1	6	9	10	12	14
76.	1	6	12	13	15	16
77.	1	7	8	10	11	14
78.	1	7	8	11	13	15
79.	1	7	8	12	13	16
80.	1	7	9	12	13	14
81.	1	7	10	12	15	16
82.	1	8	10	13	14	16
83.	1	9	10	11	13	16
84.	1	9	11	14	15	16

151.	3	4	10	13	15	16
152.	3	5	6	8	10	11
153.	3	5	6	13	14	15
154.	3	5	7	8	11	13
155.	3	5	7	10	14	15
156.	3	5	9	11	12	16
157.	3	5	9	11	14	15
158.	3	5	9	12	15	16
159.	3	5	11	12	15	16
160.	3	6	7	8	11	12
161.	3	6	7	8	11	15
162.	3	6	7	9	12	14
163.	3	6	8	9	13	16
164.	3	6	8	13	15	16
165.	3	6	10	11	14	16
166.	3	6	10	12	14	16
167.	3	7	8	9	10	16
168.	3	7	8	10	15	16
169.	3	7	11	13	14	16
170.	3	7	12	13	14	16
171.	3	8	10	11	12	13
172.	3	8	10	11	13	15
173.	3	9	10	12	13	14
174.	4	5	6	7	9	15
175.	4	5	6	7	11	14
176.	4	5	6	7	12	16
177.	4	5	6	11	13	15
178.	4	5	7	10	11	15
179.	4	5	9	10	13	15
180.	4	5	10	11	13	14
181.	4	5	10	12	13	16
182.	4	6	7	9	14	16
183.	4	6	7	10	13	15
184.	4	6	8	9	12	13
185.	4	6	8	10	12	14
186.	4	6	8	10	14	15
187.	4	6	8	11	13	16
188.	4	6	9	10	11	12
189.	4	6	9	13	14	15
190.	4	7	8	9	10	12
191.	4	7	8	10	11	16
192.	4	7	8	12	13	14
193.	4	7	8	13	14	15
194.	4	7	9	10	14	15
195.	4	7	9	11	12	13
196.	4	8	11	12	15	16

No.						
85.	2	3	4	5	14	15
86.	2	3	4	6	7	9
87.	2	3	4	8	12	15
88.	2	3	4	8	12	16
89.	2	3	4	9	10	13
90.	2	3	4	11	12	14
91.	2	3	4	11	14	15
92.	2	3	5	6	7	14
93.	2	3	5	6	7	16
94.	2	3	5	8	9	12
95.	2	3	5	9	11	15
96.	2	3	5	10	13	14
97.	2	3	5	10	13	16
98.	2	3	6	8	10	14
99.	2	3	6	9	11	13
100.	2	3	6	10	12	15
101.	2	3	7	8	13	14
102.	2	3	7	9	10	11
103.	2	3	7	12	13	15
104.	2	3	9	14	15	16
105.	2	4	5	6	8	13
106.	2	4	5	7	8	10
107.	2	4	5	8	15	16
108.	2	4	5	9	11	16
109.	2	4	5	9	12	14
110.	2	4	6	7	8	11
111.	2	4	6	10	12	15
112.	2	4	6	13	14	16
197.	4	9	10	13	14	16
198.	4	9	12	14	15	16
199.	5	6	7	8	9	11
200.	5	6	7	8	10	13
201.	5	6	7	8	12	15
202.	5	6	8	9	14	15
203.	5	6	8	10	12	16
204.	5	6	9	13	14	16
205.	5	6	10	14	15	16
206.	5	6	11	12	13	14
207.	5	7	8	9	14	15
208.	5	7	8	12	13	16
209.	5	7	9	10	14	16
210.	5	7	10	11	12	14
211.	5	7	13	14	15	16
212.	5	8	9	10	11	13
213.	5	8	9	10	14	15
214.	5	8	9	13	14	15
215.	5	8	10	12	13	15
216.	5	8	11	14	15	16
217.	6	7	9	10	13	14
218.	6	7	11	12	14	15
219.	6	8	9	12	13	15
220.	6	9	10	11	15	16
221.	7	8	9	10	12	15
222.	7	9	11	13	15	16
223.	8	9	11	12	14	16
224.	10	11	12	13	14	15

LOTTERY SYSTEMS WITH A 4-WIN GUARANTEED IF 4 OF YOUR NUMBERS ARE DRAWN

SYSTEM # 17: GUARANTEED 4–WIN IF 4 OF THE NUMBERS DRAWN ARE IN YOUR SET OF 7 NUMBERS ©Copyright 2001

Winning possibilities

Guessed	6	5	4	3	%
6	1	4	-	-	71.43
	-	5	-	-	28.57
5	-	2	3	-	47.62
	-	1	4	-	47.62
	-	-	5	-	4.76
4	-	-	3	2	28.57
	-	-	2	3	57.14
	-	-	1	4	14.29
3	-	-	-	4	14.29
	-	-	-	3	57.14
	-	-	-	2	28.57

Aside from the main guarantee, the system also guarantees at least five 4-wins on guessing correctly 5 of the numbers drawn. There are 95.24% chances for one or two 5-wins (and a number of smaller prizes) if 5 of the the numbers drawn are guessed correctly. The complete system would require 7 combinations. If all of the numbers are guessed correctly, you are either a jackpot winner (plus some extra cash!) or you will get five 5-wins. The system is MATHEMATICALLY MINIMAL with respect to both the main guarantee and the guarantee two 3-wins if 3 of the the numbers drawn are guessed correctly. It is also well balanced: The numbers 1 and 4 are each in 5 combinations; the remaining 5 numbers are each in 4 combinations.

1. 1 2 3 4 5 6
2. 1 2 3 4 5 7
3. 1 2 3 4 6 7
4. 1 2 4 5 6 7
5. 1 3 4 5 6 7

SYSTEM # 18: GUARANTEED 4–WIN IF 4 OF THE NUMBERS DRAWN ARE IN YOUR SET OF 8 NUMBERS ©Copyright 2001

Winning possibilities

Guessed	**6**	**5**	**4**	**3**	%
6	1	2	4	-	21.43
	1	-	6	-	3.57
	-	4	3	-	32.14
	-	3	4	-	42.86
5	-	3	-	4	3.57
	-	1	4	2	32.14
	-	1	3	3	21.43
	-	1	2	4	10.71
	-	-	5	2	32.15
4	-	-	3	2	8.57
	-	-	3	1	5.71
	-	-	2	4	12.86
	-	-	2	2	8.57
	-	-	1	5	51.43
	-	-	1	4	12.86
3	-	-	-	4	14.29
	-	-	-	3	21.43
	-	-	-	2	64.28

Aside from the main guarantee, the system also guarantees at least five 4-wins and two 3-wins on guessing correctly 5 of the numbers drawn. There are 67.85% chances for one or three 5-wins if 5 of the the numbers drawn are guessed correctly. The complete system would require 28 combinations. If all of the numbers drawn are guessed correctly, you are either a jackpot winner (plus some extra cash!) or you will get three or four 5-wins (and a number of smaller prizes). The system is MATHEMATICALLY MINIMAL with respect to both the main guarantee and the guarantee two 3-wins if 3 of the the numbers drawn are guessed correctly. It is also well balanced: The numbers 4 and 6 are each in 6 combinations; the remaining 6 numbers are each in 5 combinations.

1. 1 2 3 4 5 6
2. 1 2 3 5 7 8
3. 1 2 4 6 7 8
4. 1 3 4 5 6 7
5. 1 3 4 5 6 8
6. 2 3 4 6 7 8
7. 2 4 5 6 7 8

SYSTEM # 19: GUARANTEED 4–WIN IF 4 OF THE NUMBERS DRAWN ARE IN YOUR SET OF 9 NUMBERS

Winning possibilities

Guessed	**6**	**5**	**4**	**3**	%
6	1	-	9	2	14.29
	-	3	6	3	85.71
5	-	1	3	7	57.14
	-	-	6	4	42.86
4	-	-	2	4	42.86
	-	-	1	7	57.14
3	-	-	-	3	85.71
	-	-	-	2	14.29

Aside from the main guarantee, the system also guarantees three 5-wins (plus six 4-wins and three 3-wins) if six of the numbers drawn are guessed correctly and six 4-wins (plus four 3-wins) on guessing correctly 5 of the numbers drawn. The system is MATHEMATICALLY MINIMAL with respect to all of the above mentioned guarantees. It is also EXCEPTIONALLY HIGHLY BALANCED: Each number is in exactly 8 combinations and each pair of numbers is in exactly 5 combinations. Every two combinations of the system differ in at least two numbers, that is, the combinations are as 'apart' as possible. The complete system would require 84 combinations.

1. 1 2 3 4 5 6
2. 1 2 3 4 8 9
3. 1 2 3 5 7 9
4. 1 2 4 5 7 8
5. 1 2 6 7 8 9
6. 1 3 4 6 7 9
7. 1 3 5 6 7 8
8. 1 4 5 6 8 9
9. 2 3 4 6 7 8
10. 2 3 5 6 8 9
11. 2 4 5 6 7 9
12. 3 4 5 7 8 9

SYSTEM # 20: GUARANTEED 4–WIN IF 4 OF THE NUMBERS DRAWN ARE IN YOUR SET OF 10 NUMBERS ©Copyright 2001

Winning possibilities

Guessed	**6**	**5**	**4**	**3**	%
6	1	-	12	4	2.38
	1	-	10	8	7.14
	-	3	8	7	28.57
	-	3	7	9	28.57
	-	2	9	8	28.57
	-	-	15	2	4.77
5	-	1	4	10	23.81
	-	1	3	11	23.81
	-	-	7	6	23.81
	-	-	5	11	23.81
	-	-	5	10	4.76
4	-	-	3	4	2.38
	-	-	3	2	4.76
	-	-	2	7	28.57
	-	-	1	9	28.57
	-	-	1	8	35.72
3	-	-	-	5	8.33
	-	-	-	4	16.67
	-	-	-	3	75.00

Aside from the main guarantee, the system also guarantees at least five 4-wins on guessing correctly 5 of the numbers drawn and at least three 3-wins if three of the numbers drawn are guessed correctly. The complete system would require 210 combinations. If all of the numbers are guessed correctly, then there are 95.23% chances that you will get at least two 5-wins (plus some extra cash). Of course, you can also win the jackpot plus a number of smaller prizes. The system is MATHEMATICALLY MINIMAL with respect to the main guarantee. It is HIGHLY BALANCED: Each number is in exactly 12 combinations. Also, every two combinations of the system differ in at least two numbers, that is, the combinations are as 'apart' as possible.

1.	1	2	3	4	8	9	11.	1	4	5	7	9	10
2.	1	2	3	5	6	7	12.	1	4	6	8	9	10
3.	1	2	3	5	9	10	13.	2	3	4	5	7	9
4.	1	2	4	5	8	10	14.	2	3	4	6	9	10
5.	1	2	4	6	7	8	15.	2	3	5	7	8	10
6.	1	2	6	7	9	10	16.	2	3	6	7	8	9
7.	1	3	4	5	6	10	17.	2	4	5	6	7	10
8.	1	3	4	5	7	8	18.	2	5	6	8	9	10

9. 1 3 5 6 8 9

10. 1 3 7 8 9 10

19. 3 4 6 7 8 10

20. 4 5 6 7 8 9

System # 21: Guaranteed 4–win if 4 of the numbers drawn are in your set of 11 numbers ©Copyright 2001

Winning possibilities

Guessed	6	5	4	3	%
6	1	2	7-8	16-17	0.87
	1	1	8-10	15-20	0.87
	1	-	8-13	13-22	5.19
	-	4	5-8	13-18	3.46
	-	3	7-12	9-19	26.84
	-	2	8-14	7-19	48.92
	-	1	10-15	7-18	12.99
	-	-	15	10-12	0.86
5	-	2	4	12	0.87
	-	2	3	13	0.43
	-	1	6	12	0.43
	-	1	5	11-14	6.93
	-	1	4	12-17	15.80
	-	1	3	14-18	11.69
	-	1	2	16-19	3.46
	-	1	1	20	0.43
	-	1	-	22	0.22
	-	-	9	7-8	1.30
	-	-	8	8-12	5.19
	-	-	7	9-13	13.20
	-	-	6	12-17	25.97
	-	-	5	14-17	14.08
4	-	-	4	1-4	1.82
	-	-	3	4-9	6.97
	-	-	2	6-11	26.06
	-	-	1	8-13	65.15
3	-	-	-	6	4.85
	-	-	-	5	8.48
	-	-	-	4	56.36
	-	-	-	3	30.31

Aside from the main guarantee, the system also guarantees at least five 4-wins (plus a number of 3-wins) if 5 of the numbers drawn are guessed correctly, and at least three 3-wins on guessing correctly 3 of the numbers drawn. The complete system would require 462 combinations. If all of the numbers are guessed correctly, then there are 99.14% chances that you will get at least one 5-win (plus some extra cash). Of course, you can also win the jackpot plus a number of smaller prizes. The system is MATHEMATICALLY MINIMAL with respect to the main guarantee. It is also well balanced: Each number is in either 17 or 18 combinations as seen from the table below.

Number(s)	Occurrences
1, 7, 8,10,11	18
2, 3, 4, 5, 6, 9	17

1.	1	2	3	4	5	7	17.	1	4	6	7	9	10
2.	1	2	3	4	6	10	18.	1	5	6	8	9	11
3.	1	2	3	4	8	11	19.	2	3	4	5	6	9
4.	1	2	3	7	8	9	20.	2	3	5	6	8	10
5.	1	2	4	7	9	11	21.	2	3	5	9	10	11
6.	1	2	5	6	8	11	22.	2	3	6	7	10	11
7.	1	2	5	7	9	10	23.	2	4	5	6	7	8
8.	1	2	6	7	9	10	24.	2	4	5	7	10	11
9.	1	2	7	8	10	11	25.	2	4	5	8	9	10
10.	1	3	4	5	8	9	26.	2	4	6	8	9	11
11.	1	3	5	6	7	11	27.	3	4	5	8	10	11
12.	1	3	5	7	8	10	28.	3	4	6	7	8	11
13.	1	3	6	8	9	11	29.	3	4	7	9	10	11
14.	1	3	8	9	10	11	30.	3	5	6	7	9	10
15.	1	4	5	6	10	11	31.	4	5	7	8	9	11
16.	1	4	6	7	8	10	32.	6	7	8	9	10	11

SYSTEM # 22: GUARANTEED 4–WIN IF 4 OF THE NUMBERS DRAWN ARE IN YOUR SET OF 12 NUMBERS ©Copyright 2001

Winning possibilities

Guessed	6	5	4	3	%
6	1	-	5-9	21-30	4.44
	-	6	-	20	0.11
	-	5	-	30	0.65
	-	3	3	29	2.16
	-	2	6-10	14-24	56.82
	-	1	11-14	14-17	35.71
	-	-	15	20	0.11
5	-	1	5	10	0.76
	-	1	4	14	3.79
	-	1	3	16-17	15.15
	-	1	2	19	7.58
	-	1	1	20	3.79
	-	-	6	13-16	37.88
	-	-	5	14-20	31.05
4	-	-	4	-	3.03
	-	-	2	8	15.15
	-	-	1	9-12	81.82
3	-	-	-	4	72.73
	-	-	-	3	27.27

Aside from the main guarantee, the system also guarantees at least five 4-wins (plus a number of 3-wins) if 5 of the numbers drawn are guessed correctly, and at least three 3-wins on guessing correctly 3 of the numbers drawn. The complete system would require 924 combinations. If all of the numbers are guessed correctly, then there are 99.89% chances that you will get at least one 5-win (plus some extra cash). Of course, you can also win the jackpot plus a number of smaller prizes. Every two combinations of the system differ in at least two numbers, that is, the combinations are as 'apart' as possible. The system is also well balanced: Each number is in either 20 or 21 combinations as seen from the table below.

Number(s)	Occurrences
4, 5, 6, 7,10,12	21
1, 2, 3, 8, 9,11	20

1. 1 2 3 4 8 9
2. 1 2 3 5 9 11
3. 1 2 3 6 7 12
4. 1 2 3 8 10 11
5. 1 2 4 5 10 12
6. 1 2 4 6 7 11
7. 1 2 5 6 7 8
8. 1 2 6 7 9 10
9. 1 2 8 9 11 12
10. 1 3 4 5 6 10
11. 1 3 4 7 11 12
12. 1 3 5 7 8 12
13. 1 3 6 8 9 11
14. 1 3 7 9 10 12
15. 1 4 5 6 9 12
16. 1 4 5 7 8 11
17. 1 4 6 8 10 12
18. 1 4 7 9 10 11
19. 1 5 6 10 11 12
20. 1 5 7 8 9 10
21. 2 3 4 5 7 10
22. 2 3 4 6 11 12
23. 2 3 5 6 8 12
24. 2 3 6 9 10 12
25. 2 3 7 8 9 11
26. 2 4 5 6 8 11
27. 2 4 5 7 9 12
28. 2 4 6 9 10 11
29. 2 4 7 8 10 12
30. 2 5 6 8 9 10
31. 2 5 7 10 11 12
32. 3 4 5 6 7 9
33. 3 4 5 8 11 12
34. 3 4 6 7 8 10
35. 3 4 9 10 11 12
36. 3 5 6 7 10 11
37. 3 5 8 9 10 12
38. 4 5 8 9 10 11
39. 4 6 7 8 9 12
40. 5 6 7 9 11 12
41. 6 7 8 10 11 12

System # 23: Guaranteed 4–win if 4 of the numbers drawn are in your set of 13 numbers ©Copyright 2001

Winning possibilities

Guessed	6	5	4	3	%
6	1	3	9	26-28	0.23
	1	1	10-11	27-31	0.35
	1	-	6-13	25-40	3.26
	-	4	6-9	27-34	0.52
	-	3	4-14	21-39	11.83
	-	2	7-15	21-38	43.12
	-	1	11-17	19-32	36.66
	-	-	15-21	14-26	4.03
5	-	2	3-5	18-21	0.71
	-	1	1-7	12-30	29.36
	-	-	12	6	0.08
	-	-	11	6-8	0.16
	-	-	9	10-14	0.70
	-	-	8	14-22	3.65
	-	-	7	15-23	16.47
	-	-	6	16-25	34.50
	-	-	5	20-27	14.37
4	-	-	5	0-4	1.26
	-	-	4	4-8	1.26
	-	-	3	4-14	2.52
	-	-	2	8-17	24.62
	-	-	1	12-17	70.34
3	-	-	-	8	0.70
	-	-	-	7	0.35
	-	-	-	6	11.19
	-	-	-	5	35.31
	-	-	-	4	52.45

Aside from the main guarantee, the system also guarantees at least five 4-wins (plus a number of 3-wins) if 5 of the numbers drawn are guessed correctly, and at least four 3-wins on guessing correctly 3 of the numbers drawn. The complete system would require 1,716 combinations. If all of the numbers are guessed correctly, then there are 95.97% chances that you will get at least one 5-win (plus some extra cash). Of course, you can also win the jackpot plus a number of smaller prizes. The next table contains information on the balance of the system.

Number(s)	Occurrences
8	32
1, 4, 6, 7	31
2, 3, 5, 9,10,11,12,13	30

1.	1	2	3	4	6	7
2.	1	2	3	5	7	9
3.	1	2	3	6	7	8
4.	1	2	3	7	10	12
5.	1	2	3	7	11	13
6.	1	2	4	5	10	11
7.	1	2	4	5	12	13
8.	1	2	4	6	7	8
9.	1	2	4	9	10	13
10.	1	2	4	9	11	12
11.	1	2	5	6	8	11
12.	1	2	6	8	9	13
13.	1	2	6	8	10	12
14.	1	3	4	5	6	9
15.	1	3	4	6	7	8
16.	1	3	4	6	10	12
17.	1	3	4	6	11	13
18.	1	3	5	8	9	10
19.	1	3	5	8	11	12
20.	1	3	5	9	11	13
21.	1	3	8	9	12	13
22.	1	3	8	10	11	13
23.	1	4	5	7	8	13
24.	1	4	7	8	9	11
25.	1	4	7	8	10	12
26.	1	5	6	7	11	12
27.	1	5	6	10	12	13
28.	1	5	7	9	10	12
29.	1	6	7	9	10	13
30.	1	6	9	10	11	12
31.	1	7	10	11	12	13
32.	2	3	4	5	8	12
33.	2	3	4	8	9	10
34.	2	3	4	8	11	13
35.	2	3	5	6	10	13
36.	2	3	5	6	11	12
37.	2	3	5	9	10	12
38.	2	3	6	9	10	11
39.	2	3	6	9	12	13
40.	2	3	10	11	12	13
41.	2	4	5	6	7	9
42.	2	4	6	7	10	12
43.	2	4	6	7	11	13
44.	2	5	7	8	9	12
45.	2	5	7	8	10	13
46.	2	5	7	9	11	13
47.	2	7	8	9	10	11
48.	2	7	8	11	12	13
49.	3	4	5	7	10	11
50.	3	4	5	7	12	13
51.	3	4	7	9	10	13
52.	3	4	7	9	11	12
53.	3	5	6	7	8	13
54.	3	6	7	8	9	11
55.	3	6	7	8	10	12
56.	4	5	6	8	9	10
57.	4	5	6	8	9	12
58.	4	5	6	9	11	13
59.	4	5	8	10	11	12
60.	4	5	9	10	11	13
61.	4	6	8	10	11	13
62.	4	6	8	11	12	13
63.	4	8	9	10	12	13
64.	5	6	7	8	10	11
65.	5	8	9	11	12	13
66.	6	7	8	9	12	13

System # 24: Guaranteed 4–win if 4 of the numbers drawn are in your set of 14 numbers

Winning possibilities

Guessed	6	5	4	3	%
6	1	-	12	24-32	0.66
	1	-	8	36-38	1.00
	1	-	5	44-46	1.00
	-	2	6-12	22-40	41.96
	-	1	11-13	26-32	43.96
	-	-	18	16	0.50
	-	-	17	22	0.67
	-	-	15	25-27	10.25
5	-	1	4	18-24	8.99
	-	1	3	23-24	4.00
	-	1	2	25-26	5.99
	-	1	1	26-27	3.00
	-	1	-	33-34	2.00
	-	-	7	15-18	5.99
	-	-	6	19-23	24.48
	-	-	5	22-25	45.55
4	-	-	5	-	1.60
	-	-	3	8	2.00
	-	-	2	8-10	9.49
	-	-	1	12-16	86.91
3	-	-	-	5	39.56
	-	-	-	4	60.44

Aside from the main guarantee, the system also guarantees at least five 4-wins (plus a number of 3-wins) if 5 of the numbers drawn are guessed correctly, and at least four 3-wins on guessing correctly 3 of the numbers drawn. The complete system would require 3,003 combinations. If all of the numbers are guessed correctly, then there are 88.57% chances that you will get at least one 5-win (plus some extra cash). Of course, you can also win the jackpot plus a number of smaller prizes. Every two combinations of the system differ in at least two numbers, that is, the combinations are as 'apart' as possible. The system is also well balanced: Each number is in either 34 or 35 combinations as seen from the table below.

Number(s)	Occurrences
8,12,13,14	35
1, 2, 3, 4, 5, 6, 7, 9,10,11	34

1.	1	2	3	4	10	11
2.	1	2	3	5	6	7
3.	1	2	3	8	9	14
4.	1	2	3	9	12	13
5.	1	2	4	5	9	10
6.	1	2	4	6	7	10
7.	1	2	4	8	10	12
8.	1	2	4	10	13	14
9.	1	2	5	8	11	14
10.	1	2	5	11	12	13
11.	1	2	6	7	8	12
12.	1	2	6	7	9	11
13.	1	2	6	7	13	14
14.	1	2	8	12	13	14
15.	1	3	4	5	7	11
16.	1	3	4	6	9	11
17.	1	3	4	8	11	12
18.	1	3	4	11	13	14
19.	1	3	5	7	8	13
20.	1	3	5	7	9	10
21.	1	3	5	7	12	14
22.	1	3	6	8	10	14
23.	1	3	6	10	12	13
24.	1	4	5	6	8	13
25.	1	4	5	6	12	14
26.	1	4	7	8	9	14
27.	1	4	7	9	12	13
28.	1	5	6	9	10	11
29.	1	5	8	9	10	12
30.	1	5	9	10	13	14
31.	1	6	8	9	11	13
32.	1	6	9	11	12	14
33.	1	7	8	10	11	13
34.	1	7	10	11	12	14
35.	2	3	4	5	6	9
36.	2	3	4	7	8	13
37.	2	3	4	7	12	14
38.	2	3	5	6	8	12
39.	2	3	5	6	10	11
40.	2	3	5	6	13	14
41.	2	3	7	9	10	11
42.	2	3	8	10	11	13
43.	2	3	10	11	12	14
44.	2	4	5	7	9	11
45.	2	4	5	8	9	13
46.	2	4	5	9	12	14
47.	2	4	6	8	11	14
48.	2	4	6	11	12	13
49.	2	5	7	8	10	14
50.	2	5	7	10	12	13
51.	2	6	8	9	10	13
52.	2	6	9	10	12	14
53.	2	7	8	9	11	12
54.	2	7	9	11	13	14
55.	3	4	5	8	10	14
56.	3	4	5	10	12	13
57.	3	4	6	7	9	10
58.	3	4	6	8	9	12
59.	3	4	6	9	13	14
60.	3	5	8	9	11	13
61.	3	5	9	11	12	14
62.	3	6	7	8	11	14
63.	3	6	7	11	12	13
64.	3	6	8	12	13	14
65.	3	7	8	9	10	12
66.	3	7	9	10	13	14
67.	4	5	6	7	10	11
68.	4	5	7	8	11	12
69.	4	5	7	11	13	14
70.	4	6	7	8	10	13
71.	4	6	7	10	12	14
72.	4	8	9	10	11	14
73.	4	8	11	12	13	14
74.	4	9	10	11	12	13
75.	5	6	7	8	9	14
76.	5	6	7	9	12	13
77.	5	6	8	10	11	12
78.	5	6	10	11	13	14
79.	5	8	10	12	13	14
80.	7	8	9	12	13	14

SYSTEM # 25: GUARANTEED 4–WIN IF 4 OF THE NUMBERS DRAWN ARE IN YOUR SET OF 15 NUMBERS ©Copyright 2001

Winning possibilities

Guessed	6	5	4	3	%
6	1	2	11-13	38-44	0.14
	1	1	5-14	39-52	0.48
	1	-	4-19	30-56	1.74
	-	5	8-13	32-44	0.16
	-	4	4-15	27-53	1.42
	-	3	6-16	26-51	3.66
	-	2	7-18	25-55	30.63
	-	1	10-20	29-53	47.85
	-	-	15-23	25-45	13.92
5	-	3	4	24-25	0.07
	-	2	1-10	16-37	0.43
	-	1	0-9	19-42	22.51
	-	-	5-12	15-38	76.99
4	-	-	7	1-2	0.15
	-	-	6	3-8	0.51
	-	-	5	4-11	1.25
	-	-	4	6-13	0.81
	-	-	3	8-19	3.08
	-	-	2	12-23	12.67
	-	-	1	12-22	81.53
3	-	-	-	7-10	10.99
	-	-	-	4-6	89.01

Aside from the main guarantee, the system also guarantees at least five 4-wins (plus a number of 3-wins) if 5 of the numbers drawn are guessed correctly, and at least four 3-wins on guessing correctly 3 of the numbers drawn. The complete system would require 5,005 combinations. If all of the numbers are guessed correctly, then there are 86.08% chances that you will get at least one 5-win (plus some extra cash). Of course, you can also win the jackpot plus a number of smaller prizes. The next table contains information on the balance of the system.

Number(s)	Occurrences
8	51
1,11,13	50
4, 6	48
2, 7, 9	47
3	46
5,10,12,14	45
15	44

1.	1	2	3	4	7	10
2.	1	2	3	5	9	13
3.	1	2	3	6	8	11
4.	1	2	3	12	14	15
5.	1	2	4	5	6	14
6.	1	2	4	6	8	14
7.	1	2	4	9	11	13
8.	1	2	4	12	13	15
9.	1	2	5	7	8	11
10.	1	2	5	10	12	15
11.	1	2	6	7	12	15
12.	1	2	6	9	10	13
13.	1	2	7	9	13	14
14.	1	2	8	9	12	13
15.	1	2	8	9	13	15
16.	1	2	8	10	11	14
17.	1	2	9	11	12	15
18.	1	3	4	5	7	8
19.	1	3	4	6	7	15
20.	1	3	4	7	9	12
21.	1	3	4	7	11	14
22.	1	3	4	11	13	14
23.	1	3	5	6	12	13
24.	1	3	5	8	11	14
25.	1	3	5	10	13	15
26.	1	3	6	7	8	13
27.	1	3	6	9	10	14
28.	1	3	8	9	11	15
29.	1	3	8	10	11	12
30.	1	4	5	7	11	13
31.	1	4	5	9	12	14
32.	1	4	5	10	14	15
33.	1	4	6	9	10	12
34.	1	4	6	11	12	13
35.	1	4	8	9	12	15
36.	1	4	8	10	11	13
37.	1	4	9	11	13	15

60.	2	3	7	11	13	15
61.	2	3	8	12	13	14
62.	2	3	9	11	12	14
63.	2	4	5	7	9	15
64.	2	4	5	8	12	13
65.	2	4	6	7	11	14
66.	2	4	6	9	14	15
67.	2	4	6	10	13	14
68.	2	4	6	12	13	14
69.	2	4	7	8	12	13
70.	2	4	8	9	11	15
71.	2	4	9	11	12	13
72.	2	5	6	7	10	13
73.	2	5	6	9	11	12
74.	2	5	8	9	10	14
75.	2	5	11	13	14	15
76.	2	6	8	10	12	13
77.	2	6	10	11	13	15
78.	2	7	8	10	14	15
79.	2	7	9	10	11	12
80.	2	8	11	12	13	15
81.	3	4	5	6	9	11
82.	3	4	5	7	13	14
83.	3	4	5	11	12	15
84.	3	4	6	8	11	12
85.	3	4	8	9	13	14
86.	3	4	8	10	12	14
87.	3	4	8	13	14	15
88.	3	5	6	7	10	14
89.	3	5	7	8	11	13
90.	3	5	7	9	14	15
91.	3	5	8	9	10	12
92.	3	6	7	11	12	13
93.	3	6	8	10	13	14
94.	3	6	9	12	13	15
95.	3	6	10	11	14	15
96.	3	7	8	10	12	15

38. 1 5 6 7 8 10
39. 1 5 6 9 11 15
40. 1 5 7 8 9 15
41. 1 5 7 8 11 12
42. 1 5 7 8 13 14
43. 1 5 7 9 10 11
44. 1 6 7 9 10 11
45. 1 6 7 13 14 15
46. 1 6 8 9 10 15
47. 1 6 8 11 12 14
48. 1 7 9 10 11 15
49. 1 7 10 12 13 14
50. 1 8 9 11 14 15
51. 2 3 4 5 10 11
52. 2 3 4 6 8 10
53. 2 3 4 6 13 14
54. 2 3 4 9 10 15
55. 2 3 4 10 12 13
56. 2 3 5 6 8 15
57. 2 3 5 7 12 14
58. 2 3 6 7 8 9
59. 2 3 6 10 12 14
97. 3 7 8 11 13 14
98. 3 7 9 10 11 13
99. 4 5 6 7 10 12
100. 4 5 6 8 13 15
101. 4 5 7 8 11 14
102. 4 5 8 9 10 13
103. 4 6 7 8 9 13
104. 4 6 10 11 12 15
105. 4 7 8 10 13 15
106. 4 7 9 10 11 14
107. 4 7 11 12 14 15
108. 5 6 7 8 11 15
109. 5 6 7 9 10 15
110. 5 6 8 9 11 13
111. 5 6 8 10 11 15
112. 5 6 8 12 14 15
113. 5 6 9 11 13 14
114. 5 7 9 12 13 15
115. 5 10 11 12 13 14
116. 6 7 8 9 12 14
117. 7 8 9 10 11 12
118. 9 10 12 13 14 15

SYSTEM # 26: GUARANTEED 4–WIN IF 4 OF THE NUMBERS DRAWN ARE IN YOUR SET OF 16 NUMBERS ©Copyright 2001

Winning possibilities

Guessed	6	5	4	3	%
6	1	2	7	56	0.80
	1	-	23	32	0.10
	1	-	3-7	64-68	1.00
	-	4	12-14	32-36	2.00
	-	4	12	36	1.60
	-	3	14	42	3.20
	-	2	6-18	32-60	12.19
	-	1	11-14	42-50	70.73
	-	-	16-20	32-40	10.38
5	-	2	8	20	1.47
	-	1	9	30	0.73
	-	1	5	26-34	1.10
	-	1	2	39	5.86
	-	1	1	36-42	10.26
	-	-	8	28	2.93
	-	-	7	25-33	21.98
	-	-	6	26-33	20.51
	-	-	5	30-33	35.16
4	-	-	10	-	0.44
	-	-	6	-	0.22
	-	-	2	12-18	20.22
	-	-	1	16-26	79.12
3	-	-	-	10	5.71
	-	-	-	6	14.29
	-	-	-	5	80.00

Aside from the main guarantee, the system also guarantees at least five 4-wins (plus a number of 3-wins) on guessing correctly 5 of the numbers drawn and at least five 3-wins if three of the numbers drawn are guessed correctly. The complete system would require 8,008 combinations. If all of the numbers are guessed correctly, then there are 89.62% chances that you will get at least one 5-win (plus some extra cash). Of course, you can also win the jackpot plus a number of smaller prizes. The system is HIGHLY BALANCED: Each number is in exactly 57 combinations.

1.	1	2	3	4	12	14
2.	1	2	3	5	8	16
3.	1	2	3	6	9	13
4.	1	2	3	7	10	15
77.	2	4	7	11	12	13
78.	2	4	8	12	15	16
79.	2	4	10	13	14	15
80.	2	5	6	10	15	16

5. 1 2 3 9 11 13
6. 1 2 4 5 7 10
7. 1 2 4 6 11 15
8. 1 2 4 8 9 13
9. 1 2 4 9 13 16
10. 1 2 5 6 9 13
11. 1 2 5 9 11 13
12. 1 2 5 12 14 15
13. 1 2 6 7 14 16
14. 1 2 6 8 10 12
15. 1 2 7 8 11 14
16. 1 2 7 9 12 13
17. 1 2 8 9 13 15
18. 1 2 9 10 13 14
19. 1 2 9 13 15 16
20. 1 2 10 11 12 16
21. 1 3 4 5 9 15
22. 1 3 4 6 7 8
23. 1 3 4 7 11 16
24. 1 3 4 10 12 13
25. 1 3 5 6 10 11
26. 1 3 5 6 11 14
27. 1 3 5 7 9 12
28. 1 3 5 8 13 16
29. 1 3 6 12 15 16
30. 1 3 7 13 14 15
31. 1 3 8 9 10 14
32. 1 3 8 11 12 15
33. 1 3 9 10 14 16
34. 1 4 5 6 12 16
35. 1 4 5 7 13 14
36. 1 4 5 8 11 12
37. 1 4 6 9 10 14
38. 1 4 6 11 13 15
39. 1 4 7 9 12 15
40. 1 4 8 10 15 16
41. 1 4 8 14 15 16
42. 1 4 9 10 11 14
43. 1 5 6 7 8 15
44. 1 5 7 11 15 16
45. 1 5 8 9 10 14
46. 1 5 9 10 14 16
47. 1 5 10 12 13 15
48. 1 6 7 9 11 12
49. 1 6 7 10 13 16
50. 1 6 8 9 11 16

81. 2 5 7 8 12 13
82. 2 5 7 9 14 15
83. 2 5 7 12 13 16
84. 2 5 8 10 11 15
85. 2 6 7 8 9 10
86. 2 6 7 12 13 15
87. 2 6 8 11 13 16
88. 2 6 9 12 14 16
89. 2 6 10 11 13 14
90. 2 7 9 10 11 16
91. 2 7 10 12 13 14
92. 2 7 11 12 13 15
93. 2 8 9 11 12 14
94. 2 8 10 13 14 16
95. 3 4 5 6 11 15
96. 3 4 5 7 12 15
97. 3 4 5 8 15 16
98. 3 4 5 10 14 15
99. 3 4 6 8 9 12
100. 3 4 6 13 14 16
101. 3 4 7 9 10 13
102. 3 4 8 11 13 14
103. 3 4 9 11 12 16
104. 3 5 6 7 11 13
105. 3 5 6 8 11 16
106. 3 5 6 9 10 11
107. 3 5 6 9 11 14
108. 3 5 6 11 12 13
109. 3 5 7 8 10 16
110. 3 5 7 8 14 16
111. 3 5 8 9 13 16
112. 3 5 8 10 12 16
113. 3 5 8 12 14 16
114. 3 6 7 9 15 16
115. 3 6 7 10 12 14
116. 3 6 8 10 13 15
117. 3 7 8 9 11 15
118. 3 7 10 11 12 14
119. 3 9 12 13 14 15
120. 3 10 11 13 15 16
121. 4 5 6 7 9 16
122. 4 5 6 8 10 13
123. 4 5 7 8 9 11
124. 4 5 9 12 13 14
125. 4 5 10 11 13 16
126. 4 6 7 10 11 15

51.	1	6	8	12	13	14
52.	1	6	9	10	14	15
53.	1	7	8	9	12	16
54.	1	7	8	10	11	13
55.	1	7	9	10	12	14
56.	1	9	10	11	14	15
57.	1	11	12	13	14	16
58.	2	3	4	5	13	15
59.	2	3	4	6	10	16
60.	2	3	4	7	9	14
61.	2	3	4	8	10	11
62.	2	3	5	6	7	11
63.	2	3	5	6	11	12
64.	2	3	5	8	9	16
65.	2	3	5	10	13	14
66.	2	3	6	8	14	15
67.	2	3	7	8	12	13
68.	2	3	7	12	13	16
69.	2	3	9	10	12	15
70.	2	3	11	14	15	16
71.	2	4	5	6	8	14
72.	2	4	5	9	10	12
73.	2	4	5	11	14	16
74.	2	4	6	7	12	13
75.	2	4	6	9	11	15
76.	2	4	7	8	15	16

127.	4	6	7	11	14	15
128.	4	6	8	11	15	16
129.	4	6	9	11	13	15
130.	4	6	10	11	12	15
131.	4	6	11	12	14	15
132.	4	7	8	10	12	14
133.	4	7	8	13	15	16
134.	4	7	10	12	14	16
135.	4	8	9	10	15	16
136.	4	8	9	14	15	16
137.	4	8	12	13	15	16
138.	5	6	7	10	12	14
139.	5	6	8	9	12	15
140.	5	6	13	14	15	16
141.	5	7	9	10	13	15
142.	5	7	10	11	12	14
143.	5	8	11	13	14	15
144.	5	9	11	12	15	16
145.	6	7	8	9	13	14
146.	6	7	8	11	12	16
147.	6	8	10	11	14	16
148.	6	9	10	12	13	16
149.	7	8	10	12	14	15
150.	7	9	11	13	14	16
151.	7	10	12	14	15	16
152.	8	9	10	11	12	13

SYSTEM # 27: GUARANTEED 4–WIN IF 4 OF THE NUMBERS DRAWN ARE IN YOUR SET OF 17 NUMBERS ©**Copyright 2001**

Winning possibilities

Guessed	6	5	4	3	%
6	1	1	11	46-57	0.16
	1	1	7	57-63	0.16
	1	-	0-8	56-83	1.20
	-	3	10-12	36-51	1.62
	-	2	8-15	36-62	18.26
	-	1	10-18	43-63	58.56
	-	-	15-19	38-53	20.04
5	-	2	5	24	0.32
	-	1	6	24-34	3.88
	-	1	4	32-42	1.31
	-	1	3	37-43	0.34
	-	1	2	37-44	2.08
	-	1	1	38-45	7.68
	-	1	-	40-46	2.29
	-	-	10	26	0.03
	-	-	9	25-32	0.26
	-	-	8	24-37	1.00
	-	-	7	25-39	6.42
	-	-	6	26-40	30.80
	-	-	5	30-40	43.59
4	-	-	7	-	0.84
	-	-	2	12-21	13.45
	-	-	1	16-25	85.71
3	-	-	-	8	0.88
	-	-	-	7	13.97
	-	-	-	6	22.35
	-	-	-	5	62.80

Aside from the main guarantee, the system also guarantees at least five 4-wins (plus a number of 3-wins) on guessing correctly 5 of the numbers drawn, and at least five 3-wins if three of the numbers drawn are guessed correctly. The complete system would require 12,376 combinations. If all of the numbers are guessed correctly, then there are 79.96% chances that you will get at least one 5-win (plus some extra cash). Of course, you can also win the jackpot plus a number of smaller prizes. The next table gives information on the balance of the system.

Number(s)	Occurrences
2	72
6	69
1, 3	68
4, 5	67
8,13	66
7, 9,10,11,12,14,15,16,17	65

1.	1	2	3	4	6	7
2.	1	2	3	4	10	13
3.	1	2	3	5	7	8
4.	1	2	3	5	9	12
5.	1	2	3	6	11	16
6.	1	2	3	8	10	14
7.	1	2	3	14	15	17
8.	1	2	4	5	8	13
9.	1	2	4	5	16	17
10.	1	2	4	8	12	14
11.	1	2	4	9	11	15
12.	1	2	4	9	14	17
13.	1	2	4	10	11	12
14.	1	2	5	6	9	14
15.	1	2	5	6	10	15
16.	1	2	5	11	12	13
17.	1	2	6	8	11	17
18.	1	2	6	8	13	15
19.	1	2	6	10	12	17
20.	1	2	6	13	14	16
21.	1	2	7	8	9	15
22.	1	2	7	9	13	17
23.	1	2	7	10	11	14
24.	1	2	7	10	16	17
25.	1	2	7	12	15	16
26.	1	2	8	9	10	16
27.	1	2	12	13	15	17
28.	1	3	4	5	11	14
29.	1	3	4	5	15	16
30.	1	3	4	6	8	9
31.	1	3	4	7	12	17
32.	1	3	5	6	13	17
33.	1	3	5	9	13	15
34.	1	3	5	10	12	16
35.	1	3	6	7	10	15
36.	1	3	6	8	12	16
37.	1	3	6	11	14	15
38.	1	3	6	12	13	14
95.	2	5	6	8	12	16
96.	2	5	6	10	15	16
97.	2	5	7	9	11	16
98.	2	5	7	10	13	15
99.	2	5	7	12	14	17
100.	2	5	8	10	12	15
101.	2	5	8	11	14	17
102.	2	5	9	10	15	17
103.	2	6	8	9	11	17
104.	2	6	9	10	11	13
105.	2	6	11	12	14	15
106.	2	6	13	14	16	17
107.	2	7	8	9	14	15
108.	2	7	8	11	12	17
109.	2	7	8	13	14	16
110.	2	8	10	11	13	17
111.	2	8	11	15	16	17
112.	2	9	13	14	15	16
113.	2	10	12	13	14	16
114.	3	4	5	6	10	17
115.	3	4	5	7	15	16
116.	3	4	5	8	12	13
117.	3	4	6	10	11	12
118.	3	4	6	13	15	16
119.	3	4	7	8	10	14
120.	3	4	7	9	11	13
121.	3	4	9	10	15	16
122.	3	4	9	13	14	17
123.	3	4	11	15	16	17
124.	3	4	12	14	15	16
125.	3	5	6	7	9	17
126.	3	5	6	8	15	17
127.	3	5	6	11	12	17
128.	3	5	6	14	16	17
129.	3	5	7	10	11	13
130.	3	5	7	12	14	15
131.	3	5	8	9	10	14
132.	3	5	8	9	11	16

39.	1	3	7	8	11	13
40.	1	3	7	9	14	16
41.	1	3	8	11	12	15
42.	1	3	8	13	16	17
43.	1	3	9	10	11	17
44.	1	4	5	6	12	15
45.	1	4	5	7	9	10
46.	1	4	5	7	12	14
47.	1	4	6	9	10	13
48.	1	4	6	10	14	16
49.	1	4	6	11	13	17
50.	1	4	7	8	11	16
51.	1	4	7	13	14	15
52.	1	4	8	10	15	17
53.	1	4	9	12	13	16
54.	1	5	6	7	13	16
55.	1	5	6	8	10	11
56.	1	5	6	9	11	16
57.	1	5	7	11	15	17
58.	1	5	8	9	12	17
59.	1	5	8	14	15	16
60.	1	5	10	13	14	17
61.	1	6	7	8	14	17
62.	1	6	7	9	11	12
63.	1	6	9	15	16	17
64.	1	7	8	10	12	13
65.	1	8	9	11	13	14
66.	1	9	10	12	14	15
67.	1	10	11	13	15	16
68.	1	11	12	14	16	17
69.	2	3	4	5	9	12
70.	2	3	4	6	7	14
71.	2	3	4	8	11	17
72.	2	3	4	8	15	16
73.	2	3	5	6	13	17
74.	2	3	5	10	11	15
75.	2	3	5	13	14	16
76.	2	3	6	8	10	14
77.	2	3	6	9	12	15
78.	2	3	7	9	10	12
79.	2	3	7	10	16	17
80.	2	3	7	11	13	15
81.	2	3	8	9	12	13
82.	2	3	9	11	12	14
83.	2	3	9	12	16	17
84.	2	4	5	6	7	11

133.	3	6	7	8	11	13
134.	3	6	7	8	12	16
135.	3	6	9	10	13	16
136.	3	6	9	11	14	15
137.	3	7	8	9	15	17
138.	3	7	11	12	13	16
139.	3	7	11	13	14	17
140.	3	8	10	11	14	16
141.	3	8	10	12	14	17
142.	3	8	10	13	14	15
143.	3	10	12	13	15	17
144.	4	5	6	8	13	14
145.	4	5	6	9	11	16
146.	4	5	7	8	13	17
147.	4	5	7	12	14	16
148.	4	5	8	10	13	16
149.	4	5	8	11	13	15
150.	4	5	9	14	15	17
151.	4	5	10	11	12	17
152.	4	6	8	11	14	15
153.	4	6	8	12	16	17
154.	4	6	9	10	13	15
155.	4	6	9	12	14	17
156.	4	7	8	9	12	15
157.	4	7	9	11	14	17
158.	4	7	10	11	12	15
159.	4	7	10	13	16	17
160.	4	8	9	10	11	12
161.	4	8	9	14	16	17
162.	4	10	11	12	13	14
163.	5	6	7	8	9	15
164.	5	6	7	10	12	14
165.	5	6	9	10	12	13
166.	5	6	11	13	14	15
167.	5	7	8	10	16	17
168.	5	7	8	11	12	14
169.	5	7	9	12	13	14
170.	5	9	10	11	14	16
171.	5	9	11	12	15	16
172.	5	9	11	13	16	17
173.	5	12	13	15	16	17
174.	6	7	9	10	13	14
175.	6	7	10	11	16	17
176.	6	7	11	14	15	16
177.	6	7	12	13	15	17
178.	6	8	9	10	13	17

85.	2	4	5	8	9	13
86.	2	4	5	10	14	15
87.	2	4	6	7	8	10
88.	2	4	6	7	9	16
89.	2	4	6	7	12	13
90.	2	4	6	7	15	17
91.	2	4	9	10	14	17
92.	2	4	10	11	12	16
93.	2	4	11	13	14	16
94.	2	4	12	13	15	17

179.	6	8	9	12	14	16
180.	6	8	10	12	15	16
181.	6	8	11	12	13	16
182.	6	10	11	14	15	17
183.	7	8	9	10	11	15
184.	7	8	9	13	15	16
185.	7	9	10	12	16	17
186.	7	10	14	15	16	17
187.	8	12	13	14	15	17
188.	9	11	12	13	15	17

SYSTEM # 28: GUARANTEED 4–WIN IF 4 OF THE NUMBERS DRAWN ARE IN YOUR SET OF 18 NUMBERS ©Copyright 2001

Winning possibilities

Guessed	6	5	4	3	%
6	1	1	-	80	0.52
	1	-	6-8	64-72	0.75
	-	2	15	44	1.29
	-	2	10-12	50-62	13.19
	-	2	6	60	1.29
	-	1	10-13	53-65	59.47
	-	-	15-19	44-60	23.49
5	-	2	-	40	0.56
	-	1	6	24-30	3.27
	-	1	1	40-47	11.20
	-	1	-	42	0.93
	-	-	7	33	11.20
	-	-	6	30-38	22.41
	-	-	5	31-42	50.43
4	-	-	7	-	0.65
	-	-	2	16	11.76
	-	-	1	16-21	87.59
3	-	-	-	7	9.80
	-	-	-	6	58.82
	-	-	-	5	31.38

Aside from the main guarantee, the system also guarantees at least five 4-wins (plus a number of 3-wins) on guessing correctly 5 of the numbers drawn, and at least five 3-wins if three of the numbers drawn are guessed correctly. The complete system would require 18,564 combinations. If all of the numbers are guessed correctly, then there are 76.51% chances that you will get at least one 5-win (plus some extra cash). Of course, you can also win the jackpot plus a number of smaller prizes. The next table gives information on the balance of the system.

Number(s)	Occurrences
1, 2, 3, 4, 5, 6, 7, 9,10,12,13,14,15,16,17,18	80
8,11	68

1.	1	2	3	4	5	10
2.	1	2	3	6	8	9
3.	1	2	3	6	9	11
119.	2	5	9	12	15	18
120.	2	5	10	13	15	16
121.	2	5	10	14	17	18

4.	1	2	3	7	12	16	122.	2	5	11	12	16	17
5.	1	2	3	12	17	18	123.	2	6	7	8	12	18
6.	1	2	3	13	14	15	124.	2	6	7	11	12	18
7.	1	2	4	6	13	17	125.	2	6	8	11	13	17
8.	1	2	4	6	15	18	126.	2	6	9	10	13	17
9.	1	2	4	7	9	16	127.	2	6	9	12	15	16
10.	1	2	4	8	12	14	128.	2	6	12	13	14	17
11.	1	2	4	11	12	14	129.	2	6	13	15	17	18
12.	1	2	5	6	10	12	130.	2	7	9	12	15	17
13.	1	2	5	7	15	16	131.	2	7	10	14	15	18
14.	1	2	5	8	13	18	132.	2	8	9	11	12	15
15.	1	2	5	9	14	17	133.	2	8	9	13	14	16
16.	1	2	5	11	13	18	134.	2	8	10	11	14	18
17.	1	2	6	7	14	16	135.	2	9	11	13	14	16
18.	1	2	7	8	11	16	136.	2	10	12	14	16	18
19.	1	2	7	10	13	16	137.	3	4	6	7	15	16
20.	1	2	7	16	17	18	138.	3	4	6	8	13	18
21.	1	2	8	10	15	17	139.	3	4	6	9	14	17
22.	1	2	9	10	14	18	140.	3	4	6	11	13	18
23.	1	2	9	12	13	15	141.	3	4	7	8	9	12
24.	1	2	10	11	15	17	142.	3	4	7	9	11	12
25.	1	3	4	6	10	12	143.	3	4	7	10	13	17
26.	1	3	4	7	13	14	144.	3	4	8	10	14	15
27.	1	3	4	8	16	17	145.	3	4	9	10	16	18
28.	1	3	4	9	15	18	146.	3	4	10	11	14	15
29.	1	3	4	11	16	17	147.	3	4	12	13	15	16
30.	1	3	5	6	13	14	148.	3	4	12	14	17	18
31.	1	3	5	6	16	18	149.	3	5	6	7	9	15
32.	1	3	5	7	9	17	150.	3	5	6	8	10	17
33.	1	3	5	8	12	15	151.	3	5	6	10	11	17
34.	1	3	5	11	12	15	152.	3	5	7	8	13	16
35.	1	3	6	7	15	17	153.	3	5	7	10	12	14
36.	1	3	7	8	10	18	154.	3	5	7	11	13	16
37.	1	3	7	10	11	18	155.	3	5	8	9	14	18
38.	1	3	8	11	13	14	156.	3	5	9	10	12	16
39.	1	3	9	10	15	16	157.	3	5	9	11	14	18
40.	1	3	9	12	13	14	158.	3	5	10	13	15	18
41.	1	3	10	13	14	17	159.	3	5	12	13	17	18
42.	1	3	13	14	16	18	160.	3	5	14	15	16	17
43.	1	4	5	6	7	8	161.	3	6	7	8	11	15
44.	1	4	5	6	7	11	162.	3	6	7	12	13	15
45.	1	4	5	9	12	17	163.	3	6	7	14	15	18
46.	1	4	5	12	13	16	164.	3	6	8	12	14	16
47.	1	4	5	14	15	18	165.	3	6	9	10	13	16
48.	1	4	6	9	14	16	166.	3	6	9	12	17	18
49.	1	4	7	10	14	17	167.	3	6	11	12	14	16

50.	1	4	7	12	15	18
51.	1	4	8	9	10	13
52.	1	4	8	11	15	18
53.	1	4	9	10	11	13
54.	1	4	10	15	16	18
55.	1	4	13	15	17	18
56.	1	5	6	9	15	17
57.	1	5	7	10	13	15
58.	1	5	7	12	14	18
59.	1	5	8	9	11	17
60.	1	5	8	10	14	16
61.	1	5	9	10	17	18
62.	1	5	9	13	16	17
63.	1	5	10	11	14	16
64.	1	6	7	9	10	12
65.	1	6	7	9	13	18
66.	1	6	8	10	11	12
67.	1	6	8	13	15	16
68.	1	6	8	14	17	18
69.	1	6	10	12	13	18
70.	1	6	10	12	14	15
71.	1	6	10	12	16	17
72.	1	6	11	13	15	16
73.	1	6	11	14	17	18
74.	1	7	8	9	14	15
75.	1	7	8	12	13	17
76.	1	7	9	11	14	15
77.	1	7	11	12	13	17
78.	1	8	9	12	16	18
79.	1	9	11	12	16	18
80.	1	12	14	15	16	17
81.	2	3	4	5	6	12
82.	2	3	4	5	7	18
83.	2	3	4	5	8	11
84.	2	3	4	5	9	13
85.	2	3	4	5	14	16
86.	2	3	4	5	15	17
87.	2	3	6	7	10	15
88.	2	3	6	10	14	18
89.	2	3	6	13	16	17
90.	2	3	7	8	14	17
91.	2	3	7	9	13	18
92.	2	3	7	11	14	17
93.	2	3	8	10	12	13
94.	2	3	8	15	16	18
95.	2	3	9	10	16	17
168.	3	7	9	10	14	16
169.	3	7	12	16	17	18
170.	3	8	9	10	11	16
171.	3	8	9	13	15	17
172.	3	8	11	12	17	18
173.	3	9	11	13	15	17
174.	3	10	12	15	17	18
175.	4	5	6	9	10	14
176.	4	5	6	10	13	15
177.	4	5	6	16	17	18
178.	4	5	7	9	13	18
179.	4	5	7	10	16	17
180.	4	5	7	12	14	15
181.	4	5	8	9	15	16
182.	4	5	8	10	12	18
183.	4	5	8	13	14	17
184.	4	5	9	11	15	16
185.	4	5	10	11	12	18
186.	4	5	11	13	14	17
187.	4	6	7	10	17	18
188.	4	6	7	12	13	16
189.	4	6	8	9	11	14
190.	4	6	8	12	15	17
191.	4	6	9	12	14	18
192.	4	6	9	13	14	15
193.	4	6	11	12	15	17
194.	4	7	8	10	11	17
195.	4	7	8	14	16	18
196.	4	7	9	10	15	17
197.	4	7	11	14	16	18
198.	4	8	11	12	13	16
199.	4	9	12	13	16	17
200.	4	10	12	13	14	16
201.	5	6	7	10	16	18
202.	5	6	7	12	14	17
203.	5	6	8	9	12	13
204.	5	6	8	11	16	18
205.	5	6	9	11	12	13
206.	5	6	12	15	16	18
207.	5	6	13	14	16	18
208.	5	7	8	11	12	14
209.	5	7	8	15	17	18
210.	5	7	9	12	14	16
211.	5	7	11	15	17	18
212.	5	8	10	11	13	15
213.	5	9	10	13	14	15

96.	2	3	9	12	14	15
97.	2	3	10	11	12	13
98.	2	3	11	15	16	18
99.	2	4	6	7	9	14
100.	2	4	6	8	10	16
101.	2	4	6	10	11	16
102.	2	4	7	8	13	15
103.	2	4	7	10	12	17
104.	2	4	7	11	13	15
105.	2	4	8	9	17	18
106.	2	4	9	10	12	15
107.	2	4	9	11	17	18
108.	2	4	10	13	14	18
109.	2	4	12	13	16	18
110.	2	4	14	15	16	17
111.	2	5	6	7	13	17
112.	2	5	6	8	14	15
113.	2	5	6	9	16	18
114.	2	5	6	11	14	15
115.	2	5	7	8	9	10
116.	2	5	7	9	10	11
117.	2	5	7	12	13	14
118.	2	5	8	12	16	17

214.	5	10	12	13	15	17
215.	6	7	8	9	16	17
216.	6	7	8	10	13	14
217.	6	7	9	11	16	17
218.	6	7	10	11	13	14
219.	6	8	9	10	15	18
220.	6	9	10	11	15	18
221.	6	10	14	15	16	17
222.	7	8	9	11	13	18
223.	7	8	10	12	15	16
224.	7	9	10	12	13	18
225.	7	9	13	14	17	18
226.	7	9	13	15	16	18
227.	7	10	11	12	15	16
228.	7	13	14	15	16	17
229.	8	9	10	12	14	17
230.	8	10	13	16	17	18
231.	8	11	14	15	16	17
232.	8	12	13	14	15	18
233.	9	10	11	12	14	17
234.	9	14	15	16	17	18
235.	10	11	13	16	17	18
236.	11	12	13	14	15	18

System # 29: Guaranteed 4–win if 4 of the numbers drawn are in your set of 19 numbers ©Copyright 2001

Winning possibilities

Guessed	6	5	4	3	%
6	1	3	0-12	80-100	0.01
	1	2	0-6	72-103	0.41
	1	1	4-18	71-97	0.17
	1	-	1-23	62-96	0.60
	-	4	6-24	48-76	0.20
	-	3	3-24	51-86	3.47
	-	2	6-24	50-83	12.38
	-	1	10-23	57-84	56.42
	-	-	15-22	52-79	26.34
5	-	3	-	40-42	0.28
	-	2	0-8	24-58	0.36
	-	1	0-15	27-60	15.22
	-	-	9-15	24-50	0.30
	-	-	5-8	33-53	83.84
4	-	-	8	0-30	0.57
	-	-	6	4-34	0.34
	-	-	3	16-43	4.46
	-	-	2	16-30	11.20
	-	-	1	20-30	83.43
3	-	-	-	33	0.10
	-	-	-	13	0.31
	-	-	-	11	1.24
	-	-	-	9	1.14
	-	-	-	8	8.98
	-	-	-	7	38.29
	-	-	-	6	49.94

Aside from the main guarantee, the system also guarantees at least five 4-wins (plus a number of 3-wins) on guessing correctly 5 of the numbers drawn, and at least six 3-wins if three of the numbers drawn are guessed correctly. The complete system would require 27,132 combinations. If all of the numbers are guessed correctly, then there are 73.66% chances that you will get at least one 5-win (plus some extra cash). Of course, you can also win the jackpot plus a number of smaller prizes. The next table gives information on the balance of the system.

Number(s)	Occurrences
11,19	105
1, 2, 3, 4, 5, 6, 8, 9,10,12,13,14,16,17,18	103
7	101
15	94

1.	1	2	3	4	6	17
2.	1	2	3	5	13	18
3.	1	2	3	7	14	15
4.	1	2	3	8	10	18
5.	1	2	3	9	12	16
6.	1	2	3	11	14	19
7.	1	2	4	5	12	14
8.	1	2	4	7	10	13
9.	1	2	4	8	9	14
10.	1	2	4	11	16	18
11.	1	2	4	15	16	18
12.	1	2	4	16	18	19
13.	1	2	5	6	8	17
14.	1	2	5	7	8	16
15.	1	2	5	9	10	11
16.	1	2	5	9	10	15
17.	1	2	5	9	10	19
18.	1	2	6	7	16	17
19.	1	2	6	9	13	17
20.	1	2	6	10	12	17
21.	1	2	6	11	15	17
22.	1	2	6	14	17	18
23.	1	2	6	15	17	19
24.	1	2	7	9	12	18
25.	1	2	7	11	17	19
26.	1	2	8	11	12	13
27.	1	2	8	12	13	15
28.	1	2	8	12	13	19
29.	1	2	10	13	14	16
30.	1	3	4	5	8	11
31.	1	3	4	5	8	15
32.	1	3	4	5	8	19
33.	1	3	4	7	9	10
34.	1	3	4	12	13	16
35.	1	3	4	14	17	18
36.	1	3	5	6	10	14
37.	1	3	5	7	9	17
38.	1	3	5	10	12	16
39.	1	3	6	7	8	13
40.	1	3	6	9	11	18

163.	2	7	8	12	14	17
164.	2	7	9	10	14	18
165.	2	7	9	11	15	18
166.	2	7	9	15	18	19
167.	2	7	10	12	15	16
168.	2	7	11	14	16	19
169.	2	8	9	11	16	17
170.	2	8	9	15	16	17
171.	2	8	9	16	17	19
172.	2	9	10	12	13	17
173.	2	9	11	15	18	19
174.	2	10	11	12	16	19
175.	2	11	13	14	15	16
176.	2	12	13	14	16	18
177.	2	13	14	15	16	19
178.	3	4	5	6	7	13
179.	3	4	5	9	10	17
180.	3	4	5	14	16	18
181.	3	4	6	8	9	16
182.	3	4	6	10	11	12
183.	3	4	6	10	12	15
184.	3	4	6	10	12	19
185.	3	4	7	8	14	18
186.	3	4	7	15	16	17
187.	3	4	8	12	13	17
188.	3	4	9	12	14	18
189.	3	4	10	13	14	18
190.	3	4	11	14	15	18
191.	3	4	11	16	17	19
192.	3	4	14	15	18	19
193.	3	5	6	8	12	18
194.	3	5	6	9	12	17
195.	3	5	7	8	14	16
196.	3	5	7	10	15	18
197.	3	5	7	11	14	19
198.	3	5	8	9	17	18
199.	3	5	9	11	15	17
200.	3	5	9	13	16	17
201.	3	5	9	15	17	19
202.	3	5	10	11	18	19

41. 1 3 6 9 15 18
42. 1 3 6 9 18 19
43. 1 3 6 12 14 16
44. 1 3 7 11 18 19
45. 1 3 7 12 16 18
46. 1 3 8 9 13 14
47. 1 3 8 12 16 17
48. 1 3 10 11 13 17
49. 1 3 10 13 15 17
50. 1 3 10 13 17 19
51. 1 3 11 12 15 16
52. 1 3 12 15 16 19
53. 1 4 5 6 9 16
54. 1 4 5 7 10 17
55. 1 4 5 9 13 18
56. 1 4 6 7 10 18
57. 1 4 6 8 12 18
58. 1 4 6 11 13 14
59. 1 4 6 13 14 15
60. 1 4 6 13 14 19
61. 1 4 7 8 10 12
62. 1 4 7 10 14 16
63. 1 4 7 11 15 19
64. 1 4 8 13 16 17
65. 1 4 9 11 12 17
66. 1 4 9 12 15 17
67. 1 4 9 12 17 19
68. 1 4 10 11 15 19
69. 1 5 6 7 12 15
70. 1 5 6 11 12 19
71. 1 5 6 13 16 18
72. 1 5 7 11 12 19
73. 1 5 7 13 14 18
74. 1 5 8 9 12 14
75. 1 5 8 10 13 18
76. 1 5 11 13 15 18
77. 1 5 11 14 16 17
78. 1 5 12 13 17 18
79. 1 5 13 15 18 19
80. 1 5 14 15 16 17
81. 1 5 14 16 17 19
82. 1 6 7 8 9 14
83. 1 6 7 11 16 19
84. 1 6 8 10 11 16
85. 1 6 8 10 15 16
86. 1 6 8 10 16 19

203. 3 5 11 12 13 14
204. 3 5 12 13 14 15
205. 3 5 12 13 14 19
206. 3 6 7 9 13 14
207. 3 6 7 10 13 16
208. 3 6 7 11 13 15
209. 3 6 7 13 15 19
210. 3 6 7 13 17 18
211. 3 6 8 11 14 17
212. 3 6 8 14 15 17
213. 3 6 8 14 17 19
214. 3 6 10 16 17 18
215. 3 6 11 13 15 19
216. 3 7 8 9 12 15
217. 3 7 8 11 12 19
218. 3 7 9 10 11 19
219. 3 7 10 12 14 17
220. 3 7 11 16 17 19
221. 3 8 9 11 12 19
222. 3 8 11 13 16 18
223. 3 8 13 15 16 18
224. 3 8 13 16 18 19
225. 3 9 10 11 14 16
226. 3 9 10 12 13 18
227. 3 9 10 14 15 16
228. 3 9 10 14 16 19
229. 4 5 6 8 10 14
230. 4 5 6 11 17 18
231. 4 5 6 15 17 18
232. 4 5 6 17 18 19
233. 4 5 7 8 16 18
234. 4 5 7 9 14 15
235. 4 5 7 11 17 19
236. 4 5 8 13 14 17
237. 4 5 9 11 14 19
238. 4 5 10 11 13 16
239. 4 5 10 13 15 16
240. 4 5 10 13 16 19
241. 4 6 7 8 11 19
242. 4 6 7 9 12 16
243. 4 6 7 12 14 17
244. 4 6 8 10 13 17
245. 4 6 9 11 15 16
246. 4 6 9 13 16 18
247. 4 6 9 14 16 17
248. 4 6 9 15 16 19

87.	1	6	9	10	12	13
88.	1	7	8	11	13	19
89.	1	7	8	15	17	18
90.	1	7	9	11	14	19
91.	1	7	9	13	15	16
92.	1	7	10	11	15	19
93.	1	7	12	13	14	17
94.	1	8	9	10	14	17
95.	1	8	9	11	14	15
96.	1	8	9	14	15	19
97.	1	8	9	14	16	18
98.	1	8	11	17	18	19
99.	1	9	10	16	17	18
100.	1	9	11	13	16	19
101.	1	10	11	12	14	18
102.	1	10	12	14	15	18
103.	1	10	12	14	18	19
104.	2	3	4	5	7	12
105.	2	3	4	6	14	18
106.	2	3	4	7	11	19
107.	2	3	4	8	10	16
108.	2	3	4	9	11	13
109.	2	3	4	9	13	15
110.	2	3	4	9	13	19
111.	2	3	5	6	11	16
112.	2	3	5	6	15	16
113.	2	3	5	6	16	19
114.	2	3	5	8	10	13
115.	2	3	5	9	14	17
116.	2	3	6	7	12	13
117.	2	3	6	8	9	10
118.	2	3	7	8	10	17
119.	2	3	7	9	16	18
120.	2	3	8	10	11	15
121.	2	3	8	10	12	14
122.	2	3	8	10	15	19
123.	2	3	11	12	17	18
124.	2	3	12	15	17	18
125.	2	3	12	17	18	19
126.	2	3	13	14	16	17
127.	2	4	5	6	12	13
128.	2	4	5	8	9	12
129.	2	4	5	10	12	18
130.	2	4	5	11	12	15
131.	2	4	5	12	15	19
132.	2	4	5	12	16	17

249.	4	7	8	9	13	17
250.	4	7	9	11	16	19
251.	4	7	10	11	15	19
252.	4	7	11	12	18	19
253.	4	7	11	13	14	19
254.	4	7	12	13	15	18
255.	4	8	9	10	11	18
256.	4	8	9	10	15	18
257.	4	8	9	10	18	19
258.	4	8	11	12	14	16
259.	4	8	11	13	15	17
260.	4	8	12	14	15	16
261.	4	8	12	14	16	19
262.	4	8	13	15	17	19
263.	4	9	10	12	13	14
264.	4	10	12	16	17	18
265.	4	11	12	13	18	19
266.	5	6	7	8	16	17
267.	5	6	7	9	11	19
268.	5	6	8	9	11	13
269.	5	6	8	9	13	15
270.	5	6	8	9	13	19
271.	5	6	9	10	14	18
272.	5	6	10	11	14	15
273.	5	6	10	12	14	16
274.	5	6	10	13	14	17
275.	5	6	10	14	15	19
276.	5	7	8	9	10	16
277.	5	7	8	11	15	16
278.	5	7	8	12	13	16
279.	5	7	8	15	16	19
280.	5	7	9	10	12	13
281.	5	7	10	11	18	19
282.	5	7	12	14	17	18
283.	5	8	10	11	12	17
284.	5	8	10	12	15	17
285.	5	8	10	12	17	19
286.	5	8	11	15	16	19
287.	5	9	11	12	16	18
288.	5	9	12	15	16	18
289.	5	9	12	16	18	19
290.	6	7	8	10	12	18
291.	6	7	9	10	15	17
292.	6	7	10	11	14	19
293.	6	7	11	17	18	19
294.	6	7	14	15	16	18

133. 2 4 6 7 8 15
134. 2 4 6 8 11 19
135. 2 4 6 9 10 16
136. 2 4 7 9 17 18
137. 2 4 7 13 14 16
138. 2 4 8 13 17 18
139. 2 4 10 11 14 17
140. 2 4 10 14 15 17
141. 2 4 10 14 17 19
142. 2 5 6 7 9 18
143. 2 5 6 7 10 14
144. 2 5 7 11 13 19
145. 2 5 7 13 15 17
146. 2 5 8 11 14 18
147. 2 5 8 14 15 18
148. 2 5 8 14 18 19
149. 2 5 9 13 14 16
150. 2 5 10 16 17 18
151. 2 5 11 13 17 19
152. 2 6 7 11 12 19
153. 2 6 8 12 16 18
154. 2 6 8 13 14 16
155. 2 6 9 11 12 14
156. 2 6 9 12 14 15
157. 2 6 9 12 14 19
158. 2 6 10 11 13 18
159. 2 6 10 13 15 18
160. 2 6 10 13 18 19
161. 2 7 8 9 13 18
162. 2 7 8 10 11 19
295. 6 8 9 12 17 18
296. 6 8 11 12 15 18
297. 6 8 12 13 14 18
298. 6 8 12 15 18 19
299. 6 9 10 11 17 19
300. 6 11 12 13 16 17
301. 6 11 14 16 18 19
302. 6 12 13 15 16 17
303. 6 12 13 16 17 19
304. 7 8 9 11 17 19
305. 7 8 10 13 14 15
306. 7 8 11 14 18 19
307. 7 9 11 12 13 19
308. 7 9 12 14 16 17
309. 7 10 11 12 16 19
310. 7 10 11 13 17 19
311. 7 10 13 16 17 18
312. 7 11 12 14 15 17
313. 7 11 13 16 18 19
314. 7 12 14 15 17 19
315. 8 9 10 12 13 16
316. 8 10 11 13 14 19
317. 8 10 14 16 17 18
318. 9 10 11 12 13 15
319. 9 10 12 13 15 19
320. 9 11 13 14 17 18
321. 9 13 14 15 17 18
322. 9 13 14 17 18 19
323. 10 11 15 16 17 18
324. 10 15 16 17 18 19
325. 11 12 14 15 17 19

LOTTERY SYSTEMS WITH A 4-WIN GUARANTEED IF 5 OF YOUR NUMBERS ARE DRAWN

SYSTEM # 30: GUARANTEED 4–WIN IF 5 OF THE NUMBERS DRAWN ARE IN YOUR SET OF 9 NUMBERS

Winning possibilities

Guessed	6	5	4	3	%
6	1	-	-	2	3.57
	-	1	1	1	64.29
	-	-	3	-	32.14
5	-	1	-	1	14.29
	-	-	2	-	21.43
	-	-	1	2	64.28
4	-	-	1	1	14.29
	-	-	1	-	21.43
	-	-	-	2	64.28
3	-	-	-	2	3.57
	-	-	-	1	64.29
	-	-	-	-	32.14

Aside from the main guarantee, the system also guarantees at least two 3-wins if four of the numbers drawn are guessed correctly. The complete system would require 84 combinations. If all of the numbers are guessed correctly, you will either win the jackpot, or you will get a 5-win (plus a 4-win and a 3-win), or three 4-wins. The system is MATHEMATICALLY MINIMAL with respect to both the main guarantee and the guarantee three 4-wins if 6 numbers are guessed correctly. It is HIGHLY BALANCED: Each number is in exactly 2 combinations. Also, every two combinations of the system differ in at least three numbers, that is, the combinations are as 'apart' as possible.

1. 1 2 3 5 7 9
2. 1 4 5 6 8 9
3. 2 3 4 6 7 8

System # 31: Guaranteed 4–win if 5 of the numbers drawn are in your set of 10 numbers ©Copyright 2001

Winning possibilities

Guessed	6	5	4	3	%
6	1	2	3	-	2.86
	1	-	-	-	0.48
	-	4	2	-	4.29
	-	3	-	4	3.81
	-	1	4	2	34.29
	-	1	-	4	11.43
	-	-	4	2	17.14
	-	-	3	4	25.70
5	-	2	4	-	2.38
	-	1	2	3	9.52
	-	1	-	-	2.38
	-	-	4	2	14.29
	-	-	3	1	4.76
	-	-	1	5	42.86
	-	-	1	3	9.52
	-	-	1	2	14.29
4	-	-	6	-	0.48
	-	-	2	4	11.43
	-	-	1	2	17.14
	-	-	1	-	7.14
	-	-	-	4	29.52
	-	-	-	2	34.29
3	-	-	-	6	3.33
	-	-	-	2	30.00
	-	-	-	1	36.67
	-	-	-	-	30.00

Aside from the main guarantee, the system also guarantees at least two 3-wins if four of the numbers drawn are guessed correctly. The complete system would require 210 combinations. If all of the numbers are guessed correctly, you will either win the jackpot, or you will get between one and four 5-wins (plus additional prizes), or at least three 4-wins and a number of 3-wins. Information on the balance of the system is given in the table below.

Number(s)	Occurrences
2, 3, 8, 9	6
1, 4, 5, 6, 7,10	3

1. 1 2 3 5 8 9
2. 1 2 3 7 8 9
3. 1 4 5 6 7 10
4. 2 3 4 6 8 9
5. 2 3 4 8 9 10
6. 2 3 5 7 8 9
7. 2 3 6 8 9 10

SYSTEM # 32: GUARANTEED 4–WIN IF 5 OF THE NUMBERS DRAWN ARE IN YOUR SET OF 11 NUMBERS

Winning possibilities

Guessed	6	5	4	3	%
6	1	2	2	4	0.87
	1	-	4	4	0.22
	1	-	-	4-8	1.09
	-	4	3	-	0.43
	-	3	3	2	1.73
	-	2	3-5	2-4	4.33
	-	1	1-6	2-7	47.61
	-	-	3-7	0-6	43.72
5	-	2	3	2	0.87
	-	1	0-4	2-6	11.25
	-	-	5	2-4	1.95
	-	-	4	2	3.46
	-	-	3	0-5	11.26
	-	-	2	2-6	22.51
	-	-	1	4-8	48.70
4	-	-	5	-	0.30
	-	-	2	4	4.85
	-	-	1	0-5	34.24
	-	-	-	3-7	60.61
3	-	-	-	5	2.42
	-	-	-	1-3	82.43
	-	-	-	-	15.15

Aside from the main guarantee, the system also guarantees at least three 3-wins if four of the numbers drawn are guessed correctly. The complete system would require 462 combinations. If all of the numbers are guessed correctly, you will either win the jackpot (plus some extra cash!), or you will get anywhere between one and four 5-wins (and additional prizes), or at least three 4-wins and a number of 3-wins. Below is information on the balance of the system.

Number(s)	Occurrences
1, 3, 5, 7	7
2, 4, 6, 8	5
9,10,11	4

1.	1	2	3	4	5	7
2.	1	2	3	5	7	8
3.	1	2	5	6	9	11
4.	1	3	4	5	6	7
5.	1	3	5	6	7	8
6.	1	3	5	7	9	10
7.	1	4	5	8	10	11
8.	2	3	6	7	10	11
9.	2	4	6	8	9	10
10.	3	4	7	8	9	11

SYSTEM # 33: GUARANTEED 4–WIN IF 5 OF THE NUMBERS DRAWN ARE IN YOUR SET OF 12 NUMBERS

Winning possibilities

Guessed	6	5	4	3	%
6	1	-	1	8	0.65
	1	-	-	10	0.87
	-	2	2	4	1.30
	-	1	2-3	5-8	51.95
	-	-	3-6	2-10	45.23
5	-	1	1	4	1.52
	-	1	-	5	9.09
	-	-	4	-	1.52
	-	-	3	1-3	7.58
	-	-	2	4-6	48.48
	-	-	1	6-8	31.81
4	-	-	2	-	0.61
	-	-	1	0-3	41.21
	-	-	-	5	19.39
	-	-	-	4	38.79
3	-	-	-	2	34.55
	-	-	-	1	58.18
	-	-	-	-	7.27

Aside from the main guarantee, the system also guarantees at least four 3-wins if four of the numbers drawn are guessed correctly. The complete system would require 924 combinations. If all of the numbers are guessed correctly, you will either win the jackpot (plus some extra cash!), or you will get one or two 5-wins (and additional prizes), or at least three 4-wins and a number of 3-wins. The system is HIGHLY BALANCED: Each number is in exactly 7 combinations. It also has the following nice property: Every two combinations of the system differ in at least two numbers, that is, the combinations are as 'apart' as possible.

1.	1	2	4	5	6	10	8.	2	3	4	5	7	9
2.	1	2	5	7	8	12	9.	2	3	4	6	8	11
3.	1	2	8	9	10	11	10.	2	3	5	6	9	12
4.	1	3	4	9	10	12	11.	2	3	7	10	11	12
5.	1	3	5	8	10	11	12.	4	5	8	9	11	12
6.	1	3	6	7	8	9	13.	4	6	7	8	10	12
7.	1	4	6	7	11	12	14.	5	6	7	9	10	11

System # 34: Guaranteed 4–win if 5 of the numbers drawn are in your set of 13 numbers

Winning possibilities

Guessed	**6**	**5**	**4**	**3**	%
6	1	-	0-1	10-13	1.22
	-	2	2	8-9	1.40
	-	1	0-6	0-11	48.60
	-	-	8	0-1	2.80
	-	-	7	-	0.17
	-	-	6	6-8	12.12
	-	-	5	8-9	13.29
	-	-	4	7-12	14.69
	-	-	3	10-13	5.71
5	-	1	1	6	1.86
	-	1	-	0-8	7.93
	-	-	4	0-3	1.40
	-	-	3	1-6	17.25
	-	-	2	6-8	40.56
	-	-	1	6-9	31.00
4	-	-	2	-	0.84
	-	-	1	0-5	42.38
	-	-	-	4-6	56.78
3	-	-	-	3	5.59
	-	-	-	2	37.06
	-	-	-	1	55.94
	-	-	-	-	1.41

Aside from the main guarantee, the system also guarantees at least four 3-wins if four of the numbers drawn are guessed correctly. The complete system would require 1,716 combinations. If all of the numbers are guessed correctly, you will either win the jackpot (plus some extra cash!), or you will get one or two 5-wins (and additional prizes), or at least three 4-wins and a number of 3-wins. This system has the property of the preceding one: Every two combinations differ in at least two numbers, that is, the combinations are as 'apart' as possible. The next table gives information on the balance of the system.

Number(s)	Occurrences
4	11
1, 5, 6, 7, 8,10,13	10
2, 3, 9,11,12	9

1.	1	2	3	5	6	10
2.	1	2	4	5	7	11
3.	1	2	4	8	9	10
4.	1	2	5	8	12	13
5.	1	3	4	5	7	12
6.	1	3	5	8	11	13
7.	1	3	7	9	10	13
8.	1	4	6	9	11	13
9.	1	5	6	10	11	12
10.	1	6	7	8	9	12
11.	2	3	4	7	8	13
12.	2	3	4	9	11	12
13.	2	4	6	7	10	12
14.	2	5	6	7	9	13
15.	2	6	8	10	11	13
16.	3	4	5	6	8	9
17.	3	4	6	7	10	11
18.	3	6	8	10	12	13
19.	4	5	9	10	12	13
20.	4	7	8	11	12	13
21.	5	7	8	9	10	11

System # 35: Guaranteed 4–win if 5 of the numbers drawn are in your set of 14 numbers

Winning possibilities

Guessed	6	5	4	3	%
6	1	-	1-2	16	1.00
	1	-	-	-	0.03
	-	2	2-3	12	2.40
	-	1	0-6	10-14	44.76
	-	-	10	-	0.80
	-	-	8	7	6.39
	-	-	7	0-16	4.00
	-	-	6	10-18	7.46
	-	-	5	11	12.79
	-	-	4	8-16	13.18
	-	-	3	12	7.19
5	-	1	2	8	0.60
	-	1	1	8	2.40
	-	1	-	9-10	6.00
	-	1	-	-	0.29
	-	-	4	6	2.40
	-	-	3	1-12	28.37
	-	-	2	9-13	27.57
	-	-	1	6-11	32.37
4	-	-	3	-	0.20
	-	-	2	-	1.20
	-	-	1	0-6	43.46
	-	-	-	4-9	55.14
3	-	-	-	3	15.38
	-	-	-	2	39.56
	-	-	-	1	45.06

Aside from the main guarantee, the system also guarantees at least four 3-wins if four of the numbers drawn are guessed correctly. The complete system would require 3,003 combinations. If all of the numbers are guessed correctly, you will either win the jackpot (plus some extra cash!), or you will get one or two 5-wins (and additional prizes), or at least three 4-wins and a number of 3-wins. Again, every two combinations of the system differ in at least two numbers. The next table gives information on the balance of the system.

Number(s)	Occurrences
1, 2, 3, 4, 5, 6, 7, 8	15
9,10,11,12,13,14	11

1.	1	2	3	4	9	12
2.	1	2	3	4	11	13
3.	1	2	5	6	9	11
4.	1	2	5	6	10	14
5.	1	2	5	6	12	13
6.	1	2	7	8	9	13
7.	1	2	7	8	11	12
8.	1	3	5	7	9	10
9.	1	3	5	7	11	14
10.	1	3	6	8	10	12
11.	1	3	6	8	13	14
12.	1	4	5	8	9	14
13.	1	4	5	8	10	11
14.	1	4	6	7	10	13
15.	1	4	6	7	12	14
16.	2	3	5	8	10	13
17.	2	3	5	8	12	14
18.	2	3	6	7	9	14
19.	2	3	6	7	10	11
20.	2	4	5	7	10	12
21.	2	4	5	7	13	14
22.	2	4	6	8	9	10
23.	2	4	6	8	11	14
24.	3	4	5	6	9	13
25.	3	4	5	6	11	12
26.	3	4	7	8	9	11
27.	3	4	7	8	10	14
28.	3	4	7	8	12	13
29.	5	6	7	8	9	12
30.	5	6	7	8	11	13
31.	9	10	11	12	13	14

System # 36: Guaranteed 4–win if 5 of the numbers drawn are in your set of 15 numbers

Winning possibilities

Guessed	6	5	4	3	%
6	1	-	0-3	12-19	0.82
	-	3	1-2	9-12	0.06
	-	2	0-6	7-18	2.06
	-	1	0-7	7-22	39.04
	-	-	3-10	3-21	57.12
5	-	1	2	4-11	0.70
	-	1	1	6-10	2.33
	-	1	-	6-14	5.16
	-	-	6	5	0.03
	-	-	5	4-7	0.30
	-	-	4	2-9	3.40
	-	-	3	3-11	17.35
	-	-	2	6-14	42.52
	-	-	1	8-15	28.21
4	-	-	3	-	0.07
	-	-	2	1-6	1.83
	-	-	1	0-8	41.17
	-	-	-	5-10	56.93
3	-	-	-	3-5	12.53
	-	-	-	1-2	87.26
	-	-	-	-	0.21

Aside from the main guarantee, the system also guarantees at least five 3-wins if four of the numbers drawn are guessed correctly. The complete system would require 5,005 combinations. If all of the numbers are guessed correctly, you will either win the jackpot (plus some extra cash!), or you will get anywhere between one and three 5-wins (and additional prizes), or at least three 4-wins and a number of 3-wins. Every two combinations of the system differ in at least two numbers. The table below contains information on the balance of the system.

Number(s)	Occurrences
1, 2, 5, 6, 7,10,11,12	17
3, 8, 9,13,14	16
4,15	15

1.	1	2	3	4	11	13
2.	1	2	3	5	9	10
3.	1	2	3	6	12	15
4.	1	2	4	6	9	12
5.	1	2	5	7	12	13
6.	1	2	5	8	10	14
7.	1	2	6	7	11	14
8.	1	2	9	11	13	15
9.	1	3	4	7	10	15
10.	1	3	5	8	12	13
11.	1	3	7	8	9	14
12.	1	4	5	8	9	15
13.	1	4	6	8	13	14
14.	1	5	6	7	10	11
15.	1	5	9	10	12	13
16.	1	6	9	10	11	14
17.	1	8	11	12	14	15
18.	2	3	4	7	8	15
19.	2	3	5	7	10	12
20.	2	3	6	8	11	14
21.	2	4	5	6	10	13
22.	2	4	9	10	14	15
23.	2	5	6	8	9	11
24.	2	5	10	11	12	15
25.	2	7	10	13	14	15
26.	2	8	9	12	13	14
27.	3	4	5	6	12	14
28.	3	4	6	7	9	13
29.	3	4	8	10	11	12
30.	3	5	11	13	14	15
31.	3	6	8	10	13	15
32.	3	6	10	12	13	14
33.	3	7	9	11	12	15
34.	4	5	7	8	11	12
35.	4	5	7	9	11	14
36.	4	6	11	12	13	15
37.	4	7	10	11	12	14
38.	5	6	7	8	13	15
39.	5	6	7	9	14	15
40.	6	7	8	9	10	12
41.	7	8	9	10	11	13

System # 37: Guaranteed 4–win if 5 of the numbers drawn are in your set of 16 numbers ©Copyright 2001

Winning possibilities

Guessed	6	5	4	3	%
6	1	-	1-7	7-24	0.67
	-	4	1-2	3-10	0.25
	-	3	1	12	0.20
	-	2	0-7	7-23	3.80
	-	1	0-8	9-25	31.27
	-	-	9	10-14	0.55
	-	-	8	7-16	2.65
	-	-	7	11-18	3.85
	-	-	6	10-20	15.48
	-	-	5	12-22	20.44
	-	-	4	13-22	19.38
	-	-	3	16-24	1.46
5	-	1	3	2-6	1.83
	-	1	2	5-6	1.10
	-	1	1	5-13	3.11
	-	1	-	5-14	1.37
	-	-	6	3-9	0.55
	-	-	5	7-10	1.83
	-	-	4	6-12	2.93
	-	-	3	4-14	10.26
	-	-	2	8-15	42.67
	-	-	1	9-15	34.35
4	-	-	2	0-7	6.48
	-	-	1	0-11	31.54
	-	-	-	4-14	61.98
3	-	-	-	4	11.43
	-	-	-	3	8.57
	-	-	-	2	41.43
	-	-	-	1	38.57

Aside from the main guarantee, the system also guarantees at least four 3-wins if four of the numbers drawn are guessed correctly. The complete system would require 8,008 combinations. If all of the numbers are guessed correctly, you will either win the jackpot (plus some extra cash!), or you will get anywhere between one and four 5-wins (and additional prizes), or at least three 4-wins and a number of 3-wins. Every two combinations of the system differ in at least two numbers. The next table gives information on the balance of the system.

Number(s)	Occurrences
2, 4, 6, 8	22
1, 3, 5, 7	21
9,10,11,12,13,14,15,16	19

1.	1	2	3	4	10	12
2.	1	2	3	4	14	16
3.	1	2	5	7	10	14
4.	1	2	5	7	12	16
5.	1	2	6	8	10	14
6.	1	2	9	10	11	16
7.	1	2	9	11	12	14
8.	1	2	12	13	15	16
9.	1	3	5	6	9	13
10.	1	3	5	6	11	15
11.	1	3	5	8	9	15
12.	1	3	5	8	11	13
13.	1	3	6	7	9	15
14.	1	3	6	7	11	13
15.	1	3	7	8	11	15
16.	1	4	5	7	10	16
17.	1	4	5	7	12	14
18.	1	4	6	8	10	16
19.	1	4	6	8	12	14
20.	1	4	9	11	12	16
21.	1	4	10	13	14	15
22.	2	3	5	7	10	16
23.	2	3	5	7	12	14
24.	2	3	6	8	10	16
25.	2	3	6	8	12	14
26.	2	3	9	11	12	16
27.	2	3	10	13	14	15
28.	2	4	5	6	9	13
29.	2	4	5	8	9	15
30.	2	4	5	8	11	13
31.	2	4	6	7	9	15
32.	2	4	6	7	11	13
33.	2	4	7	8	9	13
34.	2	4	7	8	11	15
35.	2	4	10	12	14	16
36.	3	4	5	7	12	16
37.	3	4	6	8	10	14
38.	3	4	6	8	12	16
39.	3	4	9	10	11	14
40.	3	4	10	13	15	16
41.	3	4	12	13	14	15
42.	5	6	7	8	9	11
43.	5	6	7	8	13	15
44.	5	6	9	10	12	15
45.	5	6	10	11	12	13
46.	5	6	11	14	15	16
47.	5	8	9	13	14	16
48.	5	8	10	11	12	15
49.	6	7	9	13	14	16
50.	6	7	10	11	12	15
51.	6	8	9	11	13	15
52.	7	8	9	10	12	13
53.	7	8	9	14	15	16
54.	7	8	11	13	14	16

SYSTEM # 38: GUARANTEED 4–WIN IF 5 OF THE NUMBERS DRAWN ARE IN YOUR SET OF 17 NUMBERS ©Copyright 2001

Winning possibilities

Guessed	6	5	4	3	%
6	1	1	5-8	11-13	0.08
	1	-	0-9	8-24	0.48
	-	9	1	1	0.01
	-	5	3	14	0.01
	-	3	1-7	10-22	0.35
	-	2	0-9	9-24	2.29
	-	1	0-11	8-28	31.50
	-	-	3-11	9-28	65.28
5	-	2	7	1-2	0.06
	-	2	5	-	0.02
	-	1	0-9	0-18	6.63
	-	-	10	-	0.02
	-	-	8	6	0.02
	-	-	6	7-10	0.10
	-	-	3-5	5-18	19.90
	-	-	1-2	7-21	73.25
4	-	-	4	5-6	0.25
	-	-	3	4-7	0.42
	-	-	2	2-9	2.31
	-	-	1	0-10	37.23
	-	-	-	5-13	59.79
3	-	-	-	4-7	8.38
	-	-	-	1-3	91.03
	-	-	-	-	0.59

Aside from the main guarantee, the system also guarantees at least five 3-wins if four of the numbers drawn are guessed correctly. The complete system would require 12,376 combinations. If all of the numbers are guessed correctly, you will either win the jackpot (plus some extra cash!), or you will get anywhere between one and nine 5-wins (and additional prizes), or at least three 4-wins and a number of 3-wins. The next table gives information on the balance of the system.

Number(s)	Occurrences
1	29
13,14	26
2, 3, 5,10,15,17	25
4, 7, 8, 9,11	24
6,12,16	23

1.	1	2	3	4	7	8
2.	1	2	3	4	10	16
3.	1	2	3	6	7	10
4.	1	2	3	12	13	14
5.	1	2	4	5	10	15
6.	1	2	4	8	11	17
7.	1	2	5	6	7	17
8.	1	2	5	6	11	15
9.	1	2	7	10	14	15
10.	1	2	8	9	16	17
11.	1	2	9	10	11	15
12.	1	3	4	6	9	13
13.	1	3	4	7	10	12
14.	1	3	5	6	14	16
15.	1	3	5	8	10	13
16.	1	3	5	9	11	14
17.	1	3	7	11	13	16
18.	1	3	8	9	11	12
19.	1	4	5	7	14	15
20.	1	4	5	12	16	17
21.	1	4	8	11	14	15
22.	1	4	10	14	16	17
23.	1	5	7	9	12	15
24.	1	6	7	8	14	17
25.	1	6	8	12	15	16
26.	1	6	10	11	12	17
27.	1	7	9	10	12	17
28.	1	8	13	14	15	17
29.	1	9	10	14	15	16
30.	2	3	4	5	11	12
31.	2	3	4	7	10	17
32.	2	3	5	7	9	16
33.	2	3	6	8	11	13
34.	2	3	12	14	15	17
35.	2	4	5	13	15	16
36.	2	4	6	9	12	14
37.	2	4	7	10	13	15
38.	2	5	8	10	12	14
39.	2	5	9	11	13	17
40.	2	6	8	14	15	16
41.	2	6	10	13	16	17
42.	2	7	8	9	13	15
43.	2	7	11	12	14	16
44.	3	4	6	9	15	17
45.	3	4	6	10	11	14
46.	3	4	8	13	14	16
47.	3	5	6	7	12	13
48.	3	5	8	10	15	17
49.	3	6	8	12	16	17
50.	3	7	8	9	10	14
51.	3	7	11	15	16	17
52.	3	9	10	12	13	16
53.	4	5	6	8	9	10
54.	4	5	11	13	14	17
55.	4	6	7	9	11	16
56.	4	7	8	12	13	17
57.	4	8	9	12	15	16
58.	4	10	11	12	13	15
59.	5	6	10	12	15	16
60.	5	6	11	13	14	17
61.	5	7	8	10	11	16
62.	5	7	9	13	14	17
63.	5	9	11	12	13	17
64.	5	9	11	13	14	15
65.	5	9	13	14	16	17
66.	6	7	8	11	12	15
67.	6	7	10	13	14	15
68.	6	8	12	13	15	16
69.	8	9	11	13	14	17
70.	9	10	11	13	14	17

System # 39: Guaranteed 4–win if 5 of the numbers drawn are in your set of 18 numbers ©Copyright 2001

Winning possibilities

Guessed	6	5	4	3	%
6	1	1	10	10	0.19
	1	-	-	8-20	0.24
	-	12	-	-	0.02
	-	3	9	10	0.97
	-	2	2-6	12-24	1.44
	-	1	1-6	14-22	25.22
	-	-	9	12-14	1.29
	-	-	8	16	2.91
	-	-	7	20	2.91
	-	-	6	16-20	10.02
	-	-	5	14-24	16.48
	-	-	4	16-24	25.21
	-	-	3	16-28	13.10
5	-	2	10	-	0.21
	-	1	3	14	2.10
	-	1	-	4-10	3.15
	-	-	5	13	4.20
	-	-	4	8	4.20
	-	-	3	12	4.20
	-	-	2	9-13	29.41
	-	-	1	10-17	52.53
4	-	-	4	8	1.47
	-	-	1	0-8	33.82
	-	-	-	6-10	64.71
3	-	-	-	6	7.35
	-	-	-	5	0.74
	-	-	-	2	58.82
	-	-	-	1	33.09

Aside from the main guarantee, the system also guarantees at least six 3-wins if four of the numbers drawn are guessed correctly. The complete system would require 18,564 combinations. If all of the numbers are guessed correctly, you will either win the jackpot (plus some extra cash!), or you will get up to twelve 5-wins (and additional prizes), or at least three 4-wins and a number of 3-wins. The system is HIGHLY BALANCED: Each number is in exactly 27 combinations.

1.	1	2	3	5	7	9
2.	1	2	4	11	14	16
41.	2	5	8	10	15	16
42.	2	5	8	13	14	16

3.	1	2	4	12	15	18
4.	1	2	6	10	15	17
5.	1	2	6	12	13	14
6.	1	2	8	10	13	16
7.	1	2	8	11	17	18
8.	1	3	4	10	13	17
9.	1	3	4	12	15	18
10.	1	3	6	11	14	17
11.	1	3	6	13	16	18
12.	1	3	8	10	11	12
13.	1	3	8	14	15	16
14.	1	4	5	6	8	9
15.	1	4	7	10	12	15
16.	1	4	7	11	12	18
17.	1	4	7	12	13	18
18.	1	4	7	12	14	15
19.	1	4	7	15	16	18
20.	1	4	7	15	17	18
21.	1	5	9	10	14	18
22.	1	5	9	11	13	15
23.	1	5	9	12	16	17
24.	1	6	7	10	11	16
25.	1	6	7	12	15	18
26.	1	7	8	12	15	18
27.	1	7	8	13	14	17
28.	2	3	4	6	7	8
29.	2	3	7	10	14	18
30.	2	3	7	11	13	15
31.	2	3	7	12	16	17
32.	2	4	5	10	13	16
33.	2	4	5	14	15	17
34.	2	4	9	10	11	12
35.	2	4	9	13	17	18
36.	2	5	6	10	13	16
37.	2	5	6	11	12	18
38.	2	5	8	10	11	16
39.	2	5	8	10	12	13
40.	2	5	8	10	13	17
43.	2	5	8	13	16	18
44.	2	6	9	11	14	17
45.	2	6	9	15	16	18
46.	2	8	9	10	13	16
47.	2	8	9	12	14	15
48.	3	4	5	11	16	18
49.	3	4	5	12	13	14
50.	3	4	9	10	15	16
51.	3	4	9	11	14	17
52.	3	5	6	10	12	15
53.	3	5	6	11	14	17
54.	3	5	8	10	13	16
55.	3	5	8	15	17	18
56.	3	6	9	10	11	17
57.	3	6	9	11	12	14
58.	3	6	9	11	14	16
59.	3	6	9	11	17	18
60.	3	6	9	13	14	17
61.	3	6	9	14	15	17
62.	3	8	9	11	14	17
63.	3	8	9	12	13	18
64.	4	5	7	10	11	17
65.	4	5	7	12	15	18
66.	4	6	8	10	14	18
67.	4	6	8	11	13	15
68.	4	6	8	12	16	17
69.	4	7	9	12	15	18
70.	4	7	9	13	14	16
71.	5	6	7	13	17	18
72.	5	6	7	14	15	16
73.	5	7	8	10	13	16
74.	5	7	8	11	12	14
75.	6	7	9	10	12	13
76.	6	7	9	11	14	17
77.	7	8	9	10	15	17
78.	7	8	9	11	16	18
79.	10	11	13	14	15	18
80.	10	12	14	16	17	18
81.	11	12	13	15	16	17

SYSTEM # 40: GUARANTEED 4–WIN IF 5 OF THE NUMBERS DRAWN ARE IN YOUR SET OF 19 NUMBERS ©Copyright 2001

Winning possibilities

Guessed	6	5	4	3	%
6	1	1	1-3	7-25	0.05
	1	-	0-6	9-28	0.37
	-	3-5	0-5	5-27	0.11
	-	2	0-7	11-31	2.31
	-	1	0-9	5-36	28.02
	-	-	3-12	10-36	69.14
5	-	2	0-1	5-11	0.06
	-	1	0-4	3-23	5.81
	-	-	4-6	2-17	7.29
	-	-	1-3	6-27	86.84
4	-	-	3	2-6	0.26
	-	-	2	0-9	4.10
	-	-	1	0-12	35.53
	-	-	-	6-15	60.11
3	-	-	-	4-9	7.43
	-	-	-	3	34.57
	-	-	-	2	43.03
	-	-	-	1	14.97

Aside from the main guarantee, the system also guarantees at least six 3-wins if four of the numbers drawn are guessed correctly. The complete system would require 27,132 combinations. If all of the numbers are guessed correctly, you will either win the jackpot (plus some extra cash!), or you will get up to twelve 5-wins (and additional prizes), or at least three 4-wins and a number of 3-wins. The next table gives information on the balance of the system.

Number(s)	Occurrences
18	39
1, 6, 7,11,17	38
2, 3, 4, 8, 9,14,15	36
5,10,12,13,19	35
16	34

1. 1 2 3 4 10 18
2. 1 2 3 9 11 12
3. 1 2 4 5 11 15

58. 2 5 10 12 13 16
59. 2 6 7 9 12 15
60. 2 6 9 10 14 18

4.	1	2	5	7	9	14
5.	1	2	6	13	16	17
6.	1	2	6	16	17	19
7.	1	2	7	8	10	15
8.	1	2	8	11	12	15
9.	1	2	8	13	14	18
10.	1	2	9	12	14	18
11.	1	3	4	5	13	18
12.	1	3	4	7	10	19
13.	1	3	5	7	9	16
14.	1	3	5	8	11	19
15.	1	3	6	14	15	17
16.	1	3	7	11	15	18
17.	1	3	8	11	12	16
18.	1	3	9	10	11	13
19.	1	4	6	7	8	14
20.	1	4	6	8	9	17
21.	1	4	7	12	15	16
22.	1	4	10	11	14	16
23.	1	4	11	12	13	15
24.	1	4	12	14	18	19
25.	1	5	6	10	12	17
26.	1	5	7	8	13	15
27.	1	5	8	14	16	18
28.	1	5	9	15	18	19
29.	1	5	11	12	13	19
30.	1	6	7	11	17	18
31.	1	6	12	13	16	19
32.	1	7	8	12	15	19
33.	1	7	9	12	13	14
34.	1	8	9	15	17	18
35.	1	8	10	13	14	18
36.	1	9	10	11	14	19
37.	1	9	10	15	16	18
38.	1	10	13	16	17	19
39.	2	3	4	6	7	13
40.	2	3	5	6	7	8
41.	2	3	5	9	17	18
42.	2	3	6	8	10	11
43.	2	3	7	8	12	17
44.	2	3	7	9	10	17
45.	2	3	13	14	15	16
46.	2	3	13	14	15	19
47.	2	4	5	6	14	18
48.	2	4	5	12	16	19
49.	2	4	6	11	12	14

61.	2	7	11	13	16	18
62.	2	7	11	13	18	19
63.	2	8	10	12	16	19
64.	2	9	11	13	15	17
65.	3	4	5	11	16	17
66.	3	4	6	7	10	16
67.	3	4	6	7	12	13
68.	3	4	6	9	11	17
69.	3	4	8	9	14	15
70.	3	4	11	12	17	19
71.	3	5	6	7	9	19
72.	3	5	6	8	11	13
73.	3	5	10	12	14	15
74.	3	6	8	12	18	19
75.	3	6	9	12	16	18
76.	3	7	8	10	13	17
77.	3	7	11	14	17	18
78.	3	7	11	16	18	19
79.	3	8	10	16	17	18
80.	3	9	10	17	18	19
81.	3	9	12	13	17	18
82.	3	14	15	16	18	19
83.	4	5	6	11	14	19
84.	4	5	6	15	16	18
85.	4	5	7	13	14	17
86.	4	5	7	15	17	19
87.	4	5	8	9	10	12
88.	4	6	10	11	13	14
89.	4	6	10	15	18	19
90.	4	7	8	9	11	18
91.	4	8	9	13	16	19
92.	4	10	13	15	17	18
93.	4	12	14	16	17	18
94.	5	6	9	11	14	16
95.	5	6	9	13	14	18
96.	5	6	10	13	18	19
97.	5	6	13	16	17	19
98.	5	7	8	15	16	17
99.	5	7	10	11	12	18
100.	5	8	14	17	18	19
101.	5	9	11	13	15	17
102.	6	7	8	10	14	19
103.	6	7	8	12	14	16
104.	6	7	9	10	13	15
105.	6	7	11	14	15	18
106.	6	8	10	11	15	16

50. 2 4 7 10 14 17
51. 2 4 8 9 13 19
52. 2 4 8 9 16 18
53. 2 4 10 11 15 17
54. 2 4 12 15 17 18
55. 2 5 6 8 15 18
56. 2 5 8 11 14 17
57. 2 5 9 10 16 19

107. 6 8 12 13 15 18
108. 6 9 11 12 15 19
109. 7 9 10 14 16 17
110. 7 9 12 14 17 19
111. 7 10 12 13 17 19
112. 7 11 14 15 16 19
113. 8 10 11 15 17 19
114. 8 11 12 13 14 17
115. 9 11 12 15 16 17

SYSTEM # 41: GUARANTEED 4–WIN IF 5 OF THE NUMBERS DRAWN ARE IN YOUR SET OF 20 NUMBERS

Winning possibilities

Guessed	6	5	4	3	%
6	1	-	0-9	8-35	0.37
	-	2	0-12	11-37	3.08
	-	1	0-10	10-43	25.27
	-	-	3-13	10-41	71.28
5	-	1	0-4	3-23	5.61
	-	-	4-8	10-25	6.79
	-	-	1-3	8-27	87.60
4	-	-	4	0-1	0.50
	-	-	3	0-11	0.12
	-	-	2	0-15	2.81
	-	-	1	0-16	36.92
	-	-	-	6-17	59.65
3	-	-	-	5-8	3.61
	-	-	-	2-4	87.63
	-	-	-	1	8.76

Aside from the main guarantee, the system also guarantees at least six 3-wins if four of the numbers drawn are guessed correctly. The complete system would require 38,760 combinations. If all of the numbers are guessed correctly, you will either win the jackpot (plus some extra cash!), or you will get one or two 5-wins (plus additional prizes), or at least three 4-wins and a number of 3-wins. Every two combinations of the system differ in at least two numbers. Below is information on the balance of the system.

Number(s)	Occurrences
13	53
1, 5	45
17,19	44
2, 3, 4, 6, 7, 8, 9,10,11,12,14,15,16,18	43
20	37

1.	1	2	3	4	10	19
2.	1	2	3	12	13	18
3.	1	2	3	15	17	20
4.	1	2	4	8	13	14
5.	1	2	4	9	17	20
73.	2	7	12	13	15	19
74.	2	7	12	14	16	17
75.	2	8	11	14	15	18
76.	2	9	10	13	15	19
77.	2	11	13	16	17	19

6.	1	2	5	6	7	13
7.	1	2	6	15	16	19
8.	1	2	7	9	11	20
9.	1	2	8	10	16	20
10.	1	2	8	12	17	19
11.	1	2	10	11	12	20
12.	1	3	4	6	18	20
13.	1	3	4	7	14	20
14.	1	3	5	6	8	20
15.	1	3	5	10	15	20
16.	1	3	7	10	13	16
17.	1	3	7	15	18	19
18.	1	3	8	9	11	13
19.	1	3	11	14	17	19
20.	1	4	5	7	12	19
21.	1	4	5	9	10	20
22.	1	4	6	9	14	19
23.	1	4	6	10	11	13
24.	1	4	12	13	15	16
25.	1	4	16	17	18	20
26.	1	5	8	16	17	20
27.	1	5	9	13	14	16
28.	1	5	9	15	17	19
29.	1	5	10	11	16	19
30.	1	5	11	12	17	20
31.	1	5	11	13	15	18
32.	1	5	13	17	19	20
33.	1	6	8	12	14	20
34.	1	6	9	12	13	17
35.	1	6	9	15	18	20
36.	1	6	11	12	18	19
37.	1	6	11	14	16	20
38.	1	7	8	12	18	20
39.	1	7	8	13	15	17
40.	1	7	8	14	16	19
41.	1	7	9	14	15	20
42.	1	7	11	16	18	20
43.	1	8	9	10	18	19
44.	1	10	12	14	15	20
45.	1	10	13	14	17	18
46.	2	3	4	5	11	16
47.	2	3	5	8	15	16
48.	2	3	5	9	12	14
49.	2	3	6	9	10	14
50.	2	3	6	11	13	19
51.	2	3	7	8	13	20
78.	3	4	5	13	17	19
79.	3	4	6	7	8	12
80.	3	4	8	9	12	15
81.	3	4	8	10	12	17
82.	3	4	8	11	12	16
83.	3	4	9	11	15	16
84.	3	4	9	13	15	19
85.	3	4	11	14	16	18
86.	3	5	6	9	10	18
87.	3	5	7	9	17	18
88.	3	5	7	11	13	19
89.	3	5	12	14	16	18
90.	3	6	7	9	16	17
91.	3	6	7	11	12	15
92.	3	6	10	12	16	17
93.	3	6	13	14	15	19
94.	3	7	9	10	12	17
95.	3	8	10	13	14	19
96.	3	8	13	17	18	19
97.	3	8	14	15	16	18
98.	3	9	12	16	19	20
99.	3	10	11	12	15	17
100.	3	10	11	13	18	20
101.	3	11	13	14	17	20
102.	4	5	6	13	16	19
103.	4	5	6	14	15	17
104.	4	5	7	10	14	15
105.	4	5	7	12	13	20
106.	4	5	8	14	15	18
107.	4	6	7	8	9	16
108.	4	6	7	11	15	17
109.	4	6	8	10	15	17
110.	4	7	8	10	11	17
111.	4	7	9	13	18	19
112.	4	8	9	10	16	17
113.	4	8	11	15	19	20
114.	4	9	11	12	14	18
115.	4	10	12	13	18	19
116.	4	10	13	14	16	20
117.	4	12	13	14	17	19
118.	5	6	7	14	17	18
119.	5	6	8	11	14	17
120.	5	6	9	11	13	20
121.	5	6	10	12	16	18
122.	5	6	12	13	15	19
123.	5	7	8	9	13	19

52. 2 3 7 9 14 17
53. 2 3 9 14 16 18
54. 2 4 5 8 11 18
55. 2 4 5 9 11 12
56. 2 4 5 11 14 15
57. 2 4 6 12 13 20
58. 2 4 6 15 17 18
59. 2 4 7 10 15 18
60. 2 4 7 13 16 19
61. 2 5 6 10 14 17
62. 2 5 7 10 17 18
63. 2 5 8 9 12 15
64. 2 5 9 12 16 18
65. 2 5 10 13 17 19
66. 2 5 14 18 19 20
67. 2 6 7 10 14 18
68. 2 6 8 9 13 19
69. 2 6 8 11 17 18
70. 2 6 10 12 14 16
71. 2 6 13 15 16 20
72. 2 7 8 10 11 18
124. 5 7 8 10 11 14
125. 5 7 12 16 17 18
126. 5 7 13 15 16 20
127. 5 8 10 12 13 19
128. 5 8 11 12 13 16
129. 6 7 8 10 11 15
130. 6 7 9 10 12 16
131. 6 7 9 11 15 16
132. 6 7 10 17 19 20
133. 6 7 13 14 18 19
134. 6 8 13 16 18 19
135. 7 11 12 13 14 19
136. 8 9 10 13 18 20
137. 8 9 11 12 15 16
138. 8 9 12 14 15 18
139. 8 9 13 14 17 20
140. 9 10 11 13 14 19
141. 9 10 11 15 16 17
142. 9 11 13 17 18 19
143. 10 13 15 16 18 19
144. 12 13 15 17 18 20
145. 13 14 15 16 17 19

System # 42: Guaranteed 4–win if 5 of the numbers drawn are in your set of 21 numbers ©Copyright 2001

Winning possibilities

Guessed	6	5	4	3	%
6	1	1	0-8	18-30	0.05
	1	-	0-9	8-33	0.26
	-	3	2-7	18-29	0.02
	-	2	0-9	14-35	2.32
	-	1	0-9	8-41	23.28
	-	-	3-11	10-45	74.07
5	-	2	0-2	8-15	0.07
	-	1	0-4	0-23	4.85
	-	-	6	10-13	0.14
	-	-	5	8-20	0.71
	-	-	4	8-22	3.32
	-	-	3	8-22	19.21
	-	-	2	10-25	34.16
	-	-	1	11-28	37.54
4	-	-	4	0-1	0.47
	-	-	3	0-3	0.17
	-	-	2	2-10	2.16
	-	-	1	0-13	35.67
	-	-	-	6-14	61.53
3	-	-	-	5	0.60
	-	-	-	4	12.41
	-	-	-	3	33.01
	-	-	-	2	48.50
	-	-	-	1	5.48

Aside from the main guarantee, the system also guarantees at least six 3-wins if four of the numbers drawn are guessed correctly. The complete system would require 54,264 combinations. If all of the numbers are guessed correctly, you will either win the jackpot (plus some extra cash!), or you will get anywhere between one and three 5-wins (and additional prizes), or at least three 4-wins and a number of 3-wins. The number 13 is the most represented (53 occurrences) in the system, while the least represented number is 20 (37 occurrences). The next table gives the number of occurrences of each of the remaining numbers.

Number(s)	Occurrences
1,15	51
5,16,21	50
2, 3, 4, 6, 7, 8, 9,11,12,14,17,18	49
10	43
19	41

1.	1	2	3	4	19	21
2.	1	2	3	12	13	18
3.	1	2	3	15	17	20
4.	1	2	4	8	10	14
5.	1	2	4	8	13	14
6.	1	2	5	6	7	10
7.	1	2	5	6	7	13
8.	1	2	5	15	17	21
9.	1	2	6	15	16	19
10.	1	2	7	9	11	20
11.	1	2	8	12	17	19
12.	1	2	9	10	16	18
13.	1	2	11	12	20	21
14.	1	3	4	6	18	20
15.	1	3	4	9	13	15
16.	1	3	5	6	8	20
17.	1	3	5	10	12	14
18.	1	3	7	10	16	21
19.	1	3	7	13	16	21
20.	1	3	7	15	18	19
21.	1	3	8	9	10	11
22.	1	3	11	14	17	19
23.	1	4	5	7	12	19
24.	1	4	5	9	20	21
25.	1	4	6	9	14	19
26.	1	4	6	11	13	21
27.	1	4	7	10	11	17
28.	1	4	10	12	15	16
29.	1	4	16	17	18	20
30.	1	5	8	16	17	20
31.	1	5	9	13	14	16
32.	1	5	9	15	17	19
33.	1	5	10	11	15	18
34.	1	5	11	13	15	18
35.	1	5	11	16	19	21
36.	1	6	7	14	18	21
37.	1	6	8	10	15	21
38.	1	6	9	10	12	17
39.	1	6	9	12	13	17

85.	2	9	13	15	19	21
86.	2	10	11	13	14	15
87.	2	11	13	16	17	19
88.	3	4	5	9	10	15
89.	3	4	5	13	17	19
90.	3	4	6	7	8	12
91.	3	4	7	10	14	20
92.	3	4	8	9	12	15
93.	3	4	8	11	12	16
94.	3	4	8	12	17	21
95.	3	4	9	11	15	16
96.	3	4	11	14	16	18
97.	3	5	6	9	18	21
98.	3	5	7	9	17	18
99.	3	5	7	11	13	19
100.	3	5	10	15	20	21
101.	3	5	12	14	16	18
102.	3	6	7	9	16	17
103.	3	6	7	11	12	15
104.	3	6	10	13	16	17
105.	3	6	12	16	17	21
106.	3	6	13	14	15	19
107.	3	7	9	12	17	21
108.	3	8	9	10	11	13
109.	3	8	10	17	18	19
110.	3	8	13	14	19	21
111.	3	8	14	15	16	18
112.	3	9	12	16	19	20
113.	3	11	12	15	17	21
114.	3	11	13	14	17	20
115.	3	11	13	18	20	21
116.	4	5	6	10	16	19
117.	4	5	6	14	15	17
118.	4	5	7	12	13	20
119.	4	5	7	14	15	21
120.	4	5	8	10	13	18
121.	4	5	8	14	15	18
122.	4	6	7	8	9	16
123.	4	6	7	11	15	17

No.						
40.	1	6	11	12	18	19
41.	1	6	11	14	16	20
42.	1	7	8	12	18	20
43.	1	7	8	13	15	17
44.	1	7	8	14	16	19
45.	1	7	9	14	15	20
46.	1	8	9	18	19	21
47.	1	8	11	12	13	16
48.	1	10	13	16	19	20
49.	1	10	14	17	18	21
50.	1	12	14	15	20	21
51.	1	13	14	17	18	21
52.	2	3	4	5	11	16
53.	2	3	5	8	15	16
54.	2	3	5	9	12	14
55.	2	3	6	9	14	21
56.	2	3	6	10	11	19
57.	2	3	7	8	13	20
58.	2	3	7	9	14	17
59.	2	3	9	14	16	18
60.	2	3	10	12	13	18
61.	2	4	5	8	11	18
62.	2	4	5	9	11	12
63.	2	4	5	11	14	15
64.	2	4	6	12	13	20
65.	2	4	6	15	17	18
66.	2	4	7	13	16	19
67.	2	4	7	15	18	21
68.	2	4	9	10	17	20
69.	2	5	6	14	17	21
70.	2	5	7	17	18	21
71.	2	5	8	9	12	15
72.	2	5	9	12	16	18
73.	2	5	10	13	17	21
74.	2	5	14	18	19	20
75.	2	6	7	14	18	21
76.	2	6	8	9	13	19
77.	2	6	8	11	17	18
78.	2	6	12	14	16	21
79.	2	6	13	15	16	20
80.	2	7	8	11	18	21
81.	2	7	10	12	15	19
82.	2	7	12	14	16	17
83.	2	8	10	16	20	21
84.	2	8	11	14	15	18
124.	4	6	8	15	17	21
125.	4	6	10	11	13	21
126.	4	7	8	11	17	21
127.	4	7	9	13	18	19
128.	4	8	9	16	17	21
129.	4	8	11	15	19	20
130.	4	9	11	12	14	18
131.	4	10	12	13	15	16
132.	4	10	12	18	19	21
133.	4	12	13	14	17	19
134.	4	13	14	16	20	21
135.	5	6	7	14	17	18
136.	5	6	8	11	14	17
137.	5	6	9	11	13	20
138.	5	6	12	13	15	19
139.	5	6	12	16	18	21
140.	5	7	8	9	10	19
141.	5	7	8	11	14	21
142.	5	7	12	16	17	18
143.	5	7	13	15	16	20
144.	5	8	12	13	19	21
145.	5	9	10	13	14	16
146.	5	10	11	12	17	20
147.	6	7	8	11	15	21
148.	6	7	9	11	15	16
149.	6	7	9	12	16	21
150.	6	7	10	13	14	18
151.	6	7	17	19	20	21
152.	6	8	10	12	14	20
153.	6	8	13	16	18	19
154.	6	9	10	15	18	20
155.	7	8	10	13	15	17
156.	7	9	10	12	13	21
157.	7	10	11	16	18	20
158.	7	11	12	13	14	19
159.	8	9	11	12	15	16
160.	8	9	12	14	15	18
161.	8	9	13	14	17	20
162.	8	9	13	18	20	21
163.	8	10	11	12	15	16
164.	9	10	11	14	19	21
165.	9	11	13	17	18	19
166.	9	11	15	16	17	21
167.	10	14	15	16	17	19
168.	12	13	15	17	18	20
169.	13	15	16	18	19	21

SYSTEM # 43: GUARANTEED 4–WIN IF 5 OF THE NUMBERS DRAWN ARE IN YOUR SET OF 22 NUMBERS ©Copyright 2001

Winning possibilities

Guessed	6	5	4	3	%
6	1	-	-	40	0.23
	1	-	-	-	0.03
	-	1	4	30	20.26
	-	1	-	22-30	4.05
	-	-	9	20	4.50
	-	-	7	24	3.38
	-	-	6	30	27.02
	-	-	4	22-34	27.02
	-	-	3	24-40	13.51
5	-	1	-	20	3.83
	-	1	-	-	0.48
	-	-	3	16	38.28
	-	-	1	12-22	57.41
4	-	-	1	8	34.45
	-	-	1	-	4.31
	-	-	-	10	45.93
	-	-	-	6	15.31
3	-	-	-	3	72.73
	-	-	-	1	27.27

Aside from the main guarantee, the system also guarantees at least six 3-wins if four of the numbers drawn are guessed correctly. The complete system would require 74,613 combinations. If all of the numbers are guessed correctly, you will either win the jackpot, or you will get a 5-win (plus some additional prizes), or at least three 4-wins and a number of 3-wins. Every two combinations differ in at least three numbers, that is, the combinations of the system are as 'apart' as possible. The next table gives information on the balance of the system.

Number(s)	Occurrences
1, 2, 3, 4, 5, 6, 7, 8, 9,10,11,12,13,14,15,16,17,18,19,20,21	53
22	21

1. 1 2 3 4 21 22
2. 1 2 5 6 17 18
3. 1 2 5 7 10 11
4. 1 2 5 8 14 16

95. 3 4 5 7 9 12
96. 3 4 5 8 13 15
97. 3 4 6 7 14 16
98. 3 4 6 8 10 11

5.	1	2	6	7	13	15
6.	1	2	6	8	9	12
7.	1	2	7	8	19	20
8.	1	2	9	10	18	19
9.	1	2	9	11	14	15
10.	1	2	10	12	13	16
11.	1	2	11	12	17	20
12.	1	2	13	14	17	19
13.	1	2	15	16	18	20
14.	1	3	5	6	14	15
15.	1	3	5	7	17	19
16.	1	3	5	8	11	12
17.	1	3	6	7	9	10
18.	1	3	6	8	18	20
19.	1	3	7	8	13	16
20.	1	3	9	11	17	18
21.	1	3	9	12	15	16
22.	1	3	10	11	13	14
23.	1	3	10	12	19	20
24.	1	3	13	15	18	19
25.	1	3	14	16	17	20
26.	1	4	5	6	10	12
27.	1	4	5	7	15	16
28.	1	4	5	8	18	19
29.	1	4	6	7	17	20
30.	1	4	6	8	13	14
31.	1	4	7	8	9	11
32.	1	4	9	10	14	16
33.	1	4	9	12	17	19
34.	1	4	10	11	18	20
35.	1	4	11	12	13	15
36.	1	4	13	16	17	18
37.	1	4	14	15	19	20
38.	1	5	9	13	20	22
39.	1	5	10	14	19	21
40.	1	5	11	15	18	21
41.	1	5	12	16	17	21
42.	1	6	9	14	17	21
43.	1	6	10	13	18	21
44.	1	6	11	16	19	22
45.	1	6	12	15	20	21
46.	1	7	9	15	19	21
47.	1	7	10	16	20	21
48.	1	7	11	13	17	21
49.	1	7	12	14	18	22
50.	1	8	9	16	18	21

99.	3	4	7	8	17	18
100.	3	4	9	10	17	20
101.	3	4	9	11	13	16
102.	3	4	10	12	14	15
103.	3	4	11	12	18	19
104.	3	4	13	14	18	20
105.	3	4	15	16	17	19
106.	3	5	9	15	17	21
107.	3	5	10	16	18	22
108.	3	5	11	13	19	21
109.	3	5	12	14	20	21
110.	3	6	9	16	20	21
111.	3	6	10	15	19	21
112.	3	6	11	14	18	21
113.	3	6	12	13	17	22
114.	3	7	9	13	18	21
115.	3	7	10	14	17	21
116.	3	7	11	15	20	22
117.	3	7	12	16	19	21
118.	3	8	9	14	19	22
119.	3	8	10	13	20	21
120.	3	8	11	16	17	21
121.	3	8	12	15	18	21
122.	4	5	9	16	19	21
123.	4	5	10	15	20	21
124.	4	5	11	14	17	22
125.	4	5	12	13	18	21
126.	4	6	9	15	18	22
127.	4	6	10	16	17	21
128.	4	6	11	13	20	21
129.	4	6	12	14	19	21
130.	4	7	9	14	20	21
131.	4	7	10	13	19	22
132.	4	7	11	16	18	21
133.	4	7	12	15	17	21
134.	4	8	9	13	17	21
135.	4	8	10	14	18	21
136.	4	8	11	15	19	21
137.	4	8	12	16	20	22
138.	5	6	7	8	21	22
139.	5	6	9	10	17	19
140.	5	6	9	12	14	16
141.	5	6	10	11	13	15
142.	5	6	11	12	18	20
143.	5	6	13	14	18	19
144.	5	6	15	16	17	20

51.	1	8	10	15	17	22
52.	1	8	11	14	20	21
53.	1	8	12	13	19	21
54.	2	3	5	6	9	11
55.	2	3	5	7	13	14
56.	2	3	5	8	17	20
57.	2	3	6	7	18	19
58.	2	3	6	8	15	16
59.	2	3	7	8	10	12
60.	2	3	9	10	13	15
61.	2	3	9	12	18	20
62.	2	3	10	11	17	19
63.	2	3	11	12	14	16
64.	2	3	13	16	19	20
65.	2	3	14	15	17	18
66.	2	4	5	6	13	16
67.	2	4	5	7	18	20
68.	2	4	5	8	9	10
69.	2	4	6	7	11	12
70.	2	4	6	8	17	19
71.	2	4	7	8	14	15
72.	2	4	9	11	19	20
73.	2	4	9	12	13	14
74.	2	4	10	11	15	16
75.	2	4	10	12	17	18
76.	2	4	13	15	17	20
77.	2	4	14	16	18	19
78.	2	5	9	14	18	21
79.	2	5	10	13	17	21
80.	2	5	11	16	20	21
81.	2	5	12	15	19	22
82.	2	6	9	13	19	21
83.	2	6	10	14	20	22
84.	2	6	11	15	17	21
85.	2	6	12	16	18	21
86.	2	7	9	16	17	22
87.	2	7	10	15	18	21
88.	2	7	11	14	19	21
89.	2	7	12	13	20	21
90.	2	8	9	15	20	21
91.	2	8	10	16	19	21
92.	2	8	11	13	18	22
93.	2	8	12	14	17	21
94.	3	4	5	6	19	20

145.	5	7	9	10	14	15
146.	5	7	9	11	18	19
147.	5	7	10	12	17	20
148.	5	7	11	12	13	16
149.	5	7	13	15	17	18
150.	5	7	14	16	19	20
151.	5	8	9	11	15	16
152.	5	8	9	12	17	18
153.	5	8	10	11	19	20
154.	5	8	10	12	13	14
155.	5	8	13	16	17	19
156.	5	8	14	15	18	20
157.	6	7	9	11	13	14
158.	6	7	9	12	19	20
159.	6	7	10	11	17	18
160.	6	7	10	12	15	16
161.	6	7	13	16	18	20
162.	6	7	14	15	17	19
163.	6	8	9	10	13	16
164.	6	8	9	11	17	20
165.	6	8	10	12	18	19
166.	6	8	11	12	14	15
167.	6	8	13	15	19	20
168.	6	8	14	16	17	18
169.	7	8	9	10	18	20
170.	7	8	9	12	13	15
171.	7	8	10	11	14	16
172.	7	8	11	12	17	19
173.	7	8	13	14	17	20
174.	7	8	15	16	18	19
175.	9	10	11	12	21	22
176.	9	10	13	14	17	18
177.	9	10	15	16	19	20
178.	9	11	13	15	17	19
179.	9	11	14	16	18	20
180.	9	12	13	16	18	19
181.	9	12	14	15	17	20
182.	10	11	13	16	17	20
183.	10	11	14	15	18	19
184.	10	12	13	15	18	20
185.	10	12	14	16	17	19
186.	11	12	13	14	19	20
187.	11	12	15	16	17	18
188.	13	14	15	16	21	22
189.	17	18	19	20	21	22

System # 44: Guaranteed 4–win if 5 of the numbers drawn are in your set of 23 numbers ©Copyright 2001

Winning possibilities

Guessed	6	5	4	3	%
6	1	1	0-2	1-7	0.04
	1	-	0-5	17-44	0.19
	-	3	0-4	1-12	0.02
	-	2	0-6	4-34	0.53
	-	1	0-7	16-37	21.97
	-	-	3-10	15-48	77.25
5	-	2	-	0-2	0.06
	-	1	0-3	0-22	3.95
	-	-	6	1	0.01
	-	-	5	3-6	0.14
	-	-	4	6-19	0.54
	-	-	3	8-21	30.87
	-	-	2	13-26	12.49
	-	-	1	15-28	51.94
4	-	-	3	2	0.02
	-	-	2	0-8	1.56
	-	-	1	2-11	35.61
	-	-	-	7-13	62.81
3	-	-	-	4	4.69
	-	-	-	3	60.98
	-	-	-	2	22.59
	-	-	-	1	11.74

Aside from the main guarantee, the system also guarantees at least seven 3-wins if four of the numbers drawn are guessed correctly. The complete system would require 100,947 combinations. If all of the numbers are guessed correctly, you will either win the jackpot, or you will get anywhere between one and three 5-wins (plus some additional prizes), or at least three 4-wins and a number of 3-wins. Below is information on the balance of the system.

Number(s)	Occurrences
1, 2, 7, 9,10,11,12,14,15,16,20,21,22	62
3, 5, 6,13,17,18,19,23	61
4, 8	40

1.	1	2	3	5	9	13
2.	1	2	3	6	10	21
3.	1	2	3	19	22	23
4.	1	2	4	7	11	20
5.	1	2	4	8	11	12
6.	1	2	5	10	12	14
7.	1	2	5	16	17	22
8.	1	2	6	12	17	23
9.	1	2	6	13	16	18
10.	1	2	7	8	11	20
11.	1	2	9	12	18	19
12.	1	2	9	15	17	21
13.	1	2	10	15	18	22
14.	1	2	13	14	15	23
15.	1	2	14	16	19	21
16.	1	3	4	12	15	16
17.	1	3	5	6	7	17
18.	1	3	5	11	14	19
19.	1	3	6	18	19	20
20.	1	3	7	10	14	23
21.	1	3	7	13	18	22
22.	1	3	8	12	15	16
23.	1	3	9	10	11	18
24.	1	3	9	17	20	23
25.	1	3	11	17	21	22
26.	1	3	13	14	20	21
27.	1	4	5	18	21	23
28.	1	4	6	9	14	22
29.	1	4	7	8	10	22
30.	1	4	8	9	14	15
31.	1	4	8	16	20	21
32.	1	4	10	13	17	19
33.	1	5	6	10	11	16
34.	1	5	6	12	13	20
35.	1	5	7	9	10	15
36.	1	5	7	12	19	22
37.	1	5	8	18	21	23
38.	1	5	9	16	19	20
39.	1	5	11	13	15	22
40.	1	5	14	15	17	20
41.	1	6	7	13	15	21
42.	1	6	7	16	19	23
43.	1	6	8	9	14	22
44.	1	6	10	15	20	23
45.	1	6	11	12	19	21
46.	1	6	11	15	17	18

115.	3	4	7	9	19	21
116.	3	5	6	9	16	18
117.	3	5	6	12	14	21
118.	3	5	7	11	15	18
119.	3	5	8	10	20	22
120.	3	5	9	14	15	23
121.	3	5	12	13	18	19
122.	3	5	13	15	17	21
123.	3	5	16	17	19	23
124.	3	6	7	14	15	20
125.	3	6	8	11	13	23
126.	3	6	9	10	15	17
127.	3	6	10	14	16	19
128.	3	6	12	17	19	22
129.	3	6	15	18	21	22
130.	3	7	8	9	19	21
131.	3	7	10	11	16	17
132.	3	7	11	12	14	22
133.	3	7	12	13	17	20
134.	3	7	16	18	20	23
135.	3	9	10	12	13	14
136.	3	9	11	14	16	20
137.	3	9	12	18	22	23
138.	3	9	13	16	17	22
139.	3	10	12	17	21	23
140.	3	10	13	16	18	21
141.	3	10	15	18	19	23
142.	3	11	12	18	20	21
143.	3	11	15	17	19	20
144.	3	13	14	15	19	22
145.	3	14	16	21	22	23
146.	4	5	7	13	14	16
147.	4	5	9	11	12	17
148.	4	6	7	10	12	18
149.	4	6	8	13	17	18
150.	4	6	8	13	19	23
151.	4	6	16	17	20	21
152.	4	7	8	9	12	20
153.	4	7	8	11	15	21
154.	4	7	15	17	22	23
155.	4	8	9	10	11	16
156.	4	8	10	12	14	21
157.	4	8	11	14	20	22
158.	4	8	12	15	16	22
159.	4	8	17	18	19	23
160.	4	9	13	15	18	20

47.	1	7	9	12	13	23
48.	1	7	9	16	17	18
49.	1	7	10	16	21	22
50.	1	7	12	14	17	21
51.	1	7	14	15	18	19
52.	1	8	10	13	17	19
53.	1	9	10	12	20	21
54.	1	9	11	13	16	21
55.	1	9	11	15	19	23
56.	1	10	11	12	22	23
57.	1	10	14	16	18	20
58.	1	11	12	13	14	18
59.	1	11	14	16	17	23
60.	1	12	17	18	20	22
61.	1	13	16	20	22	23
62.	1	15	19	20	21	22
63.	2	3	4	14	17	18
64.	2	3	5	7	12	23
65.	2	3	5	11	16	21
66.	2	3	6	7	16	22
67.	2	3	6	9	12	20
68.	2	3	7	10	13	15
69.	2	3	8	14	17	18
70.	2	3	9	11	15	22
71.	2	3	10	11	12	19
72.	2	3	13	16	19	20
73.	2	3	15	20	21	23
74.	2	4	5	6	15	19
75.	2	4	7	8	14	16
76.	2	4	8	9	21	22
77.	2	4	8	10	15	20
78.	2	4	9	10	16	23
79.	2	4	12	13	21	22
80.	2	5	6	8	15	19
81.	2	5	7	9	18	22
82.	2	5	7	10	17	21
83.	2	5	9	14	20	21
84.	2	5	10	11	13	18
85.	2	5	11	14	22	23
86.	2	5	12	16	18	20
87.	2	5	13	17	20	23
88.	2	6	7	9	13	17
89.	2	6	7	14	21	23
90.	2	6	9	11	18	21
91.	2	6	10	11	17	22
92.	2	6	10	13	14	20

161.	4	10	11	14	15	21
162.	4	11	16	18	19	22
163.	4	12	14	19	20	23
164.	5	6	7	9	20	23
165.	5	6	7	11	21	22
166.	5	6	9	10	13	21
167.	5	6	10	14	17	23
168.	5	6	11	14	18	20
169.	5	6	12	16	22	23
170.	5	6	13	17	18	22
171.	5	7	8	13	14	16
172.	5	7	10	11	19	23
173.	5	7	12	15	20	21
174.	5	7	17	18	19	20
175.	5	8	9	11	12	17
176.	5	9	10	14	18	19
177.	5	9	13	19	22	23
178.	5	9	15	16	21	22
179.	5	10	12	13	15	23
180.	5	10	12	16	19	21
181.	5	10	15	16	17	18
182.	5	11	13	19	20	21
183.	5	11	15	16	20	23
184.	5	12	14	15	18	22
185.	5	14	17	19	21	22
186.	6	7	8	10	12	18
187.	6	7	9	11	15	16
188.	6	7	11	14	17	19
189.	6	7	13	19	20	22
190.	6	8	16	17	20	21
191.	6	9	10	11	19	20
192.	6	9	12	13	16	19
193.	6	9	12	15	21	23
194.	6	9	17	18	19	23
195.	6	10	13	15	16	22
196.	6	10	19	21	22	23
197.	6	11	12	15	20	22
198.	6	12	13	14	15	17
199.	6	13	14	18	19	21
200.	6	14	15	16	18	23
201.	7	8	15	17	22	23
202.	7	9	10	11	13	22
203.	7	9	10	14	17	20
204.	7	9	11	14	18	23
205.	7	9	12	16	20	22
206.	7	10	13	20	21	23

93.	2	6	11	12	14	16
94.	2	6	18	20	22	23
95.	2	7	9	12	14	15
96.	2	7	10	14	19	22
97.	2	7	12	16	17	19
98.	2	7	13	18	19	23
99.	2	7	15	16	18	21
100.	2	8	9	10	16	23
101.	2	8	12	13	21	22
102.	2	9	11	13	14	19
103.	2	9	17	19	20	22
104.	2	10	12	15	17	20
105.	2	10	18	19	20	21
106.	2	11	12	15	18	23
107.	2	11	13	15	16	17
108.	2	11	17	19	21	23
109.	2	14	15	16	20	22
110.	3	4	5	6	8	17
111.	3	4	5	8	13	18
112.	3	4	5	8	19	23
113.	3	4	5	10	20	22
114.	3	4	6	11	13	23

207.	7	10	15	16	19	20
208.	7	11	12	13	15	19
209.	7	11	12	16	21	23
210.	7	11	13	17	18	21
211.	7	14	18	20	21	22
212.	8	9	13	15	18	20
213.	8	10	11	14	15	21
214.	8	11	16	18	19	22
215.	8	12	14	19	20	23
216.	9	10	12	15	19	22
217.	9	10	17	18	21	22
218.	9	11	20	21	22	23
219.	9	12	14	16	18	21
220.	9	13	14	17	21	23
221.	9	14	15	16	17	19
222.	10	11	12	13	16	20
223.	10	11	17	18	20	23
224.	10	12	14	16	17	22
225.	10	13	14	18	22	23
226.	11	13	14	17	20	22
227.	12	13	16	17	18	23
228.	12	15	17	18	19	21
229.	13	15	16	19	21	23

SYSTEM # 45: GUARANTEED 4–WIN IF 5 OF THE NUMBERS DRAWN ARE IN YOUR SET OF 24 NUMBERS ©Copyright 2001

Winning possibilities

Guessed	6	5	4	3	%
6	1	2	0-2	1-6	0.05
	1	1	13-16	21-33	0.01
	1	-	9-18	20-38	0.02
	1	-	-	40-43	0.12
	-	4	10-13	22-34	0.04
	-	3	0-15	11-39	0.44
	-	2	2-15	4-36	0.26
	-	1	0-17	21-41	19.34
	-	-	3-10	20-53	79.72
5	-	3	-	0-22	0.05
	-	2	8	29	0.01
	-	1	0-10	0-32	3.59
	-	-	10	29	0.25
	-	-	4-6	7-19	0.61
	-	-	3	13-21	30.13
	-	-	2	14-21	4.74
	-	-	1	16-29	60.62
4	-	-	6	30	0.11
	-	-	2-4	0-32	1.41
	-	-	1	3-12	33.03
	-	-	-	7-14	65.45
3	-	-	-	36	0.05
	-	-	-	4-6	4.89
	-	-	-	3	64.82
	-	-	-	1-2	30.24

Aside from the main guarantee, the system also guarantees at least seven 3-wins if four of the numbers drawn are guessed correctly. The complete system would require 134,596 combinations. If all of the numbers are guessed correctly, you will either win the jackpot (plus some extra cash!), or you will get anywhere between one and four 5-wins (and additional prizes), or at least three 4-wins and a number of 3-wins. The table below contains information on the balance of the system.

Number(s)	Occurrences
11,12,13,15,16,17,19,20,21,22,23,24	69
1, 2, 3, 5, 7, 9,10,14,18	67
4, 6, 8	57

1.	1	2	3	5	9	13
2.	1	2	3	10	21	24
3.	1	2	3	19	22	23
4.	1	2	4	6	8	14
5.	1	2	4	7	11	20
6.	1	2	5	10	12	14
7.	1	2	5	16	17	22
8.	1	2	6	7	11	20
9.	1	2	7	8	11	20
10.	1	2	9	12	18	19
11.	1	2	9	15	17	21
12.	1	2	10	15	18	22
13.	1	2	12	17	23	24
14.	1	2	13	14	15	23
15.	1	2	13	16	18	24
16.	1	2	14	16	19	21
17.	1	3	4	6	8	10
18.	1	3	4	12	15	16
19.	1	3	5	7	17	24
20.	1	3	5	11	14	19
21.	1	3	6	12	15	16
22.	1	3	7	10	14	23
23.	1	3	7	13	18	22
24.	1	3	8	12	15	16
25.	1	3	9	10	11	18
26.	1	3	9	17	20	23
27.	1	3	11	17	21	22
28.	1	3	13	14	20	21
29.	1	3	18	19	20	24
30.	1	4	5	6	8	9
31.	1	4	5	18	21	23
32.	1	4	6	7	8	18
33.	1	4	9	14	22	24
34.	1	4	10	13	17	19
35.	1	5	6	18	21	23
36.	1	5	7	9	10	15
37.	1	5	7	12	19	22
38.	1	5	8	18	21	23
39.	1	5	9	16	19	20
40.	1	5	10	11	16	24
41.	1	5	11	13	15	22
42.	1	5	12	13	20	24
43.	1	5	14	15	17	20
44.	1	6	9	14	22	24
45.	1	6	10	13	17	19
46.	1	7	9	12	13	23
134.	3	6	11	13	23	24
135.	3	7	8	9	19	21
136.	3	7	10	11	16	17
137.	3	7	11	12	14	22
138.	3	7	12	13	17	20
139.	3	7	14	15	20	24
140.	3	7	16	18	20	23
141.	3	8	11	13	23	24
142.	3	9	10	12	13	14
143.	3	9	10	15	17	24
144.	3	9	11	14	16	20
145.	3	9	12	18	22	23
146.	3	9	13	16	17	22
147.	3	10	12	17	21	23
148.	3	10	13	16	18	21
149.	3	10	14	16	19	24
150.	3	10	15	18	19	23
151.	3	11	12	18	20	21
152.	3	11	15	17	19	20
153.	3	12	17	19	22	24
154.	3	13	14	15	19	22
155.	3	14	16	21	22	23
156.	3	15	18	21	22	24
157.	4	5	6	7	8	14
158.	4	5	7	13	14	16
159.	4	5	9	11	12	17
160.	4	6	7	8	9	10
161.	4	6	8	10	14	18
162.	4	6	8	11	12	17
163.	4	6	8	11	13	15
164.	4	6	8	11	15	22
165.	4	6	8	11	16	21
166.	4	6	8	11	19	20
167.	4	6	8	11	23	24
168.	4	6	8	12	13	23
169.	4	6	8	12	15	20
170.	4	6	8	12	16	22
171.	4	6	8	12	19	24
172.	4	6	8	12	21	22
173.	4	6	8	13	16	19
174.	4	6	8	13	17	24
175.	4	6	8	13	19	22
176.	4	6	8	13	20	21
177.	4	6	8	15	16	23
178.	4	6	8	15	17	19
179.	4	6	8	15	21	24

47.	1	7	9	16	17	18
48.	1	7	10	16	21	22
49.	1	7	12	14	17	21
50.	1	7	13	15	21	24
51.	1	7	14	15	18	19
52.	1	7	16	19	23	24
53.	1	8	9	14	22	24
54.	1	8	10	13	17	19
55.	1	9	10	12	20	21
56.	1	9	11	13	16	21
57.	1	9	11	15	19	23
58.	1	10	11	12	22	23
59.	1	10	14	16	18	20
60.	1	10	15	20	23	24
61.	1	11	12	13	14	18
62.	1	11	12	19	21	24
63.	1	11	14	16	17	23
64.	1	11	15	17	18	24
65.	1	12	17	18	20	22
66.	1	13	16	20	22	23
67.	1	15	19	20	21	22
68.	2	3	4	6	7	8
69.	2	3	4	14	17	18
70.	2	3	5	7	12	23
71.	2	3	5	11	16	21
72.	2	3	6	14	17	18
73.	2	3	7	10	13	15
74.	2	3	7	16	22	24
75.	2	3	8	14	17	18
76.	2	3	9	11	15	22
77.	2	3	9	12	20	24
78.	2	3	10	11	12	19
79.	2	3	13	16	19	20
80.	2	3	15	20	21	23
81.	2	4	5	6	8	10
82.	2	4	5	15	19	24
83.	2	4	6	8	9	18
84.	2	4	9	10	16	23
85.	2	4	12	13	21	22
86.	2	5	6	15	19	24
87.	2	5	7	9	18	22
88.	2	5	7	10	17	21
89.	2	5	8	15	19	24
90.	2	5	9	14	20	21
91.	2	5	10	11	13	18
92.	2	5	11	14	22	23

180.	4	6	8	16	17	21
181.	4	6	8	16	20	24
182.	4	6	8	17	20	22
183.	4	6	8	17	20	23
184.	4	6	8	19	21	23
185.	4	6	8	22	23	24
186.	4	7	10	12	18	24
187.	4	7	15	17	22	23
188.	4	9	13	15	18	20
189.	4	10	11	14	15	21
190.	4	11	16	18	19	22
191.	4	12	14	19	20	23
192.	4	16	17	20	21	24
193.	5	6	7	13	14	16
194.	5	6	9	11	12	17
195.	5	7	8	13	14	16
196.	5	7	9	20	23	24
197.	5	7	10	11	19	23
198.	5	7	11	21	22	24
199.	5	7	12	15	20	21
200.	5	7	17	18	19	20
201.	5	8	9	11	12	17
202.	5	9	10	13	21	24
203.	5	9	10	14	18	19
204.	5	9	13	19	22	23
205.	5	9	15	16	21	22
206.	5	10	12	13	15	23
207.	5	10	12	16	19	21
208.	5	10	14	17	23	24
209.	5	10	15	16	17	18
210.	5	11	13	19	20	21
211.	5	11	14	18	20	24
212.	5	11	15	16	20	23
213.	5	12	14	15	18	22
214.	5	12	16	22	23	24
215.	5	13	17	18	22	24
216.	5	14	17	19	21	22
217.	6	7	10	12	18	24
218.	6	7	15	17	22	23
219.	6	9	13	15	18	20
220.	6	10	11	14	15	21
221.	6	11	16	18	19	22
222.	6	12	14	19	20	23
223.	6	16	17	20	21	24
224.	7	8	10	12	18	24
225.	7	8	15	17	22	23

93.	2	5	12	16	18	20
94.	2	5	13	17	20	23
95.	2	6	9	10	16	23
96.	2	6	12	13	21	22
97.	2	7	9	12	14	15
98.	2	7	9	13	17	24
99.	2	7	10	14	19	22
100.	2	7	12	16	17	19
101.	2	7	13	18	19	23
102.	2	7	14	21	23	24
103.	2	7	15	16	18	21
104.	2	8	9	10	16	23
105.	2	8	12	13	21	22
106.	2	9	11	13	14	19
107.	2	9	11	18	21	24
108.	2	9	17	19	20	22
109.	2	10	11	17	22	24
110.	2	10	12	15	17	20
111.	2	10	13	14	20	24
112.	2	10	18	19	20	21
113.	2	11	12	14	16	24
114.	2	11	12	15	18	23
115.	2	11	13	15	16	17
116.	2	11	17	19	21	23
117.	2	14	15	16	20	22
118.	2	18	20	22	23	24
119.	3	4	5	6	8	18
120.	3	4	5	10	20	22
121.	3	4	6	8	9	14
122.	3	4	7	9	19	21
123.	3	4	11	13	23	24
124.	3	5	6	10	20	22
125.	3	5	7	11	15	18
126.	3	5	8	10	20	22
127.	3	5	9	14	15	23
128.	3	5	9	16	18	24
129.	3	5	12	13	18	19
130.	3	5	12	14	21	24
131.	3	5	13	15	17	21
132.	3	5	16	17	19	23
133.	3	6	7	9	19	21

226.	7	9	10	11	13	22
227.	7	9	10	14	17	20
228.	7	9	11	14	18	23
229.	7	9	11	15	16	24
230.	7	9	12	16	20	22
231.	7	10	13	20	21	23
232.	7	10	15	16	19	20
233.	7	11	12	13	15	19
234.	7	11	12	16	21	23
235.	7	11	13	17	18	21
236.	7	11	14	17	19	24
237.	7	13	19	20	22	24
238.	7	14	18	20	21	22
239.	8	9	13	15	18	20
240.	8	10	11	14	15	21
241.	8	11	16	18	19	22
242.	8	12	14	19	20	23
243.	8	16	17	20	21	24
244.	9	10	11	19	20	24
245.	9	10	12	15	19	22
246.	9	10	17	18	21	22
247.	9	11	20	21	22	23
248.	9	12	13	16	19	24
249.	9	12	14	16	18	21
250.	9	12	15	21	23	24
251.	9	13	14	17	21	23
252.	9	14	15	16	17	19
253.	9	17	18	19	23	24
254.	10	11	12	13	16	20
255.	10	11	17	18	20	23
256.	10	12	14	16	17	22
257.	10	13	14	18	22	23
258.	10	13	15	16	22	24
259.	10	19	21	22	23	24
260.	11	12	15	20	22	24
261.	11	13	14	17	20	22
262.	12	13	14	15	17	24
263.	12	13	16	17	18	23
264.	12	15	17	18	19	21
265.	13	14	18	19	21	24
266.	13	15	16	19	21	23
267.	14	15	16	18	23	24

Lottery systems with a 4-win guaranteed if 6 of your numbers are drawn

System # 46: Guaranteed 4–win if 6 of the numbers drawn are in your set of 10 numbers ©Copyright 2001

Winning possibilities

Guessed	**6**	**5**	**4**	**3**	%
6	1	-	1	-	0.95
	1	-	-	-	0.48
	-	2	-	-	1.90
	-	1	1	0-1	11.43
	-	1	-	1-2	19.05
	-	-	3	-	2.86
	-	-	2	0-1	44.29
	-	-	1	2	19.04
5	-	1	1	-	1.59
	-	1	-	0-1	5.55
	-	-	2	-	7.14
	-	-	1	0-2	55.56
	-	-	-	3	19.05
	-	-	-	2	11.11
4	-	-	2	-	0.48
	-	-	1	0-1	20.48
	-	-	-	2	30.48
	-	-	-	1	45.71
	-	-	-	-	2.85
3	-	-	-	2	3.33
	-	-	-	1	43.33
	-	-	-	-	53.34

The complete system would require 210 combinations. If all of the numbers are guessed correctly, you will either win the jackpot, or you will get one or two 5-wins, or anywhere between one and three 4-wins. Every two combinations of the system differ in at least two numbers. The system is MATHEMATICALLY MINIMAL with respect to the main guarantee. It is also well balanced: Each number is in either one or two of the combinations of the system, as seen from the next table.

Number(s)	Occurrences
2, 3, 4, 5, 6, 7, 8, 9	2
1,10	1

1. 1 2 4 5 6 10

2. 2 3 4 7 8 9

3. 3 5 6 7 8 9

System # 47: Guaranteed 4–win if 6 of the numbers drawn are in your set of 11 numbers ©Copyright 2001

Winning possibilities

Guessed	6	5	4	3	%
6	1	-	1	1-3	0.87
	1	-	0-1	1-2	0.22
	-	2	-	1-3	1.73
	-	1	0-3	0-4	29.00
	-	-	3	0-2	16.23
	-	-	2	1-3	29.22
	-	-	1	2-4	22.73
5	-	1	1	1-2	1.73
	-	1	-	0-3	4.76
	-	-	3	0-1	1.30
	-	-	2	0-2	14.07
	-	-	1	0-3	47.40
	-	-	-	2-4	30.74
4	-	-	2	1	0.61
	-	-	1	0-2	21.52
	-	-	-	1-4	74.25
	-	-	-	-	3.62
3	-	-	-	3	1.21
	-	-	-	2	4.24
	-	-	-	1	48.48
	-	-	-	-	46.07

If all of the numbers are guessed correctly, you will either win the jackpot, or you will get one or two 5-wins, or anywhere between one and three 4-wins. The complete system would require 462 combinations. Every two combinations of the system differ in at least two numbers. Information on the balance of the system is given in the table below.

Number(s)	Occurrences
10	4
3, 4, 6, 7, 8,11	3
1, 2, 5, 9	2

1. 1 3 4 6 10 11
2. 1 5 6 7 8 10
3. 2 3 4 5 9 11
4. 2 6 7 8 9 10
5. 3 4 7 8 10 11

System # 48: Guaranteed 4–win if 6 of the numbers drawn are in your set of 12 numbers ©Copyright 2001

Winning possibilities

Guessed	**6**	**5**	**4**	**3**	%
6	1	-	-	4	0.65
	-	1	1	2	23.38
	-	-	3	-	23.38
	-	-	1	4	52.59
5	-	1	-	2	4.55
	-	-	2	1	13.64
	-	-	1	2	40.91
	-	-	-	3	40.90
4	-	-	1	2	7.27
	-	-	1	-	10.91
	-	-	-	2	65.45
	-	-	-	-	16.37
3	-	-	-	3	1.82
	-	-	-	1	49.09
	-	-	-	-	49.09

The system gives you, in only six combinations, a 4-win or more if all of the six numbers drawn are guessed correctly. You can also be a jackpot winner, or you can get a 5-win plus some extra cash in this case. The complete system would require 924 combinations. The system is HIGHLY BALANCED: Each number is in exactly 3 combinations. In addition, the combinations of the system are maximally 'apart': Every two combinations differ in at least three numbers.

1. 1 2 3 5 7 9
2. 1 4 5 6 8 9
3. 1 5 9 10 11 12
4. 2 3 4 6 7 8
5. 2 3 7 10 11 12
6. 4 6 8 10 11 12

System # 49: Guaranteed 4–win if 6 of the numbers drawn are in your set of 13 numbers ©Copyright 2001

Winning possibilities

Guessed	6	5	4	3	%
6	1	1	1	2	0.12
	1	1	-	5	0.12
	1	-	0-2	2-5	0.35
	-	3	-	2	0.12
	-	2	0-3	0-5	1.86
	-	1	0-4	0-6	20.16
	-	-	1-5	0-7	77.27
5	-	2	0-1	2-3	0.16
	-	1	0-2	1-4	4.35
	-	-	1-5	0-5	58.75
	-	-	-	3-7	36.74
4	-	-	3	2	0.14
	-	-	2	0-3	1.54
	-	-	1	0-4	17.58
	-	-	-	1-5	80.00
	-	-	-	-	0.84
3	-	-	-	5	0.35
	-	-	-	1-3	54.55
	-	-	-	-	45.10

The complete system would require 1,716 combinations. If all of the numbers are guessed correctly, you will either win the jackpot, or you will get between one or three 5-wins, or anywhere between one and five 4-wins. The system is well balanced: Each number is in either four or five of the combinations of the system, as seen from the table below.

Number(s)	Occurrences
2, 3, 5, 6, 8, 9,11,12	5
1, 4, 7,10,13	4

1.	1	2	4	8	10	13
2.	1	2	5	6	8	12
3.	1	3	5	9	10	11
4.	1	4	6	7	12	13
5.	2	3	6	8	9	11
6.	2	3	8	9	11	12
7.	2	6	7	8	10	12
8.	3	4	5	7	9	11
9.	3	5	7	9	11	13
10.	4	5	6	10	12	13

SYSTEM # 50: GUARANTEED 4–WIN IF 6 OF THE NUMBERS DRAWN ARE IN YOUR SET OF 14 NUMBERS ©Copyright 2001

Winning possibilities

Guessed	6	5	4	3	%
6	1	-	-	4	0.47
	-	1	0-2	2-8	22.38
	-	-	4	1-3	3.49
	-	-	3	3-5	28.90
	-	-	2	4-7	33.56
	-	-	1	6-10	11.20
5	-	1	-	1-3	4.20
	-	-	2	1-3	12.59
	-	-	1	2-5	58.75
	-	-	-	4-7	24.46
4	-	-	1	0-2	20.98
	-	-	-	1-4	79.02
3	-	-	-	2	7.69
	-	-	-	1	61.54
	-	-	-	-	30.77

The system guarantees you, in only 14 combinations, a 4-win or more if all of the six numbers drawn are guessed correctly. You can also be a jackpot winner, or you can get a 5-win in this case. The complete system would require 3,003 combinations. The system is HIGHLY BALANCED: Each number is in exactly 6 combinations. It also has an additional nice property: Every two combinations of the system differ in at least three numbers, that is, the combinations are as 'apart' as possible.

1.	1	2	6	9	12	14
2.	1	2	7	10	12	13
3.	1	3	4	7	11	12
4.	1	3	6	8	10	13
5.	1	4	5	8	9	10
6.	1	5	7	8	11	14
7.	2	3	4	6	7	8
8.	2	3	5	9	11	13
9.	2	4	10	11	13	14
10.	2	5	6	8	11	12
11.	3	4	5	10	12	14
12.	3	8	9	12	13	14
13.	4	5	6	7	9	13
14.	6	7	9	10	11	14

System # 51: Guaranteed 4–win if 6 of the numbers drawn are in your set of 15 numbers ©Copyright 2001

Winning possibilities

Guessed	6	5	4	3	%
6	1	-	0-2	2-7	0.38
	-	2	0-2	0-7	0.48
	-	1	0-4	0-10	19.54
	-	-	5	1-4	0.36
	-	-	4	0-7	6.04
	-	-	3	2-8	27.18
	-	-	2	4-11	32.85
	-	-	1	7-12	13.17
5	-	1	1	1-4	0.80
	-	1	-	1-6	3.00
	-	-	3	1-3	0.77
	-	-	2	1-5	13.39
	-	-	1	2-7	55.54
	-	-	-	4-10	26.50
4	-	-	2	0-1	0.44
	-	-	1	0-4	19.99
	-	-	-	5-6	1.68
	-	-	-	2-4	75.31
	-	-	-	1	2.20
	-	-	-	-	0.38
3	-	-	-	3	1.32
	-	-	-	2	9.45
	-	-	-	1	60.66
	-	-	-	-	28.57

If all of the numbers are guessed correctly, you will either win the jackpot, or you will get one or two 5-wins, or anywhere between one and five 4-wins. The complete system would require 5,005 combinations. Every two combinations of the system differ in at least two numbers. Information on the balance of the system is given in the table below.

Number(s)	Occurrences
1, 2, 3, 5, 6, 7,11,12,13,14	8
4, 8, 9,15	7
10	6

1.	1	2	3	4	5	14
2.	1	2	7	8	13	15
3.	1	2	9	10	11	12
4.	1	3	4	5	11	13
5.	1	3	6	8	9	12
6.	1	4	5	7	9	12
7.	1	6	7	10	11	14
8.	1	6	12	13	14	15
9.	2	3	5	7	12	14
10.	2	3	9	11	13	14
11.	2	4	6	7	8	11
12.	2	4	6	10	12	13
13.	2	5	6	9	11	15
14.	3	4	7	9	10	15
15.	3	5	6	8	10	15
16.	3	5	7	11	12	13
17.	4	8	11	12	14	15
18.	5	8	9	10	13	14
19.	6	7	8	13	14	15

SYSTEM # 52: GUARANTEED 4–WIN IF 6 OF THE NUMBERS DRAWN ARE IN YOUR SET OF 16 NUMBERS

Winning possibilities

Guessed	6	5	4	3	%
6	1	-	0-2	0-8	0.31
	-	3	-	1	0.02
	-	2	0-2	4-5	0.37
	-	1	0-3	4-11	17.91
	-	-	6	-	0.09
	-	-	5	2-6	1.40
	-	-	4	0-8	9.63
	-	-	3	0-10	22.13
	-	-	2	6-12	28.79
	-	-	1	8-12	19.35
5	-	1	2	-	0.14
	-	1	1	1-4	0.55
	-	1	-	0-5	2.75
	-	-	3	1-4	1.92
	-	-	2	2-6	13.87
	-	-	1	2-8	51.51
	-	-	-	5-10	29.26
4	-	-	2	0-1	0.49
	-	-	1	0-4	19.62
	-	-	-	5-6	5.28
	-	-	-	2-4	71.93
	-	-	-	1	2.64
	-	-	-	-	0.04
3	-	-	-	3	4.64
	-	-	-	2	5.36
	-	-	-	1	64.64
	-	-	-	-	25.36

If all of the numbers are guessed correctly, you will either win the jackpot (plus some extra cash!), or you will get up to three 5-wins (and additional prizes), or anywhere between one and six 4-wins (plus a number of 3-wins). The complete system would require 8,008 combinations. Every two combinations of the system differ in at least two numbers. The next table gives information on the balance of the system.

Number(s)	Occurrences
7, 9,10,11,13,16	10
1, 2, 3, 4, 5, 6, 8,12,14,15	9

1.	1	2	3	6	9	11
2.	1	2	4	5	7	13
3.	1	2	10	14	15	16
4.	1	3	5	11	12	13
5.	1	3	8	10	11	14
6.	1	4	6	7	8	9
7.	1	4	7	12	15	16
8.	1	5	8	13	15	16
9.	1	6	9	10	12	14
10.	2	3	5	8	11	13
11.	2	3	11	12	15	16
12.	2	4	7	8	15	16
13.	2	4	7	10	12	14
14.	2	5	6	9	12	13
15.	2	6	8	9	10	14
16.	3	4	5	6	14	15
17.	3	4	7	8	11	12
18.	3	5	7	9	10	16
19.	3	7	9	10	13	15
20.	4	6	10	11	13	16
21.	4	9	11	13	14	16
22.	5	7	9	10	11	15
23.	5	8	10	12	13	14
24.	6	7	11	13	14	16
25.	6	8	9	12	15	16

System # 53: Guaranteed 4–win if 6 of the numbers drawn are in your set of 17 numbers ©Copyright 2001

Winning possibilities

Guessed	6	5	4	3	%
6	1	-	0-2	3-12	0.27
	-	2	0-2	1-10	0.20
	-	1	0-5	2-14	17.75
	-	-	7	4	0.01
	-	-	6	2-5	0.26
	-	-	5	1-9	1.83
	-	-	4	2-11	10.20
	-	-	3	4-13	26.31
	-	-	2	5-14	32.95
	-	-	1	9-16	10.22
5	-	1	0-2	0-9	3.31
	-	-	4	0-4	0.06
	-	-	3	1-6	1.45
	-	-	2	2-8	15.26
	-	-	1	2-11	55.14
	-	-	-	4-12	24.78
4	-	-	2	0-2	0.25
	-	-	1	0-5	20.92
	-	-	-	6-7	1.64
	-	-	-	2-5	76.64
	-	-	-	1	0.50
	-	-	-	-	0.05
3	-	-	-	3-4	1.77
	-	-	-	2	13.82
	-	-	-	1	66.32
	-	-	-	-	18.09

If all of the numbers are guessed correctly, you will either win the jackpot (plus some extra cash!), or you will get one or two 5-wins (and additional prizes), or anywhere between one and seven 4-wins (plus a number of 3-wins). The complete system would require 12,376 combinations. Every two combinations of the system differ in at least two numbers. Below is information on the balance of the system.

Number(s)	Occurrences
6,11	14
1, 2, 3, 4, 5, 8,10,12,14,16,17	12
7, 9,13,15	11

1.	1	2	3	8	14	16
2.	1	2	4	12	15	17
3.	1	2	5	9	13	14
4.	1	3	5	7	14	17
5.	1	3	6	10	15	16
6.	1	3	8	11	13	17
7.	1	4	5	8	10	12
8.	1	4	6	9	11	12
9.	1	4	7	12	13	16
10.	1	5	6	11	16	17
11.	1	6	7	10	14	17
12.	1	7	8	9	11	15
13.	2	3	4	6	7	8
14.	2	3	5	12	14	16
15.	2	3	7	10	11	12
16.	2	4	6	10	11	16
17.	2	4	9	10	14	16
18.	2	5	8	10	15	17
19.	2	6	8	11	12	13
20.	2	6	9	11	15	17
21.	2	7	13	15	16	17
22.	3	4	5	11	15	16
23.	3	4	6	10	11	14
24.	3	4	9	10	13	17
25.	3	5	6	12	13	17
26.	3	8	9	12	14	15
27.	4	5	7	11	14	17
28.	4	6	8	13	14	15
29.	5	6	7	9	12	15
30.	5	6	8	9	10	11
31.	5	7	8	10	13	16
32.	6	7	9	11	13	16
33.	8	9	12	14	16	17
34.	10	11	12	13	14	15

System # 54: Guaranteed 4–win if 6 of the numbers drawn are in your set of 18 numbers ©Copyright 2001

Winning possibilities

Guessed	6	5	4	3	%
6	1	-	-	6-8	0.23
	-	1	2	5	0.87
	-	1	1	6-10	11.93
	-	1	-	11-12	3.49
	-	-	6	2	0.44
	-	-	4	4-8	9.16
	-	-	3	5-11	32.43
	-	-	2	9-12	32.29
	-	-	1	12-14	9.16
5	-	1	-	2-4	2.94
	-	-	2	3-6	14.81
	-	-	1	4-8	58.61
	-	-	-	8-10	23.64
4	-	-	1	0-4	20.59
	-	-	-	2-5	79.41
3	-	-	-	5	0.74
	-	-	-	3	3.31
	-	-	-	1	89.34
	-	-	-	-	6.61

Aside from the main guarantee, the system also guarantees at least two 3-wins on guessing correctly four of the numbers drawn. The complete system would require 18,564 combinations. If all of the numbers are guessed correctly, you will either win the jackpot, or you will get a 5-win (plus additional prizes), or anywhere between one and six 4-wins and a number of 3-wins. The system is HIGHLY BALANCED: Each number is in exactly 14 combinations. In addition, the combinations of the system are maximally 'apart': Every two combinations differ in at least three numbers.

1.	1	2	3	5	7	9
2.	1	2	4	10	12	13
3.	1	2	6	11	12	14
4.	1	2	8	12	15	18
5.	1	3	4	14	15	16
6.	1	3	6	13	16	18
7.	1	3	8	10	11	16
8.	1	4	5	6	8	9
9.	1	4	7	11	17	18
10.	1	5	9	10	14	18
22.	2	5	8	10	13	16
23.	2	6	9	10	13	17
24.	2	8	9	11	14	17
25.	3	4	5	13	17	18
26.	3	4	9	10	11	12
27.	3	5	6	10	11	17
28.	3	5	8	14	15	17
29.	3	6	9	12	14	15
30.	3	8	9	12	13	18
31.	4	5	7	10	12	15

11.	1	5	9	11	13	15
12.	1	5	9	12	16	17
13.	1	6	7	10	15	17
14.	1	7	8	13	14	17
15.	2	3	4	6	7	8
16.	2	3	7	10	14	18
17.	2	3	7	11	13	15
18.	2	3	7	12	16	17
19.	2	4	5	11	14	16
20.	2	4	9	15	17	18
21.	2	5	6	15	16	18

32.	4	6	8	10	14	18
33.	4	6	8	11	13	15
34.	4	6	8	12	16	17
35.	4	7	9	13	14	16
36.	5	6	7	12	13	14
37.	5	7	8	11	12	18
38.	6	7	9	11	16	18
39.	7	8	9	10	15	16
40.	10	11	13	14	15	18
41.	10	12	14	16	17	18
42.	11	12	13	15	16	17

System # 55: Guaranteed 4–win if 6 of the numbers drawn are in your set of 19 numbers ©Copyright 2001

Winning possibilities

Guessed	6	5	4	3	%
6	1	-	4	10	0.07
	1	-	-	4-10	0.13
	-	2	3-4	5-10	0.54
	-	1	0-5	5-14	14.46
	-	-	8	6	0.07
	-	-	6	0-3	0.44
	-	-	5	6-7	1.19
	-	-	4	9-13	15.19
	-	-	3	8-13	17.16
	-	-	2	11-16	40.00
	-	-	1	16	10.75
5	-	1	2	7	0.62
	-	1	-	2-10	2.17
	-	-	4	2-4	1,70
	-	-	3	8	0.62
	-	-	2	4-9	12.38
	-	-	1	4-8	55.88
	-	-	-	8-14	26.63
4	-	-	3	3	0.31
	-	-	1	0-5	19.97
	-	-	-	3-9	79.72
3	-	-	-	6	1.24
	-	-	-	3	4.95
	-	-	-	2	3.72
	-	-	-	1	81.73
	-	-	-	-	8.36

Aside from the main guarantee, the system also guarantees at least three 3-wins on guessing correctly four of the numbers drawn. The complete system would require 27,132 combinations. If all of the numbers are guessed correctly, you will either win the jackpot (plus some extra cash!), or you will get one or two 5-wins (and additional prizes), or up to eight 4-wins (plus a number of 3-wins). Every two combinations of the system differ in at least two numbers. In addition, the system is well balanced: The number 19 is in 18 combinations; each of the remaining numbers is in 17 combinations.

1.	1	2	3	6	8	19
2.	1	2	4	6	9	19
3.	1	2	5	6	7	19
28.	2	5	8	12	15	18
29.	3	4	5	6	7	19
30.	3	4	5	10	11	12

4.	1	2	6	10	11	12	31.	3	4	5	13	17	18
5.	1	2	6	13	17	18	32.	3	4	5	14	15	16
6.	1	2	6	14	15	16	33.	3	6	9	10	13	16
7.	1	3	4	5	8	19	34.	3	6	9	11	14	17
8.	1	3	7	8	9	19	35.	3	6	9	12	15	18
9.	1	3	8	10	15	17	36.	4	6	8	10	14	18
10.	1	3	8	11	16	18	37.	4	6	8	11	13	15
11.	1	3	8	12	13	14	38.	4	6	8	12	16	17
12.	1	4	7	10	13	16	39.	5	6	7	8	9	19
13.	1	4	7	11	14	17	40.	5	6	7	10	15	17
14.	1	4	7	12	15	18	41.	5	6	7	11	16	18
15.	1	5	9	10	14	18	42.	5	6	7	12	13	14
16.	1	5	9	11	13	15	43.	7	8	9	10	11	12
17.	1	5	9	12	16	17	44.	7	8	9	13	17	18
18.	2	3	4	5	9	19	45.	7	8	9	14	15	16
19.	2	3	7	10	14	18	46.	10	11	12	13	14	19
20.	2	3	7	11	13	15	47.	10	11	12	15	17	19
21.	2	3	7	12	16	17	48.	10	11	12	16	18	19
22.	2	4	7	8	9	19	49.	10	13	15	17	18	19
23.	2	4	9	10	15	17	50.	10	14	15	16	17	19
24.	2	4	9	11	16	18	51.	11	13	16	17	18	19
25.	2	4	9	12	13	14	52.	11	14	15	16	18	19
26.	2	5	8	10	13	16	53.	12	13	14	15	16	19
27.	2	5	8	11	14	17	54.	12	13	14	17	18	19

SYSTEM # 56: GUARANTEED 4–WIN IF 6 OF THE NUMBERS DRAWN ARE IN YOUR SET OF 20 NUMBERS

Winning possibilities

Guessed	6	5	4	3	%
6	1	2	4	-	0.05
	1	-	6	-	0.01
	1	-	-	8	0.12
	-	4	3	-	0.07
	-	3	4	-	0.09
	-	3	-	10	0.19
	-	1	0-4	7-17	13.09
	-	-	7	6	0.03
	-	-	6	4-10	0.28
	-	-	5	4-13	3.91
	-	-	4	6-16	11.07
	-	-	3	6-18	25.34
	-	-	2	8-20	24.63
	-	-	1	11-22	21.12
5	-	3	-	4	0.04
	-	1	4	2	0.35
	-	1	3	3	0.23
	-	1	2	4	0.12
	-	1	-	4	1.74
	-	-	5	2	0.35
	-	-	3	4-8	2.32
	-	-	2	5-10	13.93
	-	-	1	2-11	50.50
	-	-	-	6-15	30.42
4	-	-	3	1-2	0.62
	-	-	2	2-4	0.93
	-	-	1	0-5	16.72
	-	-	-	1-7	81.73
3	-	-	-	3-5	5.80
	-	-	-	2	20.00
	-	-	-	1	55.26
	-	-	-	-	18.94

If all of the numbers are guessed correctly, you will either win the jackpot (plus some extra cash!), or you will get between one and four 5-wins (and additional prizes), or up to seven 4-wins (plus a number of 3-wins). The complete system would require 38,760 combinations. The next table contains information on the balance of the system.

Number(s)	Occurrences
10,12,14,16,17,18	21
1, 2, 3, 4, 5, 6, 7, 8, 9,11,13,15	20
19,20	15

1.	1	2	3	5	7	9
2.	1	2	4	11	14	16
3.	1	2	6	10	15	17
4.	1	2	6	12	13	14
5.	1	2	8	11	17	18
6.	1	3	4	10	13	17
7.	1	3	6	13	16	18
8.	1	3	8	10	11	12
9.	1	3	8	14	15	16
10.	1	4	5	6	8	9
11.	1	4	7	12	18	19
12.	1	4	7	15	19	20
13.	1	4	12	15	18	19
14.	1	4	12	18	19	20
15.	1	5	9	10	14	18
16.	1	5	9	11	13	15
17.	1	5	9	12	16	17
18.	1	6	7	10	11	16
19.	1	7	8	13	14	17
20.	1	7	12	15	18	20
21.	2	3	4	6	7	8
22.	2	3	7	10	14	18
23.	2	3	7	11	13	15
24.	2	3	7	12	16	17
25.	2	4	5	14	15	17
26.	2	4	9	10	11	12
27.	2	4	9	13	17	18
28.	2	5	6	11	12	18
29.	2	5	8	10	16	19
30.	2	5	8	13	19	20
31.	2	5	10	13	16	20
32.	2	6	9	15	16	18
33.	2	8	9	12	14	15
34.	2	8	10	13	16	20
35.	2	10	13	16	19	20
36.	3	4	5	11	16	18
37.	3	4	5	12	13	14
38.	3	4	9	10	15	16
39.	3	5	6	10	12	15
40.	3	5	8	15	17	18
41.	3	6	9	11	19	20
42.	3	6	9	14	17	19
43.	3	6	11	14	17	20
44.	3	8	9	12	13	18
45.	3	9	11	14	17	20
46.	3	11	14	17	19	20
47.	4	5	7	10	11	17
48.	4	6	8	10	14	18
49.	4	6	8	11	13	15
50.	4	6	8	12	16	17
51.	4	7	9	13	14	16
52.	4	7	12	15	18	20
53.	5	6	7	13	17	18
54.	5	6	7	14	15	16
55.	5	7	8	11	12	14
56.	5	8	10	13	16	19
57.	5	8	10	16	19	20
58.	6	7	9	10	12	13
59.	6	9	11	14	17	19
60.	6	9	14	17	19	20
61.	7	8	9	10	15	17
62.	7	8	9	11	16	18
63.	7	12	15	18	19	20
64.	10	11	13	14	15	18
65.	10	12	14	16	17	18
66.	11	12	13	15	16	17

System # 57: Guaranteed 4–win if 6 of the numbers drawn are in your set of 21 numbers ©Copyright 2001

Winning possibilities

Guessed	6	5	4	3	%
6	1	-	0-9	2-10	0.15
	-	3	3-6	3-4	0.23
	-	2	0-6	4-15	0.25
	-	1	0-4	8-19	12.06
	-	-	5-9	4-14	5.62
	-	-	4	7-17	8.69
	-	-	3	8-19	22.76
	-	-	2	9-25	27.58
	-	-	1	11-23	22.66
5	-	1	3	6-9	0.47
	-	1	2	5-7	0.44
	-	1	1	4-6	0.24
	-	1	-	4-6	1.21
	-	-	3-6	2-10	1.36
	-	-	2	5-14	16.66
	-	-	1	2-15	46.75
	-	-	-	6-15	32.87
4	-	-	2	0-4	2.16
	-	-	1	0-9	15.74
	-	-	-	7-10	1.50
	-	-	-	4-6	62.84
	-	-	-	1-3	17.76
3	-	-	-	4-5	0.53
	-	-	-	3	9.47
	-	-	-	2	23.68
	-	-	-	1	41.95
	-	-	-	-	24.37

The complete system would require 54,264 combinations. If all of the numbers are guessed correctly, you will either win the jackpot, or you will get between one or three 5-wins, or up to nine 4-wins. Every two combinations of the system differ in at least two numbers. In addition, the system is well balanced: Each number is in either 22 or 23 of the combinations of the system, as seen from the table below.

Number(s)	Occurrences
1, 2, 3, 4, 5, 6, 7, 8, 9,10,11,12,13,14,15,16,17,18	23
19,20,21	22

1.	1	2	3	5	7	9
2.	1	2	4	11	14	16
3.	1	2	6	10	15	17
4.	1	2	6	12	13	14
5.	1	2	8	11	17	18
6.	1	3	4	10	13	17
7.	1	3	6	12	14	15
8.	1	3	6	13	16	18
9.	1	3	8	10	11	12
10.	1	3	8	14	15	16
11.	1	4	5	6	8	9
12.	1	4	7	12	19	21
13.	1	4	7	15	19	20
14.	1	4	12	18	20	21
15.	1	4	15	18	19	21
16.	1	5	9	10	14	18
17.	1	5	9	11	13	15
18.	1	5	9	12	16	17
19.	1	6	7	10	11	16
20.	1	7	8	13	14	17
21.	1	7	12	18	19	20
22.	1	7	15	18	20	21
23.	1	12	15	19	20	21
24.	2	3	4	6	7	8
25.	2	3	7	10	14	18
26.	2	3	7	11	13	15
27.	2	3	7	12	16	17
28.	2	4	5	14	15	17
29.	2	4	9	10	11	12
30.	2	4	9	13	17	18
31.	2	5	6	11	12	18
32.	2	5	8	13	19	20
33.	2	5	8	16	20	21
34.	2	5	10	13	19	21
35.	2	5	10	16	19	20
36.	2	6	9	15	16	18
37.	2	8	9	10	11	17
38.	2	8	9	12	14	15
39.	2	8	10	19	20	21
40.	2	8	13	16	19	21
41.	2	10	13	16	20	21
42.	3	4	5	11	16	18
43.	3	4	5	12	13	14
44.	3	4	9	10	15	16
45.	3	5	6	10	12	15
46.	3	5	6	13	14	16
47.	3	5	8	15	17	18
48.	3	6	9	11	19	20
49.	3	6	9	17	20	21
50.	3	6	11	17	19	21
51.	3	8	9	12	13	18
52.	3	9	11	14	19	21
53.	3	9	14	17	19	20
54.	3	11	14	17	20	21
55.	4	5	7	10	11	17
56.	4	6	8	10	14	18
57.	4	6	8	11	13	15
58.	4	6	8	12	16	17
59.	4	7	9	11	17	18
60.	4	7	9	13	14	16
61.	4	7	12	15	20	21
62.	4	7	18	19	20	21
63.	4	12	15	18	19	20
64.	5	6	7	13	17	18
65.	5	6	7	14	15	16
66.	5	7	8	11	12	14
67.	5	8	10	13	20	21
68.	5	8	10	16	19	21
69.	5	13	16	19	20	21
70.	6	7	9	10	12	13
71.	6	9	11	14	20	21
72.	6	9	14	17	19	21
73.	6	11	14	17	19	20
74.	7	8	9	10	15	17
75.	7	8	9	11	16	18
76.	7	12	15	18	19	21
77.	8	10	13	16	19	20
78.	10	11	13	14	15	18
79.	10	12	14	16	17	18
80.	11	12	13	15	16	17

System # 58: Guaranteed 4–win if 6 of the numbers drawn are in your set of 22 numbers ©Copyright 2001

Winning possibilities

Guessed	6	5	4	3	%
6	1	1	8-10	7-9	0.02
	1	-	0-12	4-9	0.12
	-	4	5-7	8-11	0.03
	-	3	4-9	5-15	0.36
	-	2	2-11	4-21	0.40
	-	1	0-13	4-24	11.09
	-	-	8-18	0-17	0.21
	-	-	5-7	4-24	6.33
	-	-	1-4	7-32	81.44
5	-	2	2	10-13	0.03
	-	1	0-5	4-15	2.27
	-	-	3-8	4-15	3.83
	-	-	1-2	3-20	59.29
	-	-	-	7-21	34.58
4	-	-	3	0-5	0.62
	-	-	2	4-8	2.41
	-	-	1	0-11	14.26
	-	-	-	1-9	82.71
3	-	-	-	5-6	1.29
	-	-	-	3-4	16.10
	-	-	-	1-2	55.71
	-	-	-	-	26.90

If all of the numbers are guessed correctly, you will either win the jackpot (plus some extra cash!), or you will get between one and four 5-wins (and additional prizes), or up to eighteen 4-wins (plus a number of 3-wins). The complete system would require 74,613 combinations. Information on the balance of the system is given in the table below.

Number(s)	Occurrences
1, 5, 6,10	30
2, 3, 4, 7,19,21	28
8, 9,11,12,13,14,15,16,17,18,20,22	27

1.	1	2	3	4	5	21
2.	1	2	3	5	7	19
52.	2	13	14	15	16	19
53.	3	4	5	10	19	21

3. 1 2 3 6 19 21
4. 1 2 3 7 10 19
5. 1 2 4 6 7 21
6. 1 2 4 10 19 21
7. 1 3 4 6 7 19
8. 1 3 4 7 10 21
9. 1 4 5 7 19 21
10. 1 5 6 12 16 18
11. 1 5 6 15 16 20
12. 1 5 8 12 15 18
13. 1 5 8 12 16 20
14. 1 5 9 11 17 22
15. 1 5 9 13 14 17
16. 1 5 10 12 16 18
17. 1 5 10 15 18 20
18. 1 5 11 13 14 22
19. 1 6 8 12 15 20
20. 1 6 8 15 16 18
21. 1 6 9 11 14 22
22. 1 6 9 13 17 22
23. 1 6 10 12 15 20
24. 1 6 10 16 18 20
25. 1 6 11 13 14 17
26. 1 8 10 12 15 16
27. 1 8 10 12 18 20
28. 1 9 10 11 13 17
29. 1 9 10 13 14 22
30. 1 10 11 14 17 22
31. 2 3 4 5 6 19
32. 2 3 4 5 7 10
33. 2 3 6 7 10 21
34. 2 3 8 12 13 22
35. 2 3 9 11 16 20
36. 2 3 14 15 17 18
37. 2 4 5 6 7 21
38. 2 4 6 7 10 19
39. 2 4 8 9 14 15
40. 2 4 11 13 18 20
41. 2 4 12 16 17 22
42. 2 5 6 7 8 10
43. 2 5 7 10 19 21
44. 2 7 8 11 16 17
45. 2 7 9 12 13 18
46. 2 7 14 15 20 22
47. 2 8 11 18 19 22
48. 2 8 13 17 20 21
54. 3 4 6 10 19 21
55. 3 4 8 9 17 18
56. 3 4 11 15 16 22
57. 3 4 12 13 14 20
58. 3 5 6 7 19 21
59. 3 5 6 8 10 21
60. 3 7 8 11 13 15
61. 3 7 9 12 14 16
62. 3 7 17 18 20 22
63. 3 8 11 14 19 20
64. 3 8 14 16 21 22
65. 3 9 12 15 19 22
66. 3 9 13 15 20 21
67. 3 11 12 17 18 21
68. 3 13 16 17 18 19
69. 4 5 6 8 10 19
70. 4 7 8 9 20 22
71. 4 7 11 14 16 18
72. 4 7 12 13 15 17
73. 4 8 9 11 12 21
74. 4 8 9 13 16 19
75. 4 11 15 17 19 20
76. 4 12 14 18 19 22
77. 4 13 15 18 21 22
78. 4 14 16 17 20 21
79. 5 6 9 11 13 14
80. 5 6 9 14 17 22
81. 5 6 11 13 17 22
82. 5 6 12 15 18 20
83. 5 8 15 16 18 20
84. 5 9 10 11 13 22
85. 5 9 10 11 14 17
86. 5 10 12 15 16 20
87. 5 10 13 14 17 22
88. 6 8 12 16 18 20
89. 6 9 10 11 13 14
90. 6 9 10 11 17 22
91. 6 10 12 15 16 18
92. 6 10 13 14 17 22
93. 7 8 12 14 17 19
94. 7 8 13 14 18 21
95. 7 9 11 15 18 19
96. 7 9 15 16 17 21
97. 7 11 12 20 21 22
98. 7 13 16 19 20 22
99. 8 10 15 16 18 20

49. 2 9 12 17 19 20
50. 2 9 16 18 21 22
51. 2 11 12 14 15 21

100. 8 15 17 19 21 22
101. 9 14 18 19 20 21
102. 11 12 13 16 19 21

System # 59: Guaranteed 4–win if 6 of the numbers drawn are in your set of 23 numbers ©Copyright 2001

Winning possibilities

Guessed	6	5	4	3	%
6	1	-	0-6	16-44	0.13
	-	3	0-3	11-24	0.09
	-	2	1-5	10-23	1.04
	-	1	0-7	6-42	10.49
	-	-	1-11	6-32	88.25
5	-	1	2	4-12	1.91
	-	1	1	16	0.10
	-	1	-	9-22	0.26
	-	-	5	2-16	0.48
	-	-	4	6-18	2.52
	-	-	3	4-17	5.58
	-	-	2	8-18	14.06
	-	-	1	2-21	34.99
	-	-	-	8-22	40.10
4	-	-	3	1-6	0.23
	-	-	2	2-10	3.04
	-	-	1	0-12	14.76
	-	-	-	1-16	81.97
3	-	-	-	7-10	1.47
	-	-	-	1-4	69.23
	-	-	-	-	29.30

If all of the numbers are guessed correctly, you will either win the jackpot (plus some extra cash!), or you will get between one and three 5-wins (and additional prizes), or up to eleven 4-wins (plus a number of 3-wins). The complete system would require 100,947 combinations. The next table gives information on the balance of the system.

Number(s)	Occurrences
1, 2, 4, 6, 7, 8, 9,11,22	34
3, 5,12,13,15,16,17,18,19,20,21,23	33
10,14	30

1. 1 2 3 15 18 22
2. 1 2 3 19 20 22
3. 1 2 4 6 8 11

64. 3 5 14 17 21 23
65. 3 6 7 11 15 18
66. 3 6 7 11 19 20

4.	1	2	4	7	9	11
5.	1	2	4	8	9	22
6.	1	2	5	10	12	22
7.	1	2	6	7	11	22
8.	1	2	10	13	17	22
9.	1	2	10	16	21	22
10.	1	2	15	19	22	23
11.	1	2	18	20	22	23
12.	1	3	4	7	15	18
13.	1	3	4	7	19	20
14.	1	3	6	9	14	23
15.	1	3	8	11	14	23
16.	1	4	5	7	10	12
17.	1	4	6	7	8	22
18.	1	4	7	10	13	17
19.	1	4	7	10	16	21
20.	1	4	7	15	19	23
21.	1	4	7	18	20	23
22.	1	5	6	9	13	21
23.	1	5	6	9	16	17
24.	1	5	8	11	13	21
25.	1	5	8	11	16	17
26.	1	6	9	12	13	16
27.	1	6	9	12	17	21
28.	1	6	9	14	15	20
29.	1	6	9	14	18	19
30.	1	7	8	9	11	22
31.	1	8	11	12	13	16
32.	1	8	11	12	17	21
33.	1	8	11	14	15	20
34.	1	8	11	14	18	19
35.	2	3	4	6	14	23
36.	2	3	7	8	14	23
37.	2	3	9	11	15	18
38.	2	3	9	11	19	20
39.	2	4	5	6	13	21
40.	2	4	5	6	16	17
41.	2	4	6	7	9	22
42.	2	4	6	12	13	16
43.	2	4	6	12	17	21
44.	2	4	6	14	15	20
45.	2	4	6	14	18	19
46.	2	5	7	8	13	21
47.	2	5	7	8	16	17
48.	2	5	9	10	11	12
49.	2	6	8	9	11	22

67.	3	6	8	15	18	22
68.	3	6	8	19	20	22
69.	3	7	9	14	22	23
70.	3	10	13	15	17	18
71.	3	10	13	17	19	20
72.	3	10	15	16	18	21
73.	3	10	16	19	20	21
74.	3	12	13	14	21	23
75.	3	12	13	15	19	21
76.	3	12	13	18	20	21
77.	3	12	14	16	17	23
78.	3	12	15	16	17	19
79.	3	12	16	17	18	20
80.	3	15	18	19	20	23
81.	4	5	8	9	10	12
82.	4	5	11	13	21	22
83.	4	5	11	16	17	22
84.	4	6	7	8	9	11
85.	4	8	9	10	13	17
86.	4	8	9	10	16	21
87.	4	8	9	15	19	23
88.	4	8	9	18	20	23
89.	4	11	12	13	16	22
90.	4	11	12	17	21	22
91.	4	11	14	15	20	22
92.	4	11	14	18	19	22
93.	5	6	7	10	11	12
94.	5	6	8	10	12	22
95.	5	7	9	13	21	22
96.	5	7	9	16	17	22
97.	5	10	12	15	18	23
98.	5	10	12	19	20	23
99.	5	12	13	16	17	21
100.	5	13	14	15	20	21
101.	5	13	14	18	19	21
102.	5	13	15	16	18	23
103.	5	13	16	19	20	23
104.	5	14	15	16	17	20
105.	5	14	16	17	18	19
106.	5	15	17	18	21	23
107.	5	17	19	20	21	23
108.	6	7	10	11	13	17
109.	6	7	10	11	16	21
110.	6	7	11	15	19	23
111.	6	7	11	18	20	23
112.	6	8	10	13	17	22

50.	2	7	8	12	13	16
51.	2	7	8	12	17	21
52.	2	7	8	14	15	20
53.	2	7	8	14	18	19
54.	2	9	10	11	13	17
55.	2	9	10	11	16	21
56.	2	9	11	15	19	23
57.	2	9	11	18	20	23
58.	3	4	8	9	15	18
59.	3	4	8	9	19	20
60.	3	4	11	14	22	23
61.	3	5	10	12	15	19
62.	3	5	10	12	18	20
63.	3	5	13	14	16	23

113.	6	8	10	16	21	22
114.	6	8	15	19	22	23
115.	6	8	18	20	22	23
116.	7	9	12	13	16	22
117.	7	9	12	17	21	22
118.	7	9	14	15	20	22
119.	7	9	14	18	19	22
120.	10	13	15	17	19	23
121.	10	13	17	18	20	23
122.	10	15	16	19	21	23
123.	10	16	18	20	21	23
124.	12	13	14	15	16	20
125.	12	13	14	16	18	19
126.	12	14	15	17	20	21
127.	12	14	17	18	19	21

System # 60: Guaranteed 4–win if 6 of the numbers drawn are in your set of 24 numbers ©Copyright 2001

Winning possibilities

Guessed	6	5	4	3	%
6	1	2	3-9	9-16	0.04
	1	1	4-5	15-22	0.02
	1	-	0-13	0-25	0.06
	-	6	1-3	14-19	0.01
	-	4	4-9	8-21	0.09
	-	3	2-9	10-25	0.20
	-	2	0-13	8-29	0.54
	-	1	0-15	8-29	10.22
	-	-	1-15	7-34	88.82
5	-	3	3-6	10-17	0.02
	-	2	0-2	9-18	0.06
	-	1	0-11	0-18	1.98
	-	-	2-12	6-23	12.78
	-	-	1	6-23	58.66
	-	-	-	11-25	26.50
4	-	-	3-9	0-17	0.58
	-	-	2	0-15	2.22
	-	-	1	0-18	15.28
	-	-	-	4-17	81.92
3	-	-	-	9-16	1.19
	-	-	-	3-5	7.51
	-	-	-	2	24.31
	-	-	-	1	66.99

If all of the numbers are guessed correctly, you will either win the jackpot (plus some extra cash!), or you will get between one and six 5-wins (and additional prizes), or up to 15 4-wins (plus a number of 3-wins). The complete system would require 134,596 combinations. Below is information on the balance of the system.

Number(s)	Occurrences
1	40
2, 5, 6, 8,10,13,18,19,20,21,24	39
3, 4, 7, 9,11,12,14,16,17,22,23	38
15	37

1.	1	2	3	7	8	16
2.	1	2	4	10	12	15
3.	1	2	4	12	20	24
4.	1	2	5	11	20	22
5.	1	2	6	9	13	21
6.	1	2	10	15	17	24
7.	1	2	14	18	19	23
8.	1	3	4	14	20	21
9.	1	3	5	10	15	19
10.	1	3	5	10	19	24
11.	1	3	6	10	15	24
12.	1	3	9	11	12	18
13.	1	3	13	17	22	23
14.	1	4	5	13	16	18
15.	1	4	6	7	11	23
16.	1	4	8	9	19	22
17.	1	4	10	15	17	24
18.	1	5	6	10	15	24
19.	1	5	7	9	14	17
20.	1	5	8	12	21	23
21.	1	5	10	18	21	24
22.	1	6	8	17	18	20
23.	1	6	10	15	19	24
24.	1	6	12	14	16	22
25.	1	7	10	18	22	24
26.	1	7	10	21	22	24
27.	1	7	12	13	19	20
28.	1	7	15	18	21	22
29.	1	8	10	11	15	24
30.	1	8	10	13	15	24
31.	1	8	10	14	15	24
32.	1	8	11	13	14	24
33.	1	8	13	16	20	23
34.	1	9	10	16	23	24
35.	1	9	10	20	21	24
36.	1	9	15	16	20	23
37.	1	10	11	13	14	15
38.	1	10	12	15	17	24
39.	1	10	16	20	23	24
40.	1	11	16	17	19	21
41.	2	3	4	5	12	17
42.	2	3	4	6	12	17
43.	2	3	4	12	17	19
44.	2	3	5	15	19	24
45.	2	3	9	14	22	24
46.	2	3	10	13	18	20
78.	3	5	6	8	11	14
79.	3	5	6	8	13	19
80.	3	5	6	9	19	20
81.	3	5	6	11	13	19
82.	3	5	6	13	14	19
83.	3	5	6	16	19	20
84.	3	5	6	18	21	22
85.	3	5	6	19	20	23
86.	3	5	8	9	16	23
87.	3	6	7	18	19	22
88.	3	6	9	16	19	23
89.	3	6	18	19	21	22
90.	3	7	10	12	14	23
91.	3	7	11	17	20	24
92.	3	8	9	10	17	21
93.	3	8	11	13	14	19
94.	3	8	12	15	20	22
95.	3	12	13	16	21	24
96.	3	14	15	16	17	18
97.	4	5	6	12	17	19
98.	4	5	7	8	10	20
99.	4	5	9	11	21	24
100.	4	5	14	15	22	23
101.	4	6	8	15	16	21
102.	4	6	9	10	14	18
103.	4	6	13	20	22	24
104.	4	7	12	17	18	21
105.	4	7	12	17	18	22
106.	4	7	14	16	19	24
107.	4	9	12	16	20	23
108.	4	9	16	17	20	23
109.	4	10	13	19	21	23
110.	4	11	15	18	19	20
111.	5	6	8	11	14	19
112.	5	6	9	16	19	23
113.	5	7	11	12	15	16
114.	5	7	18	19	21	22
115.	5	8	16	17	22	24
116.	5	9	10	12	13	22
117.	5	10	11	17	18	23
118.	5	12	14	18	20	24
119.	5	13	15	17	20	21
120.	6	7	8	9	12	24
121.	6	7	8	14	21	22
122.	6	7	10	13	16	17
123.	6	9	11	15	17	22

47.	2	3	11	15	21	23
48.	2	4	5	6	13	19
49.	2	4	7	17	18	21
50.	2	4	7	17	18	22
51.	2	4	8	11	12	13
52.	2	4	8	11	13	17
53.	2	4	8	12	14	17
54.	2	4	9	16	20	23
55.	2	4	10	12	15	24
56.	2	4	11	12	14	17
57.	2	4	12	13	14	17
58.	2	4	12	17	21	22
59.	2	5	6	12	17	19
60.	2	5	7	13	23	24
61.	2	5	8	9	15	18
62.	2	5	10	14	16	21
63.	2	6	7	14	15	20
64.	2	6	8	10	22	23
65.	2	6	11	16	18	24
66.	2	7	9	10	11	19
67.	2	7	12	18	21	22
68.	2	8	19	20	21	24
69.	2	9	12	16	17	20
70.	2	9	12	16	17	23
71.	2	12	17	19	20	23
72.	2	13	15	16	19	22
73.	3	4	7	9	13	15
74.	3	4	8	18	23	24
75.	3	4	10	11	16	22
76.	3	5	6	7	18	22
77.	3	5	6	7	19	21

124.	6	10	11	12	20	21
125.	6	12	13	15	18	23
126.	6	14	17	21	23	24
127.	7	8	11	13	14	18
128.	7	8	11	13	21	22
129.	7	8	15	17	19	23
130.	7	9	16	18	20	21
131.	7	9	16	20	22	23
132.	7	9	18	20	21	23
133.	7	10	15	18	21	22
134.	7	11	13	14	21	22
135.	7	15	18	21	22	24
136.	7	16	18	21	22	23
137.	8	9	11	13	14	16
138.	8	9	11	13	14	20
139.	8	9	11	13	14	23
140.	8	10	12	16	18	19
141.	8	11	12	13	14	17
142.	8	11	13	14	18	21
143.	8	11	13	14	18	22
144.	8	11	14	16	20	23
145.	9	10	15	16	20	23
146.	9	12	14	15	19	21
147.	9	13	17	18	19	24
148.	9	15	16	20	23	24
149.	9	16	18	20	21	22
150.	9	18	20	21	22	23
151.	10	11	13	14	15	24
152.	10	14	17	19	20	22
153.	11	12	19	22	23	24
154.	11	13	14	16	20	23

System # 61: Guaranteed 4–win if 6 of the numbers drawn are in your set of 25 numbers ©Copyright 2001

Winning possibilities

Guessed	6	5	4	3	%
6	1	-	0-6	10-48	0.10
	-	3	0-3	10-32	0.05
	-	2	1-5	17-31	0.91
	-	1	0-5	9-48	9.29
	-	-	1-12	8-34	89.65
5	-	1	2	9-15	1.76
	-	1	-	11-24	0.21
	-	-	5	2-22	0.44
	-	-	4	8-23	3.07
	-	-	3	6-19	5.15
	-	-	2	8-19	13.35
	-	-	1	4-24	33.74
	-	-	-	10-19	42.28
4	-	-	3	6-8	0.09
	-	-	2	2-10	3.42
	-	-	1	0-15	13.64
	-	-	-	2-15	82.25
3	-	-	-	9-12	1.34
	-	-	-	1-4	71.91
	-	-	-	-	26.75

If all of the numbers are guessed correctly, you will either win the jackpot (plus some extra cash!), or you will get up to three 5-wins (and additional prizes), or up to twelve 4-wins (plus a number of 3-wins). The complete system would require 177,100 combinations. Below is information on the balance of the system.

Number(s)	Occurrences
2, 4, 5, 6, 7, 8, 9,10,11,12,13,14,16,17,19,21,22,24	44
1, 3,15,20,23,25	37
18	36

1.	1	2	3	9	11	20
2.	1	2	3	20	22	24
3.	1	2	4	6	18	25
4.	1	2	7	8	18	25
5.	1	2	9	11	15	23
88.	3	10	13	15	16	25
89.	3	10	14	18	21	23
90.	3	10	17	18	19	23
91.	3	12	13	14	18	23
92.	3	12	15	19	21	25

6.	1	2	15	22	23	24	93.	3	12	16	17	18	23
7.	1	3	4	7	20	24	94.	3	13	17	20	21	25
8.	1	3	4	8	9	20	95.	3	14	16	19	20	25
9.	1	3	5	10	12	15	96.	4	5	7	10	12	24
10.	1	3	5	14	17	20	97.	4	5	7	14	17	24
11.	1	3	6	7	11	20	98.	4	5	8	9	10	12
12.	1	3	6	8	20	22	99.	4	5	8	9	14	17
13.	1	3	10	13	16	20	100.	4	5	11	13	19	22
14.	1	3	12	19	20	21	101.	4	5	11	16	21	22
15.	1	3	13	15	17	21	102.	4	6	7	8	9	11
16.	1	3	14	15	16	19	103.	4	6	7	8	22	24
17.	1	3	15	20	23	25	104.	4	7	10	13	16	24
18.	1	4	7	15	23	24	105.	4	7	12	19	21	24
19.	1	4	8	9	15	23	106.	4	7	13	17	21	24
20.	1	4	11	18	22	25	107.	4	7	14	16	19	24
21.	1	5	10	12	20	23	108.	4	7	20	23	24	25
22.	1	5	13	18	19	25	109.	4	8	9	10	13	16
23.	1	5	14	15	17	23	110.	4	8	9	12	19	21
24.	1	5	16	18	21	25	111.	4	8	9	13	17	21
25.	1	6	7	11	15	23	112.	4	8	9	14	16	19
26.	1	6	8	15	22	23	113.	4	8	9	20	23	25
27.	1	6	9	18	24	25	114.	4	10	11	14	21	22
28.	1	7	9	18	22	25	115.	4	10	11	17	19	22
29.	1	8	11	18	24	25	116.	4	11	12	13	14	22
30.	1	10	13	15	16	23	117.	4	11	12	16	17	22
31.	1	10	14	18	21	25	118.	4	11	15	18	20	22
32.	1	10	17	18	19	25	119.	5	6	7	10	11	12
33.	1	12	13	14	18	25	120.	5	6	7	11	14	17
34.	1	12	15	19	21	23	121.	5	6	8	10	12	22
35.	1	12	16	17	18	25	122.	5	6	8	14	17	22
36.	1	13	17	20	21	23	123.	5	6	9	13	19	24
37.	1	14	16	19	20	23	124.	5	6	9	16	21	24
38.	2	3	4	6	18	23	125.	5	7	9	13	19	22
39.	2	3	7	8	18	23	126.	5	7	9	16	21	22
40.	2	3	9	11	15	25	127.	5	8	11	13	19	24
41.	2	3	15	22	24	25	128.	5	8	11	16	21	24
42.	2	4	5	6	13	19	129.	5	10	12	13	17	21
43.	2	4	5	6	16	21	130.	5	10	12	14	16	19
44.	2	4	6	7	9	22	131.	5	10	12	15	23	25
45.	2	4	6	8	11	24	132.	5	10	13	14	16	17
46.	2	4	6	10	14	21	133.	5	10	16	17	19	21
47.	2	4	6	10	17	19	134.	5	12	13	14	16	21
48.	2	4	6	12	13	14	135.	5	12	14	17	19	21
49.	2	4	6	12	16	17	136.	5	13	15	18	19	20
50.	2	4	6	15	18	20	137.	5	14	17	20	23	25
51.	2	4	7	9	11	24	138.	5	15	16	18	20	21

52.	2	4	8	9	22	24
53.	2	5	7	8	13	19
54.	2	5	7	8	16	21
55.	2	5	9	10	11	12
56.	2	5	9	11	14	17
57.	2	5	10	12	22	24
58.	2	5	14	17	22	24
59.	2	6	7	11	22	24
60.	2	6	8	9	11	22
61.	2	7	8	10	14	21
62.	2	7	8	10	17	19
63.	2	7	8	12	13	14
64.	2	7	8	12	16	17
65.	2	7	8	15	18	20
66.	2	9	10	11	13	16
67.	2	9	11	12	19	21
68.	2	9	11	13	17	21
69.	2	9	11	14	16	19
70.	2	9	11	20	23	25
71.	2	10	13	16	22	24
72.	2	12	19	21	22	24
73.	2	13	17	21	22	24
74.	2	14	16	19	22	24
75.	2	20	22	23	24	25
76.	3	4	7	15	24	25
77.	3	4	8	9	15	25
78.	3	4	11	18	22	23
79.	3	5	10	12	20	25
80.	3	5	13	18	19	23
81.	3	5	14	15	17	25
82.	3	5	16	18	21	23
83.	3	6	7	11	15	25
84.	3	6	8	15	22	25
85.	3	6	9	18	23	24
86.	3	7	9	18	22	23
87.	3	8	11	18	23	24
139.	6	7	10	11	13	16
140.	6	7	11	12	19	21
141.	6	7	11	13	17	21
142.	6	7	11	14	16	19
143.	6	7	11	20	23	25
144.	6	8	10	13	16	22
145.	6	8	12	19	21	22
146.	6	8	13	17	21	22
147.	6	8	14	16	19	22
148.	6	8	20	22	23	25
149.	6	9	10	14	21	24
150.	6	9	10	17	19	24
151.	6	9	12	13	14	24
152.	6	9	12	16	17	24
153.	6	9	15	18	20	24
154.	7	8	9	11	22	24
155.	7	9	10	14	21	22
156.	7	9	10	17	19	22
157.	7	9	12	13	14	22
158.	7	9	12	16	17	22
159.	7	9	15	18	20	22
160.	8	10	11	14	21	24
161.	8	10	11	17	19	24
162.	8	11	12	13	14	24
163.	8	11	12	16	17	24
164.	8	11	15	18	20	24
165.	10	12	13	14	17	19
166.	10	12	13	16	19	21
167.	10	13	16	20	23	25
168.	10	14	15	18	20	21
169.	10	15	17	18	19	20
170.	12	13	14	15	18	20
171.	12	15	16	17	18	20
172.	12	19	20	21	23	25
173.	13	14	16	17	19	21
174.	13	15	17	21	23	25
175.	14	15	16	19	23	25

System # 62: Guaranteed 4–win if 6 of the numbers drawn are in your set of 27 numbers ©Copyright 2001

Winning possibilities

Guessed	6	5	4	3	%
6	1	-	6	16-26	0.08
	-	3	3	39	0.02
	-	2	5	22-38	0.93
	-	1	4	12-29	7.77
	-	1	3	28	0.66
	-	-	12	14-16	0.08
	-	-	6-9	14-30	7.89
	-	-	3-5	12-30	19.08
	-	-	1-2	20-26	63.49
5	-	1	2	12-17	1.81
	-	-	5	26	0.10
	-	-	4	8-28	5.32
	-	-	3	18-21	3.68
	-	-	2	12-22	12.64
	-	-	1	8-17	33.11
	-	-	-	12-15	43.34
4	-	-	2	12	2.77
	-	-	2	10	0.92
	-	-	2	2	0.46
	-	-	1	17	0.92
	-	-	1	4	11.54
	-	-	-	18	0.31
	-	-	-	9	5.54
	-	-	-	8	27.69
	-	-	-	4	49.85
3	-	-	-	14	0.92
	-	-	-	12	0.31
	-	-	-	3	1.85
	-	-	-	2	72.00
	-	-	-	-	24.92

Aside from the main guarantee, the system also guarantees at least four 3-wins on guessing correctly four of the numbers drawn. If all of the numbers are guessed correctly, you will either win the jackpot (plus some extra cash!), or you will get anywhere between one and three 5-wins (and additional prizes), or up to twelve 4-wins (plus a number of 3-wins). The complete system would require 296,010 combinations. Every two combinations of the system differ in at least two numbers. In addition, the system is HIGHLY BALANCED: Each number is in exactly 54 combinations.

1. 1 2 3 4 5 6
2. 1 2 3 4 8 9
3. 1 2 4 5 7 8
4. 1 2 6 7 8 9
5. 1 2 6 10 11 12
6. 1 2 6 10 15 17
7. 1 2 6 11 16 18
8. 1 2 6 12 13 14
9. 1 2 6 13 17 18
10. 1 2 6 14 15 16
11. 1 2 6 19 22 23
12. 1 2 6 19 26 27
13. 1 2 6 20 22 25
14. 1 2 6 20 24 27
15. 1 2 6 21 23 24
16. 1 2 6 21 25 26
17. 1 3 4 6 7 9
18. 1 3 5 6 7 8
19. 1 3 8 10 11 12
20. 1 3 8 10 15 17
21. 1 3 8 11 16 18
22. 1 3 8 12 13 14
23. 1 3 8 13 17 18
24. 1 3 8 14 15 16
25. 1 3 8 19 22 23
26. 1 3 8 19 26 27
27. 1 3 8 20 22 25
28. 1 3 8 20 24 27
29. 1 3 8 21 23 24
30. 1 3 8 21 25 26
31. 1 4 7 10 13 16
32. 1 4 7 10 14 18
33. 1 4 7 11 13 15
34. 1 4 7 11 14 17
35. 1 4 7 12 15 18
36. 1 4 7 12 16 17
37. 1 4 7 19 20 21
38. 1 4 7 19 24 25
39. 1 4 7 20 23 26
40. 1 4 7 21 22 27
41. 1 4 7 22 24 26
42. 1 4 7 23 25 27
43. 1 5 9 10 13 16
44. 1 5 9 10 14 18
45. 1 5 9 11 13 15
46. 1 5 9 11 14 17
122. 4 6 8 12 15 18
123. 4 6 8 12 16 17
124. 4 6 8 19 20 21
125. 4 6 8 19 24 25
126. 4 6 8 20 23 26
127. 4 6 8 21 22 27
128. 4 6 8 22 24 26
129. 4 6 8 23 25 27
130. 5 6 7 10 11 12
131. 5 6 7 10 15 17
132. 5 6 7 11 16 18
133. 5 6 7 12 13 14
134. 5 6 7 13 17 18
135. 5 6 7 14 15 16
136. 5 6 7 19 22 23
137. 5 6 7 19 26 27
138. 5 6 7 20 22 25
139. 5 6 7 20 24 27
140. 5 6 7 21 23 24
141. 5 6 7 21 25 26
142. 7 8 9 10 11 12
143. 7 8 9 10 15 17
144. 7 8 9 11 16 18
145. 7 8 9 12 13 14
146. 7 8 9 13 17 18
147. 7 8 9 14 15 16
148. 7 8 9 19 22 23
149. 7 8 9 19 26 27
150. 7 8 9 20 22 25
151. 7 8 9 20 24 27
152. 7 8 9 21 23 24
153. 7 8 9 21 25 26
154. 10 11 12 13 17 18
155. 10 11 12 14 15 16
156. 10 11 12 19 22 23
157. 10 11 12 19 26 27
158. 10 11 12 20 22 25
159. 10 11 12 20 24 27
160. 10 11 12 21 23 24
161. 10 11 12 21 25 26
162. 10 11 13 14 16 17
163. 10 11 15 16 17 18
164. 10 12 13 14 15 17
165. 10 12 13 15 16 18
166. 10 13 16 19 20 21
167. 10 13 16 19 24 25

47.	1	5	9	12	15	18
48.	1	5	9	12	16	17
49.	1	5	9	19	20	21
50.	1	5	9	19	24	25
51.	1	5	9	20	23	26
52.	1	5	9	21	22	27
53.	1	5	9	22	24	26
54.	1	5	9	23	25	27
55.	2	3	5	6	8	9
56.	2	3	7	10	13	16
57.	2	3	7	10	14	18
58.	2	3	7	11	13	15
59.	2	3	7	11	14	17
60.	2	3	7	12	15	18
61.	2	3	7	12	16	17
62.	2	3	7	19	20	21
63.	2	3	7	19	24	25
64.	2	3	7	20	23	26
65.	2	3	7	21	22	27
66.	2	3	7	22	24	26
67.	2	3	7	23	25	27
68.	2	4	5	6	7	9
69.	2	4	9	10	11	12
70.	2	4	9	10	15	17
71.	2	4	9	11	16	18
72.	2	4	9	12	13	14
73.	2	4	9	13	17	18
74.	2	4	9	14	15	16
75.	2	4	9	19	22	23
76.	2	4	9	19	26	27
77.	2	4	9	20	22	25
78.	2	4	9	20	24	27
79.	2	4	9	21	23	24
80.	2	4	9	21	25	26
81.	2	5	8	10	13	16
82.	2	5	8	10	14	18
83.	2	5	8	11	13	15
84.	2	5	8	11	14	17
85.	2	5	8	12	15	18
86.	2	5	8	12	16	17
87.	2	5	8	19	20	21
88.	2	5	8	19	24	25
89.	2	5	8	20	23	26
90.	2	5	8	21	22	27
91.	2	5	8	22	24	26
92.	2	5	8	23	25	27
168.	10	13	16	20	23	26
169.	10	13	16	21	22	27
170.	10	13	16	22	24	26
171.	10	13	16	23	25	27
172.	10	14	18	19	20	21
173.	10	14	18	19	24	25
174.	10	14	18	20	23	26
175.	10	14	18	21	22	27
176.	10	14	18	22	24	26
177.	10	14	18	23	25	27
178.	10	15	17	19	22	23
179.	10	15	17	19	26	27
180.	10	15	17	20	22	25
181.	10	15	17	20	24	27
182.	10	15	17	21	23	24
183.	10	15	17	21	25	26
184.	11	12	13	14	16	18
185.	11	12	14	15	17	18
186.	11	13	15	19	20	21
187.	11	13	15	19	24	25
188.	11	13	15	20	23	26
189.	11	13	15	21	22	27
190.	11	13	15	22	24	26
191.	11	13	15	23	25	27
192.	11	14	17	19	20	21
193.	11	14	17	19	24	25
194.	11	14	17	20	23	26
195.	11	14	17	21	22	27
196.	11	14	17	22	24	26
197.	11	14	17	23	25	27
198.	11	16	18	19	22	23
199.	11	16	18	19	26	27
200.	11	16	18	20	22	25
201.	11	16	18	20	24	27
202.	11	16	18	21	23	24
203.	11	16	18	21	25	26
204.	12	13	14	19	22	23
205.	12	13	14	19	26	27
206.	12	13	14	20	22	25
207.	12	13	14	20	24	27
208.	12	13	14	21	23	24
209.	12	13	14	21	25	26
210.	12	15	18	19	20	21
211.	12	15	18	19	24	25
212.	12	15	18	20	23	26
213.	12	15	18	21	22	27

93.	3	4	5	7	8	9
94.	3	4	5	10	11	12
95.	3	4	5	10	15	17
96.	3	4	5	11	16	18
97.	3	4	5	12	13	14
98.	3	4	5	13	17	18
99.	3	4	5	14	15	16
100.	3	4	5	19	22	23
101.	3	4	5	19	26	27
102.	3	4	5	20	22	25
103.	3	4	5	20	24	27
104.	3	4	5	21	23	24
105.	3	4	5	21	25	26
106.	3	6	9	10	13	16
107.	3	6	9	10	14	18
108.	3	6	9	11	13	15
109.	3	6	9	11	14	17
110.	3	6	9	12	15	18
111.	3	6	9	12	16	17
112.	3	6	9	19	20	21
113.	3	6	9	19	24	25
114.	3	6	9	20	23	26
115.	3	6	9	21	22	27
116.	3	6	9	22	24	26
117.	3	6	9	23	25	27
118.	4	6	8	10	13	16
119.	4	6	8	10	14	18
120.	4	6	8	11	13	15
121.	4	6	8	11	14	17

214.	12	15	18	22	24	26
215.	12	15	18	23	25	27
216.	12	16	17	19	20	21
217.	12	16	17	19	24	25
218.	12	16	17	20	23	26
219.	12	16	17	21	22	27
220.	12	16	17	22	24	26
221.	12	16	17	23	25	27
222.	13	14	15	16	17	18
223.	13	17	18	19	22	23
224.	13	17	18	19	26	27
225.	13	17	18	20	22	25
226.	13	17	18	20	24	27
227.	13	17	18	21	23	24
228.	13	17	18	21	25	26
229.	14	15	16	19	22	23
230.	14	15	16	19	26	27
231.	14	15	16	20	22	25
232.	14	15	16	20	24	27
233.	14	15	16	21	23	24
234.	14	15	16	21	25	26
235.	19	20	22	23	24	27
236.	19	20	22	25	26	27
237.	19	20	23	24	25	26
238.	19	21	22	23	25	26
239.	19	21	22	24	25	27
240.	19	21	23	24	26	27
241.	20	21	22	23	24	25
242.	20	21	22	23	26	27
243.	20	21	24	25	26	27

LOTTERY SYSTEMS WITH A 3-WIN GUARANTEED IF 3 OF YOUR NUMBERS ARE DRAWN

SYSTEM # 63: GUARANTEED 3–WIN IF 3 OF THE NUMBERS DRAWN ARE IN YOUR SET OF 8 NUMBERS ©Copyright 2001

Winning possibilities

Guessed	**6**	**5**	**4**	**3**	%
6	1	-	3	-	14.29
	-	2	2	-	85.71
5	-	1	1	2	42.86
	-	-	3	1	57.14
4	-	-	2	-	8.57
	-	-	1	2	68.57
	-	-	-	4	22.86
3	-	-	-	2	42.86
	-	-	-	1	57.14

This is a nice small system for a 3 on 3 guarantee. The complete system would require 28 combinations. If all of the numbers are guessed correctly, you will either win the jackpot or you will get two 5-wins and two 4-wins. The system is MATHEMATICALLY MINIMAL with respect to all of the following guarantees: 1) the main guarantee, 2) the guarantee of two 5-wins if all 6 numbers are guessed correctly, 3) the guarantee of three 4-wins on 5 numbers guessed correctly. Every two combinations of the system differ in at least two numbers. Finally, the system is HIGHLY BALANCED: Each number participates in exactly 3 of the combinations of the system.

1. 1 2 3 5 6 7
2. 1 2 4 5 6 8
3. 1 3 4 5 7 8
4. 2 3 4 6 7 8

SYSTEM # 64: GUARANTEED 3–WIN IF 3 OF THE NUMBERS DRAWN ARE IN YOUR SET OF 9 NUMBERS ©Copyright 2001

Winning possibilities

Guessed	6	5	4	3	%
6	1	3	-	3	4.76
	1	1	1	4	2.38
	1	-	2	4	1.19
	-	3	-	4	2.38
	-	2	4	1	28.57
	-	2	3	2	11.90
	-	2	1	4	5.95
	-	1	5	1	23.81
	-	1	4	2	9.52
	-	-	6	1	9.54
5	-	4	-	-	0.79
	-	2	1	-	0.79
	-	1	3	1-2	15.87
	-	1	2	-	3.17
	-	1	1	4	6.35
	-	1	-	5	3.17
	-	-	4	2	4.76
	-	-	3	3-4	39.68
	-	-	2	4-5	25.42
4	-	-	4	-	3.97
	-	-	3	-	0.79
	-	-	2	1	3.17
	-	-	1	2-5	58.72
	-	-	-	5	9.52
	-	-	-	4	23.83
3	-	-	-	4	11.90
	-	-	-	3	4.76
	-	-	-	2	21.43
	-	-	-	1	61.91

Aside from the main guarantee, the system also guarantees at least two 4-wins on guessing correctly five of the numbers drawn. If all of the numbers are guessed correctly, you will either win the jackpot (plus some extra cash!), or you will get anywhere between one and three 5-wins (and additional prizes), or six 4-wins. The system is MATHEMATICALLY MINIMAL with respect to the main guarantee. The complete system would require 84 combinations. The next table gives information on the balance of the system.

Number(s)	Occurrences
8	6
2, 4, 6, 7	5
1, 3, 5, 9	4

1. 1 2 3 5 6 9
2. 1 2 4 6 7 8
3. 1 3 4 5 8 9
4. 1 3 5 7 8 9
5. 2 3 4 6 7 8
6. 2 4 5 6 7 8
7. 2 4 6 7 8 9

SYSTEM # 65: GUARANTEED 3–WIN IF 3 OF THE NUMBERS DRAWN ARE IN YOUR SET OF 10 NUMBERS ©Copyright 2001

Winning possibilities

Guessed	6	5	4	3	%
6	1	-	4	4	4.76
	-	3	2	3	4.76
	-	2	2-4	2-6	23.81
	-	1	4-5	3-5	52.38
	-	-	6-7	2-4	14.29
5	-	1	0-3	2-7	23.81
	-	-	2-5	0-7	76.19
4	-	-	2	2-3	9.52
	-	-	1	2-4	52.38
	-	-	-	4-6	38.10
3	-	-	-	3	16.67
	-	-	-	2	33.33
	-	-	-	1	50.00

This is yet another MATHEMATICALLY MINIMAL with respect to the main guarantee system. It also guarantees at least two 4-wins if 5 of the numbers drawn are guessed correctly. The system is HIGHLY BALANCED: Each number is in exactly 6 combinations. If all of the numbers are guessed correctly, you will either win the jackpot (plus some extra cash!), or you will get anywhere between one and three 5-wins (and additional prizes), or either six or seven 4-wins (plus a number of 3-wins). Every two combinations of the system differ in at least two numbers. The complete system would require 210 combinations.

1.	1	2	3	4	6	7
2.	1	2	3	5	7	10
3.	1	2	4	8	9	10
4.	1	3	4	5	9	10
5.	1	3	5	7	8	9
6.	1	5	6	8	9	10
7.	2	3	4	6	8	10
8.	2	3	5	6	7	9
9.	2	4	5	6	7	8
10.	4	6	7	8	9	10

SYSTEM # 66: GUARANTEED 3–WIN IF 3 OF THE NUMBERS DRAWN ARE IN YOUR SET OF 11 NUMBERS ©Copyright 2001

Winning possibilities

Guessed	6	5	4	3	%
6	1	-	-	10	2.38
	-	1	3	5	71.43
	-	-	6	2	11.90
	-	-	5	5	14.29
5	-	1	-	5	14.29
	-	-	3	2	11.90
	-	-	2	5	71.43
	-	-	-	10	2.38
4	-	-	1	2	50.00
	-	-	-	5	33.33
	-	-	-	4	16.67
3	-	-	-	2	33.33
	-	-	-	1	66.67

This system is MATHEMATICALLY MINIMAL with respect to the main guarantee. It is also EXCEPTIONALLY HIGHLY BALANCED: Each number is in exactly 6 combinations; each pair of numbers is in exactly 3 combinations. In addition, the combinations of the system are maximally 'apart': Every two combinations differ in at least three numbers. If all of the six numbers drawn are guessed correctly, you will either win the jackpot (plus some extra cash!), or you will get a 5-win (and additional prizes), or either five or six 4-wins (plus a number of 3-wins). There are also 97.62% chances of getting at least two 4-wins on guessing correctly five of the numbers drawn. The complete system would require 462 combinations.

1. 1 2 3 7 9 11
2. 1 2 4 8 9 10
3. 1 2 5 6 7 10
4. 1 3 4 5 10 11
5. 1 3 4 6 7 8
6. 1 5 6 8 9 11
7. 2 3 4 5 6 9
8. 2 3 6 8 10 11
9. 2 4 5 7 8 11
10. 3 5 7 8 9 10
11. 4 6 7 9 10 11

SYSTEM # 67: GUARANTEED 3–WIN IF 3 OF THE NUMBERS DRAWN ARE IN YOUR SET OF 12 NUMBERS ©Copyright 2001

Winning possibilities

Guessed	6	5	4	3	%
6	1	-	0-3	8-11	1.62
	-	2	2-3	6-7	3.03
	-	1	2-5	5-9	52.38
	-	-	7-9	0-2	1.52
	-	-	3-6	0-11	41.45
5	-	1	2	5	0.51
	-	1	1	5-6	2.53
	-	1	-	4-7	8.33
	-	-	4	5	0.51
	-	-	3	3-6	16.16
	-	-	2	4-8	47.47
	-	-	1	6-11	21.46
	-	-	-	10-12	3.03
4	-	-	2	0-4	1.41
	-	-	1	0-5	42.63
	-	-	-	4-7	55.96
3	-	-	-	3	9.09
	-	-	-	2	18.18
	-	-	-	1	72.73

This is yet another MATHEMATICALLY MINIMAL with respect to the main guarantee system. If all of the numbers are guessed correctly, you will either win the jackpot (plus some extra cash!), or you will get one or two 5-wins (and additional prizes), or at least three (up to nine) 4-wins (plus a number of 3-wins). There are also 96.97% chances of getting at least one 4-win on guessing correctly five of the numbers drawn. The complete system would require 924 combinations. Every two combinations of the system differ in at least two numbers. Information on the balance of the system is given in the table below.

Number(s)	Occurrences
6, 9	9
4, 8	8
1, 2, 3, 5, 7,10,11,12	7

1. 1 2 3 4 10 12
2. 1 2 5 6 11 12

8. 2 3 4 5 9 11
9. 2 3 4 6 7 8

3.	1	2	7	8	9	12
4.	1	3	5	6	7	9
5.	1	3	6	8	9	11
6.	1	4	5	8	9	10
7.	1	4	6	7	10	11
10.	2	4	6	8	9	10
11.	2	5	7	8	10	11
12.	3	5	6	8	10	12
13.	3	7	9	10	11	12
14.	4	5	6	7	9	12
15.	4	6	8	9	11	12

System # 68: Guaranteed 3–win if 3 of the numbers drawn are in your set of 13 numbers ©Copyright 2001

Winning possibilities

Guessed	**6**	**5**	**4**	**3**	%
6	1	2	-	8-9	0.17
	1	1	0-2	8-11	0.47
	1	-	0-2	10-13	0.58
	-	3	0-1	8-9	0.35
	-	2	1-5	4-11	3.96
	-	1	0-6	3-14	41.61
	-	-	2-8	1-15	52.86
5	-	2	1	4-5	0.31
	-	2	-	4	0.23
	-	1	2	3-6	1.40
	-	1	1	3-7	2.95
	-	1	-	2-8	4.35
	-	-	5	4	0.16
	-	-	4	2-5	0.93
	-	-	3	2-9	18.57
	-	-	2	4-9	38.62
	-	-	1	6-12	27.82
	-	-	-	10-14	4.66
4	-	-	3	0-2	0.28
	-	-	2	0-4	4.48
	-	-	1	0-6	34.27
	-	-	-	4-8	60.97
3	-	-	-	3-5	9.79
	-	-	-	2	22.38
	-	-	-	1	67.83

The complete system would require 1,716 combinations. If all of the numbers are guessed correctly, you will either win the jackpot (plus some extra cash!), or you will get anywhere between one and three 5-wins (and additional prizes), or at least two (up to eight) 4-wins (plus a number of 3-wins). There are also 95.34% chances of getting at least one 4-win on guessing correctly five of the numbers drawn. Below is information on the balance of the system.

Number(s)	Occurrences
2	11
1, 3, 8,10,11,12,13	10
4, 5, 6, 7, 9	9

1. 1 2 3 7 9 11
2. 1 2 4 6 9 10
3. 1 2 4 6 10 13
4. 1 2 5 8 11 12
5. 1 3 4 8 10 11
6. 1 3 5 6 11 13
7. 1 3 5 6 12 13
8. 1 4 5 7 10 12
9. 1 5 7 9 10 12
10. 1 6 7 8 9 13
11. 2 3 4 7 8 13
12. 2 3 4 8 12 13
13. 2 3 5 6 7 10
14. 2 3 7 8 12 13
15. 2 4 5 9 11 13
16. 2 6 8 10 11 12
17. 2 8 9 10 11 12
18. 3 4 5 6 8 9
19. 3 9 10 11 12 13
20. 4 6 7 9 11 12
21. 5 7 8 10 11 13

System # 69: Guaranteed 3–win if 3 of the numbers drawn are in your set of 14 numbers ©Copyright 2001

Winning possibilities

Guessed	6	5	4	3	%
6	1	-	8	-	0.03
	1	-	0-4	6-12	0.80
	-	2	0-5	4-11	4.53
	-	1	0-5	2-14	30.90
	-	-	9	-	0.07
	-	-	8	4	0.27
	-	-	6-7	2-10	6.14
	-	-	3-5	4-12	53.99
	-	-	1-2	13-16	3.27
5	-	1	4	3-4	1.00
	-	1	1	2-8	2.80
	-	1	-	2-13	3.70
	-	-	4	5-6	1.20
	-	-	3	2-10	11.19
	-	-	2	4-7	33.17
	-	-	1	6-9	37.16
	-	-	-	10-13	9.18
4	-	-	5	-	0.20
	-	-	2	0-4	1.40
	-	-	1	0-8	33.67
	-	-	-	4-6	64.73
3	-	-	-	5	2.20
	-	-	-	4	4.40
	-	-	-	2	15.38
	-	-	-	1	78.02

The complete system would require 3,003 combinations. If all of the numbers are guessed correctly, you will either win the jackpot (plus some extra cash!), or you will get one or two 5-wins (and additional prizes), or up to nine 4-wins (plus a number of 3-wins). There are also 90.82% chances of getting at least one 4-win on guessing correctly five of the numbers drawn. Every two combinations of the system differ in at least two numbers. The next table contains information on the balance of the system.

Number(s)	Occurrences
6, 8	13
2, 4,13,14	11
1, 3, 5, 7, 9,10,11,12	10

1.	1	2	3	10	12	14
2.	1	2	4	5	6	8
3.	1	2	7	9	12	13
4.	1	2	7	10	11	13
5.	1	3	4	5	7	13
6.	1	3	6	8	9	11
7.	1	3	6	8	10	12
8.	1	4	5	9	10	14
9.	1	4	5	11	12	14
10.	1	6	7	8	13	14
11.	2	3	4	6	7	8
12.	2	3	5	9	12	13
13.	2	3	5	10	11	13
14.	2	4	6	8	9	10
15.	2	4	6	8	11	12
16.	2	4	6	8	13	14
17.	2	5	7	9	11	14
18.	3	4	7	9	10	14
19.	3	4	7	11	12	14
20.	3	5	6	8	13	14
21.	4	9	10	11	12	13
22.	5	6	7	8	9	11
23.	5	6	7	8	10	12
24.	6	8	9	12	13	14
25.	6	8	10	11	13	14

System # 70: Guaranteed 3–win if 3 of the numbers drawn are in your set of 15 numbers ©Copyright 2001

Winning possibilities

Guessed	6	5	4	3	%
6	1	-	0-3	7-16	0.62
	-	2	1-2	7-11	1.04
	-	1	1-5	5-14	31.37
	-	-	6-8	2-9	4.04
	-	-	3-5	6-16	57.36
	-	-	2	12-17	5.57
5	-	1	2	3	0.03
	-	1	1	3-6	1.67
	-	1	-	4-10	4.50
	-	-	4	4	0.03
	-	-	3	4-7	5.83
	-	-	2	5-9	44.39
	-	-	1	6-12	31.24
	-	-	-	10-14	12.31
4	-	-	2	0-1	0.95
	-	-	1	0-5	32.16
	-	-	-	4-7	66.89
3	-	-	-	4	4.40
	-	-	-	3	0.22
	-	-	-	2	22.64
	-	-	-	1	72.74

The complete system would require 5,005 combinations. If all of the numbers are guessed correctly, you will either win the jackpot (plus some extra cash!), or you will get one or two 5-wins (and additional prizes), or up to eight 4-wins (plus a number of 3-wins). There are also 87.69% chances of getting at least one 4-win on guessing correctly five of the numbers drawn. Every two combinations of the system differ in at least two numbers. In addition, the system is well balanced: Each number is in either 12 or 13 combinations as shown in the table below.

Number(s)	Occurrences
2, 3, 5, 7, 9,15	13
1, 4, 6, 8,10,11,12,13,14	12

1. 1 2 3 5 6 7
2. 1 2 3 5 14 15

16. 2 4 5 8 11 13
17. 2 4 6 7 9 15

3.	1	2	4	10	12	13
4.	1	2	8	9	11	14
5.	1	3	4	8	12	15
6.	1	3	9	10	11	13
7.	1	4	5	9	11	12
8.	1	4	6	7	12	14
9.	1	5	7	8	12	13
10.	1	5	10	13	14	15
11.	1	6	7	8	10	13
12.	1	6	7	9	11	15
13.	2	3	4	7	9	13
14.	2	3	7	8	11	15
15.	2	3	7	10	12	14
18.	2	4	6	13	14	15
19.	2	5	9	10	11	14
20.	2	5	9	10	12	15
21.	2	6	8	10	11	12
22.	3	4	5	6	11	14
23.	3	4	7	8	9	10
24.	3	5	6	8	10	15
25.	3	5	6	9	12	13
26.	3	6	11	12	13	15
27.	3	8	9	13	14	15
28.	4	5	7	10	11	15
29.	4	6	8	9	10	14
30.	5	7	8	9	12	14
31.	7	11	12	13	14	15

SYSTEM # 71: GUARANTEED 3–WIN IF 3 OF THE NUMBERS DRAWN ARE IN YOUR SET OF 16 NUMBERS ©**Copyright 2001**

Winning possibilities

Guessed	6	5	4	3	%
6	1	-	0-2	9-14	0.47
	-	2	1-2	9-13	0.30
	-	1	0-4	6-17	27.87
	-	-	1-7	2-20	71.15
	-	-	-	20-22	0.21
5	-	1	1	4-8	0.55
	-	1	-	2-9	4.67
	-	-	3	2-9	4.44
	-	-	2	4-10	34.48
	-	-	1	6-12	47.66
	-	-	-	10-13	8.20
4	-	-	2	-	0.33
	-	-	1	1-6	27.09
	-	-	1	-	3.57
	-	-	-	4-8	69.01
3	-	-	-	4	0.54
	-	-	-	3	5.54
	-	-	-	2	23.04
	-	-	-	1	70.88

The complete system would require 8,008 combinations. If all of the numbers are guessed correctly, you will either win the jackpot (plus some extra cash!), or you will get one or two 5-wins (and additional prizes), or up to seven 4-wins (plus a number of 3-wins). There are also 91.80% chances of getting at least one 4-win on guessing correctly five of the numbers drawn. Every two combinations of the system differ in at least two numbers. In addition, the system is well balanced: Each number is in either 14 or 15 combinations as shown in the table below.

Number(s)	Occurrences
1, 2,10,14	15
3, 4, 5, 6, 7, 8, 9,11,12,13,15,16	14

1.	1	2	3	8	9	10
2.	1	2	4	5	6	8
3.	1	2	4	7	13	14
4.	1	2	4	10	12	16
20.	2	4	7	9	11	16
21.	2	5	7	8	11	12
22.	2	5	8	9	14	15
23.	2	5	8	10	13	16

5.	1	2	8	11	14	15
6.	1	3	4	6	11	12
7.	1	3	4	9	13	15
8.	1	3	5	7	10	11
9.	1	3	6	9	14	16
10.	1	4	6	10	13	16
11.	1	5	9	11	13	16
12.	1	5	10	12	14	15
13.	1	6	7	8	15	16
14.	1	6	7	10	11	13
15.	1	7	8	9	12	13
16.	2	3	4	5	15	16
17.	2	3	5	9	12	14
18.	2	3	6	7	10	15
19.	2	3	11	12	13	14

24.	2	6	9	12	13	15
25.	2	6	10	11	14	16
26.	3	4	7	8	10	14
27.	3	5	6	8	13	14
28.	3	7	9	11	14	15
29.	3	7	10	12	13	16
30.	3	8	11	12	15	16
31.	4	5	6	7	9	10
32.	4	5	6	11	14	15
33.	4	5	7	12	13	15
34.	4	8	9	12	14	16
35.	4	8	10	11	13	15
36.	5	6	7	12	14	16
37.	6	8	9	10	11	12
38.	9	10	13	14	15	16

SYSTEM # 72: GUARANTEED 3–WIN IF 3 OF THE NUMBERS DRAWN ARE IN YOUR SET OF 17 NUMBERS ©Copyright 2001

Winning possibilities

Guessed	**6**	**5**	**4**	**3**	%
6	1	-	0-3	7-15	0.36
	-	2	0-4	6-16	0.48
	-	1	0-5	4-18	22.50
	-	-	5-8	3-14	9.65
	-	-	2-4	6-18	65.94
	-	-	1	16-19	1.07
5	-	1	2	8	0.02
	-	1	1	4-9	0.94
	-	1	-	2-12	3.31
	-	-	5	1	0.03
	-	-	4	2-8	0.26
	-	-	3	3-10	3.59
	-	-	2	4-11	26.28
	-	-	1	6-13	51.84
	-	-	-	10-14	13.73
4	-	-	2	0-4	0.63
	-	-	1	0-8	26.47
	-	-	-	4-8	72.90
3	-	-	-	5	1.18
	-	-	-	4	1.18
	-	-	-	3	2.06
	-	-	-	2	17.06
	-	-	-	1	78.52

The complete system would require 12,376 combinations. If all of the numbers are guessed correctly, you will either win the jackpot (plus some extra cash!), or you will get one or two 5-wins (and additional prizes), or up to eight 4-wins (plus a number of 3-wins). There are also 86.27% chances of getting at least one 4-win on guessing correctly five of the numbers drawn. Every two combinations of the system differ in at least two numbers. Information on the balance of the system is given in the table below.

Number(s)	Occurrences
1,10	17
3, 4, 9,12,14	16
2, 5, 6, 7, 8,11,13,15,16,17	15

1.	1	2	3	5	11	15
2.	1	2	3	5	12	14
3.	1	2	3	7	8	9
4.	1	2	4	6	13	15
5.	1	2	10	11	16	17
6.	1	3	4	9	12	13
7.	1	3	5	8	13	17
8.	1	3	6	8	12	16
9.	1	3	7	10	14	17
10.	1	4	5	9	15	16
11.	1	4	7	9	15	17
12.	1	4	8	11	12	14
13.	1	4	9	10	11	13
14.	1	5	6	7	10	11
15.	1	6	9	12	14	17
16.	1	7	12	13	14	16
17.	1	8	10	12	14	15
18.	2	3	4	5	8	10
19.	2	3	4	12	16	17
20.	2	3	6	10	13	14
21.	2	4	7	9	11	14
22.	2	5	6	9	16	17
23.	2	5	7	9	13	17
24.	2	6	7	9	13	16
25.	2	6	8	11	12	13
26.	2	7	9	10	12	15
27.	2	8	14	15	16	17
28.	3	4	5	6	7	12
29.	3	4	8	11	14	15
30.	3	5	9	10	14	16
31.	3	6	9	11	15	17
32.	3	7	11	13	15	16
33.	3	10	11	12	14	15
34.	4	5	11	13	14	17
35.	4	6	8	9	10	17
36.	4	6	10	11	14	16
37.	4	6	10	12	15	16
38.	4	7	8	10	13	16
39.	5	6	7	8	14	15
40.	5	6	7	13	16	17
41.	5	8	9	11	12	16
42.	5	10	12	13	15	17
43.	7	8	10	11	12	17
44.	8	9	10	13	14	15

System # 73: Guaranteed 3–win if 3 of the numbers drawn are in your set of 18 numbers ©Copyright 2001

Winning possibilities

Guessed	6	5	4	3	%
6	1	-	-	0-8	0.26
	-	1	0-2	8-14	18.61
	-	-	6	4	0.32
	-	-	5	4-8	2.42
	-	-	4	8-10	14.54
	-	-	3	8-13	41.05
	-	-	2	12-15	20.36
	-	-	1	16	2.44
5	-	1	-	0-4	3.36
	-	-	2	5-7	18.91
	-	-	1	6-9	63.03
	-	-	-	10-12	14.70
4	-	-	1	0-4	23.53
	-	-	-	4-6	76.47
3	-	-	-	5	0.74
	-	-	-	2	14.71
	-	-	-	1	84.55

The system is MATHEMATICALLY MINIMAL with respect to the main guarantee. It is also HIGHLY BALANCED: Each number is in exactly 16 combinations. The combinations of the system are as 'apart' as possible: Every two of them differ in at least three numbers. The complete system would require 18,564 combinations. If all of the numbers are guessed correctly, you will either win the jackpot (plus some extra cash!), or you will get a 5-win (and additional prizes), or up to six 4-wins (plus a number of 3-wins). There are also 85.30% chances of getting at least one 4-win on guessing correctly five of the numbers drawn.

1.	1	2	3	5	8	13
2.	1	2	4	12	14	15
3.	1	2	5	9	11	18
4.	1	2	6	10	13	17
5.	1	2	7	11	16	17
6.	1	3	4	12	17	18
7.	1	3	5	6	14	16
8.	1	3	7	11	13	15
9.	1	3	9	10	11	14
10.	1	4	5	7	10	12
11.	1	4	6	8	11	12
25.	2	7	8	12	13	18
26.	2	8	9	10	12	17
27.	2	9	13	14	15	16
28.	3	4	5	11	15	16
29.	3	4	8	10	13	14
30.	3	5	7	10	17	18
31.	3	5	8	9	12	15
32.	3	6	8	11	17	18
33.	3	6	10	12	13	15
34.	3	7	8	12	14	16
35.	3	9	13	16	17	18

12.	1	4	9	12	13	16
13.	1	5	6	9	15	17
14.	1	6	7	13	14	18
15.	1	7	8	9	14	17
16.	1	8	10	15	16	18
17.	2	3	4	6	7	9
18.	2	3	10	11	12	16
19.	2	3	14	15	17	18
20.	2	4	5	8	16	17
21.	2	4	10	11	13	18
22.	2	5	6	12	16	18
23.	2	5	7	10	14	15
24.	2	6	8	11	14	15
36.	4	5	6	13	15	18
37.	4	5	8	9	14	18
38.	4	6	10	14	16	17
39.	4	7	8	13	15	17
40.	4	7	11	14	16	18
41.	4	9	10	11	15	17
42.	5	6	7	8	10	11
43.	5	7	9	10	13	16
44.	5	11	12	13	14	17
45.	6	7	12	15	16	17
46.	6	8	9	11	13	16
47.	6	9	10	12	14	18
48.	7	9	11	12	15	18

SYSTEM # 74: GUARANTEED 3–WIN IF 3 OF THE NUMBERS DRAWN ARE IN YOUR SET OF 19 NUMBERS ©Copyright 2001

Winning possibilities

Guessed	6	5	4	3	%
6	1	-	0-2	7-16	0.23
	-	2	0-3	7-16	0.18
	-	1	0-6	2-19	17.76
	-	-	7-8	2-10	0.09
	-	-	5-6	2-15	5.08
	-	-	3-4	7-19	51.54
	-	-	1-2	12-22	24.84
	-	-	-	20-22	0.28
5	-	1	2	6-8	0.02
	-	1	1	2-10	0.38
	-	1	-	2-12	2.86
	-	-	4	4-6	0.10
	-	-	3	1-10	1.93
	-	-	2	3-12	21.99
	-	-	1	6-14	55.07
	-	-	-	10-15	17.65
4	-	-	2	0-5	0.31
	-	-	1	0-7	23.76
	-	-	-	4-10	75.93
3	-	-	-	3-6	3.30
	-	-	-	2	21.16
	-	-	-	1	75.54

The complete system would require 27,132 combinations. If all of the numbers are guessed correctly, you will either win the jackpot (plus some extra cash!), or you will get one or two 5-wins (and additional prizes), or up to eight 4-wins (plus a number of 3-wins). There are also 82.35% chances of getting at least one 4-win on guessing correctly five of the numbers drawn. Every two combinations of the system differ in at least two numbers. The next table gives information on the balance of the system.

Number(s)	Occurrences
4	22
1, 3, 5, 6, 8, 9,10,11,12,14,15,16,18,19	20
2, 7,13,17	19

1.	1	2	3	6	9	15
2.	1	2	4	5	6	7
3.	1	2	4	10	11	16
4.	1	2	6	8	12	17
5.	1	2	13	14	18	19
6.	1	3	4	7	12	13
7.	1	3	5	8	9	14
8.	1	3	6	7	10	18
9.	1	3	11	16	17	19
10.	1	4	6	8	10	19
11.	1	4	9	12	18	19
12.	1	4	10	12	14	15
13.	1	4	11	15	17	18
14.	1	5	9	10	13	17
15.	1	5	11	12	14	18
16.	1	5	12	15	16	19
17.	1	6	11	13	14	16
18.	1	7	8	9	11	16
19.	1	7	14	15	17	19
20.	1	8	13	15	16	18
21.	2	3	4	5	8	10
22.	2	3	7	11	12	16
23.	2	3	7	13	14	15
24.	2	3	7	17	18	19
25.	2	4	7	8	9	10
26.	2	4	8	11	13	18
27.	2	4	8	12	14	19
28.	2	4	8	15	16	17
29.	2	5	9	11	14	17
30.	2	5	9	12	15	18
31.	2	5	9	13	16	19
32.	2	6	10	11	15	19
33.	2	6	10	12	13	17
34.	2	6	10	14	16	18
35.	3	4	5	6	9	10
36.	3	4	5	11	15	19
37.	3	4	5	12	13	17
38.	3	4	5	14	16	18
39.	3	5	6	7	8	9
40.	3	6	9	11	13	18
41.	3	6	9	12	14	19
42.	3	6	9	15	16	17
43.	3	8	10	11	14	17
44.	3	8	10	12	15	18
45.	3	8	10	13	16	19
46.	4	6	7	11	14	17
47.	4	6	7	12	15	18
48.	4	6	7	13	16	19
49.	4	9	10	11	12	16
50.	4	9	10	13	14	15
51.	4	9	10	17	18	19
52.	5	6	8	11	12	16
53.	5	6	8	13	14	15
54.	5	6	8	17	18	19
55.	5	7	10	11	13	18
56.	5	7	10	12	14	19
57.	5	7	10	15	16	17
58.	7	8	9	11	15	19
59.	7	8	9	12	13	17
60.	7	8	9	14	16	18
61.	11	12	13	15	17	19
62.	11	14	15	16	18	19
63.	12	13	14	16	17	18

System # 75: Guaranteed 3–win if 3 of the numbers drawn are in your set of 20 numbers ©Copyright 2001

Winning possibilities

Guessed	6	5	4	3	%
6	1	-	0-1	2-18	0.19
	-	2	0-2	8-18	0.06
	-	1	0-5	8-20	15.48
	-	-	1-8	2-27	83.35
	-	-	-	20-28	0.92
5	-	1	1	2-10	0.15
	-	1	-	0-11	2.63
	-	-	4	3-5	0.05
	-	-	3	3-8	1.46
	-	-	2	4-11	15.89
	-	-	1	6-18	61.04
	-	-	-	10-17	18.78
4	-	-	2	0-4	0.12
	-	-	1	0-6	22.04
	-	-	-	7-10	4.25
	-	-	-	4-6	73.59
3	-	-	-	4	0.18
	-	-	-	3	4.65
	-	-	-	2	16.49
	-	-	-	1	78.68

The complete system would require 38,760 combinations. If all of the numbers are guessed correctly, you will either win the jackpot (plus some extra cash!), or you will get one or two 5-wins (and additional prizes), or up to eight 4-wins (plus a number of 3-wins). There are also 81.22% chances of getting at least one 4-win on guessing correctly five of the numbers drawn. Every two combinations of the system differ in at least two numbers. Below is information on the balance of the system.

Number(s)	Occurrences
9,15	26
4, 8,11,13,17	22
1, 2, 3, 6, 7,10,12,16,19,20	21
5,14,18	20

1. 1 2 3 6 9 20
2. 1 2 4 7 9 11

37. 2 9 12 13 15 19
38. 3 4 5 9 10 11

3.	1	2	5	8	10	15
4.	1	2	12	14	16	18
5.	1	2	13	15	17	19
6.	1	3	4	8	12	19
7.	1	3	5	7	17	18
8.	1	3	9	15	16	17
9.	1	3	10	11	13	14
10.	1	4	5	6	13	16
11.	1	4	8	9	13	18
12.	1	4	10	15	18	20
13.	1	4	12	13	14	17
14.	1	5	9	14	19	20
15.	1	5	11	12	13	17
16.	1	6	7	8	14	15
17.	1	6	10	12	15	17
18.	1	6	11	15	18	19
19.	1	7	9	10	16	19
20.	1	7	9	12	13	20
21.	1	8	11	16	17	20
22.	2	3	4	13	15	18
23.	2	3	5	11	16	19
24.	2	3	7	10	12	15
25.	2	3	8	9	14	17
26.	2	4	5	12	17	20
27.	2	4	6	8	16	20
28.	2	4	6	10	14	19
29.	2	5	6	16	18	20
30.	2	5	7	9	13	14
31.	2	6	7	15	16	17
32.	2	6	8	11	12	13
33.	2	7	8	18	19	20
34.	2	8	11	14	15	20
35.	2	9	10	11	17	18
36.	2	9	10	13	16	20
39.	3	4	6	11	15	17
40.	3	4	7	14	16	20
41.	3	5	6	12	14	15
42.	3	5	8	13	15	20
43.	3	6	7	9	13	19
44.	3	6	8	10	16	18
45.	3	7	8	10	11	19
46.	3	7	10	14	18	19
47.	3	9	11	12	18	20
48.	3	9	12	13	16	17
49.	3	10	15	17	19	20
50.	4	5	7	11	15	19
51.	4	5	8	11	14	18
52.	4	5	9	14	15	18
53.	4	6	7	9	12	18
54.	4	7	8	10	13	17
55.	4	8	12	15	17	18
56.	4	9	11	13	19	20
57.	4	9	16	17	18	19
58.	4	10	11	12	15	16
59.	5	6	7	10	11	20
60.	5	6	8	9	17	19
61.	5	7	8	9	12	16
62.	5	10	12	13	18	19
63.	5	10	14	15	16	17
64.	6	8	9	10	13	15
65.	6	8	9	11	14	16
66.	6	12	15	16	19	20
67.	6	13	14	17	18	20
68.	7	9	11	15	17	20
69.	7	11	12	14	17	19
70.	7	11	13	15	16	18
71.	8	9	10	12	14	20
72.	8	13	14	15	16	19

SYSTEM # 76: GUARANTEED 3–WIN IF 3 OF THE NUMBERS DRAWN ARE IN YOUR SET OF 22 NUMBERS ©Copyright 2001

Winning possibilities

Guessed	6	5	4	3	%
6	1	-	-	-	0.10
	-	1	-	10	9.91
	-	-	3	8	12.38
	-	-	2	12	74.30
	-	-	-	20	3.31
5	-	1	-	-	1.75
	-	-	1	6	70.18
	-	-	-	10	28.07
4	-	-	1	-	15.79
	-	-	-	4	84.21
3	-	-	-	1	100.00

This system is MATHEMATICALLY MINIMAL with respect to the main guarantee. It is also EXCEPTIONALLY HIGHLY BALANCED: Each number is in exactly 21 combinations; each pair of numbers is in exactly 5 combinations; each triple is in exactly one combination. In addition, the combinations of the system are maximally 'apart': Every two combinations differ in at least four numbers. If all of the six numbers drawn are guessed correctly, you will either win the jackpot, or you will get one 5-win and ten 3-wins, or up to three 4-wins (plus a number of 3-wins). There are also 71.93% chances of getting a 4-win on guessing correctly five of the numbers drawn. The complete system would require 74,613 combinations.

1.	1	2	3	6	7	11
2.	1	2	4	8	9	10
3.	1	2	5	12	13	14
4.	1	2	15	16	17	18
5.	1	2	19	20	21	22
6.	1	3	4	5	15	19
7.	1	3	8	13	17	21
8.	1	3	9	12	16	20
9.	1	3	10	14	18	22
10.	1	4	6	14	16	21
11.	1	4	7	12	17	22
12.	1	4	11	13	18	20
13.	1	5	6	10	17	20
14.	1	5	7	9	18	21
15.	1	5	8	11	16	22
16.	1	6	8	12	18	19
39.	3	4	7	9	13	14
40.	3	4	10	11	16	17
41.	3	5	6	13	16	18
42.	3	5	7	8	10	12
43.	3	5	11	14	20	21
44.	3	6	9	10	19	21
45.	3	6	12	14	15	17
46.	3	7	15	16	21	22
47.	3	7	17	18	19	20
48.	3	8	9	11	15	18
49.	3	11	12	13	19	22
50.	4	5	6	9	11	12
51.	4	5	8	14	17	18
52.	4	5	10	13	21	22
53.	4	6	7	10	15	18
54.	4	7	8	11	19	21

17. 1 6 9 13 15 22
18. 1 7 8 14 15 20
19. 1 7 10 13 16 19
20. 1 9 11 14 17 19
21. 1 10 11 12 15 21
22. 2 3 4 12 18 21
23. 2 3 5 9 17 22
24. 2 3 8 14 16 19
25. 2 3 10 13 15 20
26. 2 4 5 7 16 20
27. 2 4 6 13 17 19
28. 2 4 11 14 15 22
29. 2 5 6 8 15 21
30. 2 5 10 11 18 19
31. 2 6 9 14 18 20
32. 2 6 10 12 16 22
33. 2 7 8 13 18 22
34. 2 7 9 12 15 19
35. 2 7 10 14 17 21
36. 2 8 11 12 17 20
37. 2 9 11 13 16 21
38. 3 4 6 8 20 22

55. 4 8 12 13 15 16
56. 4 9 15 17 20 21
57. 4 9 16 18 19 22
58. 4 10 12 14 19 20
59. 5 6 7 14 19 22
60. 5 7 11 13 15 17
61. 5 8 9 13 19 20
62. 5 9 10 14 15 16
63. 5 12 15 18 20 22
64. 5 12 16 17 19 21
65. 6 7 8 9 16 17
66. 6 7 12 13 20 21
67. 6 8 10 11 13 14
68. 6 11 15 16 19 20
69. 6 11 17 18 21 22
70. 7 9 10 11 20 22
71. 7 11 12 14 16 18
72. 8 9 12 14 21 22
73. 8 10 15 17 19 22
74. 8 10 16 18 20 21
75. 9 10 12 13 17 18
76. 13 14 15 18 19 21
77. 13 14 16 17 20 22

SYSTEM # 77: GUARANTEED 3–WIN IF 3 OF THE NUMBERS DRAWN ARE IN YOUR SET OF 23 NUMBERS ©Copyright 2001

Winning possibilities

Guessed	6	5	4	3	%
6	1	1	-	0-3	0.01
	1	-	0-1	1-17	0.07
	-	2	0-1	4-13	0.14
	-	1	0-3	4-23	10.17
	-	-	1-5	8-24	87.27
	-	-	-	20-26	2.44
5	-	2	-	-	0.02
	-	1	1	0-6	0.23
	-	1	-	0-10	1.58
	-	-	1-3	3-12	70.51
	-	-	-	10-14	27.66
4	-	-	2	-	0.43
	-	-	1	0-4	16.76
	-	-	-	4-7	82.81
3	-	-	-	2	17.45
	-	-	-	1	82.55

This is yet another MATHEMATICALLY MINIMAL with respect to the main guarantee system. The complete system would require 100,947 combinations. If all of the six numbers drawn are guessed correctly, you will either win the jackpot (plus some extra cash!), or you will get one or two 5-wins (and additional prizes), or up to five 4-wins (plus a number of 3-wins). There are also 72.34% chances of getting at least one 4-win on guessing correctly five of the numbers drawn. The system is well balanced: Each number is in either 27 or 28 combinations as seen from the table below.

Number(s)	Occurrences
8,11,23	28
1, 2, 3, 4, 5, 6, 7, 9,10,12,13,14,15,16,17,18,19,20,21,22	27

1.	1	2	3	10	14	19	53.	3	5	6	12	14	18
2.	1	2	4	7	21	22	54.	3	5	13	16	19	20
3.	1	2	5	12	20	23	55.	3	6	8	9	16	17
4.	1	2	6	8	11	18	56.	3	6	8	10	16	17
5.	1	2	9	11	17	20	57.	3	6	11	19	21	22
6.	1	2	13	15	16	17	58.	3	7	9	11	13	22

7.	1	3	4	6	15	20
8.	1	3	5	7	11	17
9.	1	3	8	12	13	22
10.	1	3	9	10	14	19
11.	1	3	16	18	21	23
12.	1	4	5	8	14	16
13.	1	4	8	9	11	23
14.	1	4	10	12	17	18
15.	1	4	11	13	19	23
16.	1	5	6	7	9	23
17.	1	5	6	10	13	21
18.	1	5	15	18	19	22
19.	1	6	7	12	16	19
20.	1	6	14	17	22	23
21.	1	7	8	10	15	23
22.	1	7	13	14	18	20
23.	1	8	9	13	18	21
24.	1	8	17	19	20	21
25.	1	9	12	15	16	22
26.	1	10	11	16	20	22
27.	1	11	12	14	15	21
28.	2	3	4	11	12	16
29.	2	3	5	8	15	21
30.	2	3	5	9	15	21
31.	2	3	6	7	13	23
32.	2	3	17	18	20	22
33.	2	4	5	6	17	19
34.	2	4	8	10	13	20
35.	2	4	9	11	13	21
36.	2	4	14	15	18	23
37.	2	5	7	10	16	18
38.	2	5	11	13	14	22
39.	2	6	9	12	13	14
40.	2	6	10	12	15	22
41.	2	6	14	16	20	21
42.	2	7	8	12	14	17
43.	2	7	9	10	16	18
44.	2	7	11	15	19	20
45.	2	8	9	19	22	23
46.	2	8	16	19	22	23
47.	2	10	11	17	21	23
48.	2	12	13	18	19	21
49.	3	4	5	10	22	23
50.	3	4	7	8	18	19
51.	3	4	9	14	15	16
52.	3	4	13	14	17	21

59.	3	7	10	12	20	21
60.	3	7	14	15	16	22
61.	3	8	11	14	20	23
62.	3	9	12	18	20	23
63.	3	10	11	13	15	18
64.	3	12	15	17	19	23
65.	4	5	6	8	9	22
66.	4	5	7	12	13	15
67.	4	5	11	18	20	21
68.	4	6	7	10	11	14
69.	4	6	8	12	21	23
70.	4	6	13	16	18	22
71.	4	7	9	10	12	23
72.	4	7	16	17	20	23
73.	4	8	11	15	17	22
74.	4	9	17	18	19	20
75.	4	10	15	16	19	21
76.	4	12	14	19	20	22
77.	5	6	7	8	20	22
78.	5	6	11	15	16	23
79.	5	7	14	19	21	23
80.	5	8	9	10	11	12
81.	5	8	10	11	12	19
82.	5	8	13	17	18	23
83.	5	9	13	16	19	20
84.	5	9	14	17	18	22
85.	5	10	14	15	17	20
86.	5	12	16	17	21	22
87.	6	7	15	17	18	21
88.	6	8	13	14	15	19
89.	6	9	10	20	21	22
90.	6	9	11	15	18	19
91.	6	10	18	19	20	23
92.	6	11	12	13	17	20
93.	7	8	9	14	15	20
94.	7	8	11	13	16	21
95.	7	9	12	17	19	21
96.	7	10	13	17	19	22
97.	7	11	12	18	22	23
98.	8	10	14	18	21	22
99.	8	12	15	16	18	20
100.	9	10	13	15	17	23
101.	9	11	14	16	21	23
102.	10	12	13	14	16	23
103.	11	14	16	17	18	19
104.	13	15	20	21	22	23

System # 78: Guaranteed 3–win if 3 of the numbers drawn are in your set of 24 numbers ©Copyright 2001

Winning possibilities

Guessed	6	5	4	3	%
6	1	-	0-4	0-29	0.09
	-	2	0-4	4-22	0.03
	-	1	0-7	4-24	9.24
	-	-	1-10	8-22	86.30
	-	-	-	20-24	4.34
5	-	1	0-3	0-20	1.64
	-	-	6	12	0.03
	-	-	3	3-17	3.24
	-	-	2	3-7	3.34
	-	-	1	6-11	57.02
	-	-	-	10-13	34.73
4	-	-	4	8	0.01
	-	-	2	-	0.05
	-	-	1	0-13	16.24
	-	-	-	4-7	83.70
3	-	-	-	8	0.10
	-	-	-	7	0.99
	-	-	-	4	0.10
	-	-	-	2	7.71
	-	-	-	1	91.10

The complete system would require 134,596 combinations. If all of the numbers are guessed correctly, you will either win the jackpot (plus some extra cash!), or you will get one or two 5-wins (and additional prizes), or up to ten 4-wins (plus a number of 3-wins). There are also 65.27% chances of getting at least one 4-win on guessing correctly five of the numbers drawn. Every two combinations of the system differ in at least two numbers. The table below contains information on the balance of the system.

Number(s)	Occurrences
9,24	39
8,22	29
1, 2, 3, 4, 5, 6, 7,10,11,12,13,14,15,16,17,18,19,20,21,23	28

1.	1	2	3	10	12	19
2.	1	2	4	7	21	22

59.	3	6	18	19	21	22
60.	3	7	8	9	14	24

3.	1	2	5	14	20	23
4.	1	2	6	8	11	18
5.	1	2	9	12	18	24
6.	1	2	13	15	16	17
7.	1	3	4	6	17	20
8.	1	3	5	7	15	18
9.	1	3	8	14	16	22
10.	1	3	9	11	22	24
11.	1	3	11	13	21	23
12.	1	4	5	8	12	13
13.	1	4	8	9	20	24
14.	1	4	10	11	14	15
15.	1	4	16	18	19	23
16.	1	5	6	10	16	21
17.	1	5	9	17	21	24
18.	1	5	11	17	19	22
19.	1	6	7	13	14	19
20.	1	6	9	10	19	24
21.	1	6	12	15	22	23
22.	1	7	8	10	17	23
23.	1	7	9	16	23	24
24.	1	7	11	12	16	20
25.	1	8	15	19	20	21
26.	1	9	13	14	15	24
27.	1	10	13	18	20	22
28.	1	12	14	17	18	21
29.	2	3	4	9	23	24
30.	2	3	4	13	14	18
31.	2	3	5	8	17	21
32.	2	3	6	7	16	23
33.	2	3	11	15	20	22
34.	2	4	5	6	15	19
35.	2	4	8	10	16	20
36.	2	4	11	12	17	23
37.	2	5	7	9	19	24
38.	2	5	7	10	11	13
39.	2	5	12	16	18	22
40.	2	6	9	11	14	24
41.	2	6	10	14	17	22
42.	2	6	12	13	20	21
43.	2	7	8	12	14	15
44.	2	7	17	18	19	20
45.	2	8	9	21	22	24
46.	2	8	13	19	22	23
47.	2	9	10	15	17	24
48.	2	9	13	16	20	24
61.	3	7	10	14	20	21
62.	3	7	12	13	17	22
63.	3	8	12	18	20	23
64.	3	9	12	19	20	24
65.	3	9	15	18	21	24
66.	3	10	11	16	17	18
67.	3	14	15	17	19	23
68.	4	5	7	14	16	17
69.	4	5	9	15	16	24
70.	4	5	11	18	20	21
71.	4	6	7	10	12	18
72.	4	6	8	14	21	23
73.	4	6	9	12	21	24
74.	4	6	11	13	16	22
75.	4	7	9	11	17	24
76.	4	7	13	15	20	23
77.	4	8	15	17	18	22
78.	4	9	10	14	18	24
79.	4	9	13	19	22	24
80.	4	10	13	17	19	21
81.	4	12	14	19	20	22
82.	5	6	7	8	20	22
83.	5	6	8	9	22	24
84.	5	6	13	17	18	23
85.	5	7	12	19	21	23
86.	5	8	10	14	18	19
87.	5	8	11	15	16	23
88.	5	9	11	18	20	24
89.	5	9	12	14	23	24
90.	5	10	12	15	17	20
91.	5	13	14	15	21	22
92.	6	7	9	13	18	24
93.	6	7	11	15	17	21
94.	6	8	12	16	17	19
95.	6	9	15	20	23	24
96.	6	10	11	19	20	23
97.	6	14	15	16	18	20
98.	7	8	13	16	18	21
99.	7	9	10	20	21	24
100.	7	9	12	15	22	24
101.	7	10	15	16	19	22
102.	7	11	14	18	22	23
103.	8	9	10	22	23	24
104.	8	9	11	15	19	24
105.	8	9	12	13	17	24
106.	8	9	16	18	22	24

49.	2	10	15	18	21	23	107.	8	10	11	12	21	22
50.	2	11	14	16	19	21	108.	8	11	13	14	17	20
51.	3	4	5	10	22	23	109.	9	10	11	12	16	24
52.	3	4	7	8	11	19	110.	9	11	13	21	23	24
53.	3	4	12	15	16	21	111.	9	14	16	19	21	24
54.	3	5	6	11	12	14	112.	9	14	17	20	22	24
55.	3	5	9	10	13	24	113.	9	17	18	19	23	24
56.	3	5	13	16	19	20	114.	10	12	13	14	16	23
57.	3	6	8	10	13	15	115.	11	12	13	15	18	19
58.	3	6	9	16	17	24	116.	16	17	20	21	22	23

SYSTEM # 79: GUARANTEED 3–WIN IF 3 OF THE NUMBERS DRAWN ARE IN YOUR SET OF 26 NUMBERS

Winning possibilities

Guessed	6	5	4	3	%
6	1	-	-	-	0.06
	-	1	-	10	6.78
	-	-	3	8	6.21
	-	-	2	12	57.59
	-	-	1	16	27.10
	-	-	-	20	2.26
5	-	1	-	-	1.19
	-	-	1	6	59.29
	-	-	-	10	39.52
4	-	-	1	-	13.04
	-	-	-	4	86.96
3	-	-	-	1	100.00

This system is MATHEMATICALLY MINIMAL with respect to the main guarantee. It is also EXCEPTIONALLY HIGHLY BALANCED: Each number is in exactly 30 combinations; each pair of numbers is in exactly 6 combinations; each triple is in exactly one combination. In addition, the combinations of the system are maximally 'apart': Every two combinations differ in at least four numbers. If all of the six numbers drawn are guessed correctly, you will either win the jackpot, or you will get a 5-win (plus ten 3-wins), or up to three 4-wins (and a number of 3-wins). There are also 60.48% chances of getting a 4-win on guessing correctly five of the numbers drawn. The complete system would require 230,230 combinations.

1.	1	2	3	7	12	17
2.	1	2	4	15	16	19
3.	1	2	5	8	22	23
4.	1	2	6	9	18	21
5.	1	2	10	11	20	24
6.	1	2	13	14	25	26
7.	1	3	4	11	13	22
8.	1	3	5	9	10	26
9.	1	3	6	8	19	20
10.	1	3	14	15	21	23
11.	1	3	16	18	24	25
12.	1	4	5	6	17	25
13.	1	4	7	9	23	24
14.	1	4	8	10	14	18
15.	1	4	12	20	21	26
66.	3	7	11	14	24	26
67.	3	8	13	18	21	26
68.	3	8	14	17	22	25
69.	3	9	12	18	22	23
70.	3	9	17	20	21	24
71.	3	10	12	13	14	20
72.	3	10	15	19	22	24
73.	3	11	12	16	19	21
74.	4	5	7	10	11	19
75.	4	5	14	15	22	26
76.	4	5	16	18	21	23
77.	4	6	10	20	22	23
78.	4	6	11	15	21	24
79.	4	6	12	13	18	19
80.	4	7	12	16	22	25

16.	1	5	7	14	16	20
17.	1	5	11	12	15	18
18.	1	5	13	19	21	24
19.	1	6	7	10	13	15
20.	1	6	11	16	23	26
21.	1	6	12	14	22	24
22.	1	7	8	11	21	25
23.	1	7	18	19	22	26
24.	1	8	9	12	13	16
25.	1	8	15	17	24	26
26.	1	9	11	14	17	19
27.	1	9	15	20	22	25
28.	1	10	12	19	23	25
29.	1	10	16	17	21	22
30.	1	13	17	18	20	23
31.	2	3	4	10	21	25
32.	2	3	5	14	18	19
33.	2	3	6	13	23	24
34.	2	3	8	9	11	15
35.	2	3	16	20	22	26
36.	2	4	5	9	13	20
37.	2	4	6	7	8	26
38.	2	4	11	12	14	23
39.	2	4	17	18	22	24
40.	2	5	6	10	12	16
41.	2	5	7	15	24	25
42.	2	5	11	17	21	26
43.	2	6	11	19	22	25
44.	2	6	14	15	17	20
45.	2	7	9	10	14	22
46.	2	7	11	13	16	18
47.	2	7	19	20	21	23
48.	2	8	10	13	17	19
49.	2	8	12	18	20	25
50.	2	8	14	16	21	24
51.	2	9	12	19	24	26
52.	2	9	16	17	23	25
53.	2	10	15	18	23	26
54.	2	12	13	15	21	22
55.	3	4	5	8	12	24
56.	3	4	6	9	14	16
57.	3	4	7	15	18	20
58.	3	4	17	19	23	26
59.	3	5	6	7	21	22
60.	3	5	11	20	23	25
61.	3	5	13	15	16	17

81.	4	7	13	14	17	21
82.	4	8	9	19	21	22
83.	4	8	11	16	17	20
84.	4	8	13	15	23	25
85.	4	9	10	12	15	17
86.	4	9	11	18	25	26
87.	4	10	13	16	24	26
88.	4	14	19	20	24	25
89.	5	6	8	11	13	14
90.	5	6	9	15	19	23
91.	5	6	18	20	24	26
92.	5	7	8	9	17	18
93.	5	7	12	13	23	26
94.	5	8	10	15	20	21
95.	5	8	16	19	25	26
96.	5	9	11	16	22	24
97.	5	9	12	14	21	25
98.	5	10	13	18	22	25
99.	5	10	14	17	23	24
100.	5	12	17	19	20	22
101.	6	7	9	11	12	20
102.	6	7	14	18	23	25
103.	6	7	16	17	19	24
104.	6	8	9	10	24	25
105.	6	8	12	17	21	23
106.	6	8	15	16	18	22
107.	6	9	13	17	22	26
108.	6	10	14	19	21	26
109.	6	13	16	20	21	25
110.	7	8	12	14	15	19
111.	7	8	13	20	22	24
112.	7	9	15	16	21	26
113.	7	10	12	18	21	24
114.	7	10	17	20	25	26
115.	7	11	15	17	22	23
116.	8	9	14	20	23	26
117.	8	10	11	12	22	26
118.	8	11	18	19	23	24
119.	9	10	11	13	21	23
120.	9	10	16	18	19	20
121.	9	13	14	15	18	24
122.	10	11	14	15	16	25
123.	11	12	13	17	24	25
124.	11	13	15	19	20	26
125.	11	14	18	20	21	22
126.	12	14	16	17	18	26

62.	3	6	10	11	17	18	127.	12	15	16	20	23	24
63.	3	6	12	15	25	26	128.	13	14	16	19	22	23
64.	3	7	8	10	16	23	129.	15	17	18	19	21	25
65.	3	7	9	13	19	25	130.	21	22	23	24	25	26

SYSTEM # 80: GUARANTEED 3–WIN IF 3 OF THE NUMBERS DRAWN ARE IN YOUR SET OF 27 NUMBERS

Winning possibilities

Guessed	6	5	4	3	%
6	1	0-1	0-2	0-16	0.05
	-	2	0-3	4-20	0.06
	-	1	0-4	3-22	6.97
	-	-	5	8-12	0.03
	-	-	4	8-14	1.48
	-	-	3	8-18	15.18
	-	-	2	12-21	49.71
	-	-	1	16-24	23.93
	-	-	-	20-26	2.59
5	-	2	-	0-4	0.01
	-	1	0-2	0-11	1.23
	-	-	3	1-7	0.15
	-	-	2	3-10	4.41
	-	-	1	6-12	55.74
	-	-	-	10-14	38.46
4	-	-	2	0-4	0.24
	-	-	1	0-5	13.79
	-	-	-	4-7	85.97
3	-	-	-	3	0.51
	-	-	-	2	13.16
	-	-	-	1	86.33

This is yet another MATHEMATICALLY MINIMAL with respect to the main guarantee system. The complete system would require 296,010 combinations. If all of the six numbers drawn are guessed correctly, you will either win the jackpot (plus some extra cash!), or you will get one or two 5-wins (and additional prizes), or up to five 4-wins (plus a number of 3-wins). There are also 61.53% chances of getting at least one 4-win on guessing correctly five of the numbers drawn. The system is well balanced: Each number is in either 37 or 38 combinations as seen from the table below.

Number(s)	Occurrences
14,17,24	38
1, 2, 3, 4, 5, 6, 7, 8, 9,10,11,12,13,15,16,18,19,20,21,22,23,25,26,27	37

1.	1	2	3	7	11	27
2.	1	2	3	7	26	27
3.	1	2	3	14	15	16
4.	1	2	4	7	10	13
5.	1	2	5	9	11	24
6.	1	2	6	19	22	25
7.	1	2	8	12	18	21
8.	1	2	17	20	23	26
9.	1	3	4	5	18	25
10.	1	3	6	8	13	20
11.	1	3	7	9	22	26
12.	1	3	10	17	21	24
13.	1	3	11	12	19	23
14.	1	4	6	15	23	24
15.	1	4	8	11	16	26
16.	1	4	9	19	20	21
17.	1	4	12	14	17	22
18.	1	4	13	19	25	27
19.	1	5	6	14	21	26
20.	1	5	6	16	21	27
21.	1	5	7	12	15	20
22.	1	5	8	10	22	23
23.	1	5	13	16	17	19
24.	1	6	7	11	17	18
25.	1	6	9	10	12	16
26.	1	7	8	14	19	24
27.	1	7	16	21	23	25
28.	1	8	9	15	17	25
29.	1	8	12	20	23	27
30.	1	9	13	14	18	23
31.	1	9	15	17	24	27
32.	1	10	11	14	20	25
33.	1	10	14	18	22	27
34.	1	10	15	18	19	26
35.	1	11	13	15	21	22
36.	1	12	13	24	25	26
37.	1	16	18	20	22	24
38.	2	3	4	11	20	22
39.	2	3	5	13	21	23
40.	2	3	6	7	12	24
41.	2	3	8	10	25	26
42.	2	3	9	17	18	19
43.	2	4	5	8	15	19
44.	2	4	6	16	17	21
45.	2	4	9	12	23	25
46.	2	4	12	17	22	27
84.	3	9	10	15	20	23
85.	3	9	13	18	23	27
86.	3	10	12	13	18	22
87.	3	10	12	19	21	27
88.	3	11	13	14	17	26
89.	3	12	16	17	20	25
90.	3	14	22	23	24	25
91.	4	5	6	11	12	13
92.	4	5	7	21	22	24
93.	4	5	9	10	17	26
94.	4	5	14	16	20	23
95.	4	6	7	20	25	26
96.	4	6	8	9	10	27
97.	4	6	8	9	18	22
98.	4	6	9	11	26	27
99.	4	7	9	11	14	15
100.	4	7	12	16	18	19
101.	4	7	15	18	21	27
102.	4	8	10	12	20	24
103.	4	8	13	14	21	25
104.	4	10	11	18	21	23
105.	4	10	15	16	22	25
106.	4	11	14	16	23	27
107.	4	11	17	19	24	25
108.	4	13	15	17	18	20
109.	4	13	19	22	23	26
110.	5	6	7	9	19	23
111.	5	6	8	16	24	25
112.	5	7	8	13	18	26
113.	5	7	10	17	23	27
114.	5	8	10	12	26	27
115.	5	8	11	17	20	21
116.	5	9	11	19	22	27
117.	5	9	13	20	22	25
118.	5	9	15	16	18	21
119.	5	10	12	19	21	25
120.	5	10	13	14	15	24
121.	5	11	14	18	19	22
122.	5	11	15	23	25	26
123.	5	12	13	14	15	27
124.	5	12	17	18	23	24
125.	6	7	8	10	15	21
126.	6	7	13	14	16	22
127.	6	7	13	20	22	27
128.	6	8	12	17	19	26
129.	6	9	14	17	20	24

47. 2 4 14 18 24 26
48. 2 5 6 10 18 20
49. 2 5 7 14 17 25
50. 2 5 8 18 25 27
51. 2 5 12 16 22 26
52. 2 6 8 11 14 23
53. 2 6 9 13 15 26
54. 2 6 15 19 23 27
55. 2 7 8 9 16 20
56. 2 7 11 19 21 26
57. 2 7 15 18 22 23
58. 2 8 13 17 22 24
59. 2 9 10 14 21 22
60. 2 9 14 20 21 27
61. 2 10 11 12 15 17
62. 2 10 13 16 24 27
63. 2 10 16 19 23 24
64. 2 11 13 16 18 25
65. 2 12 13 14 19 20
66. 2 15 20 21 24 25
67. 3 4 5 20 24 27
68. 3 4 6 10 14 19
69. 3 4 7 8 17 23
70. 3 4 9 13 16 24
71. 3 4 12 15 21 26
72. 3 5 6 15 17 22
73. 3 5 7 10 11 16
74. 3 5 8 9 12 14
75. 3 5 19 20 24 26
76. 3 6 9 11 21 25
77. 3 6 14 17 25 27
78. 3 6 16 18 23 26
79. 3 7 13 15 19 25
80. 3 7 14 18 20 21
81. 3 8 11 15 18 24
82. 3 8 15 16 22 27
83. 3 8 16 19 21 22

130. 6 10 11 22 24 26
131. 6 10 13 17 23 25
132. 6 11 12 18 24 27
133. 6 11 15 16 19 20
134. 6 12 14 15 18 25
135. 6 12 20 21 22 23
136. 6 13 18 19 21 24
137. 7 8 11 12 22 25
138. 7 8 14 19 24 27
139. 7 9 10 18 24 25
140. 7 9 12 13 17 21
141. 7 9 12 16 25 27
142. 7 10 12 14 23 26
143. 7 10 17 19 20 22
144. 7 11 13 20 23 24
145. 7 15 16 17 24 26
146. 8 9 10 11 13 19
147. 8 9 21 23 24 26
148. 8 10 14 16 17 18
149. 8 11 13 17 21 27
150. 8 12 13 15 16 23
151. 8 14 15 20 22 26
152. 8 18 19 20 23 25
153. 9 11 12 18 20 26
154. 9 11 16 17 22 23
155. 9 12 15 19 22 24
156. 9 14 16 19 25 26
157. 10 11 15 20 25 27
158. 10 13 16 20 21 26
159. 11 12 14 16 21 24
160. 13 14 15 16 26 27
161. 14 15 17 19 21 23
162. 14 17 24 25 26 27
163. 16 17 18 19 20 27
164. 17 18 19 20 26 27
165. 17 18 21 22 25 26
166. 21 22 23 24 25 27
167. 21 22 23 24 26 27

PART II
LOTTERY SYSTEMS WITH DOUBLE GUARANTEES

In this part of the book, I introduce systems where the main guarantee is two or more identical prizes. The arrangement of the systems follows the pattern from the first part of the book: First, I introduce the systems with two 5-wins guaranteed, then those with two 4-wins, and finally those with two 3-wins. Part III of the book presents systems where the main guarantee is more than two identical prizes. What is the point of playing with a double (or multiple) guarantee system? Let us focus on the double guarantee systems. The main advantage is that in some cases, due to the specifics of the combinatorial problem, **we are able to achieve the double guarantee in less than twice the number of combinations needed for the single guarantee**.

Let us consider our first example, System # 20 (you play with 10 numbers in 20 tickets and you get a 4-win whenever 4 of the numbers drawn are in your set of 10 numbers). Recall that 20 **is the minimum number of tickets** (see page 10) that will guarantee you this prize. Now, suppose you want to play for two 4-wins guaranteed whenever 4 of your numbers are drawn. The simplest way is to play twice the system # 20 (so you have to fill 40 tickets). This way you will have repeated tickets and repeated wins correspondingly. However, it is possible to have the same guarantee (two 4-wins if 4 of your numbers are drawn) in just 30 tickets and no repetition! You can find a system with this property under # 88 in the book. We should mention that 30 is again the minimum possible number of tickets, but now, it is the minimum for the double guarantee, so you have an example of another mathematically minimal system. Indeed, all of the systems in this part of the book have the following nice property: THEY GIVE YOU THE DOUBLE GUARANTEE IN A NUMBER OF TICKETS WHICH IS LESS THAN TWICE THE NUMBER OF TICKETS NEEDED FOR THE SINGLE GUARANTEE.

Part III of the book contains systems with multiple guarantees. The systems there have the same nice properties as the double guarantee systems. I have chosen to present the best systems I know, that is, the systems that give you the multiple guarantee in much less than the corresponding multiple number of tickets. Also, I have included mostly **highly balanced systems** in part III: Not only every number appears the same number of times in the combinations of the system, but in many cases every pair of numbers appears the same number of times, and in some cases every triple or even every quadruple appears the same number of times! Information on the balance is supplied in my comments to the systems.

Double Guarantees: Lottery systems with two 5-wins guaranteed if 5 of your numbers are drawn

System # 81: Guaranteed two 5–wins if 5 of the numbers drawn are in your set of 9 numbers ©Copyright 2001

Winning possibilities

Guessed	6	5	4	3	%
6	2	9	27	13	3.57
	1	10	28	12	32.14
	1	9	30	11	21.43
	-	13	25	13	32.14
	-	12	27	12	10.72
5	-	5	12	29	7.14
	-	3	16	27	21.43
	-	2	19-21	20-24	71.43
4	-	-	8	20	7.14
	-	-	7	22	21.43
	-	-	6	24	42.86
	-	-	5	27-29	28.57
3	-	-	-	13	35.71
	-	-	-	12	42.86
	-	-	-	11	21.43

The best single guarantee system (# 2) has 30 combinations. The system presented here gives you twice the guarantee in 51 combinations, that is, in just 1.7 times the number of tickets needed for the single guarantee system! It also guarantees at least five 4-wins if five of your numbers are drawn, and at least eleven 3-wins if three of your numbers are in the draw. If all of the numbers are guessed correctly, you will either win the jackpot (or even two jackpots!) plus many other prizes, or you will get at least twelve 5-wins and a number of other prizes. The possibility of a double jackpot comes from the fact that this system is one of the few systems with repeated combinations in the book. You will notice that the combinations 1 and 2 are the same and so are 33 and 34 as well as 38 and 39. Nevertheless, the system is the best with the main guarantee. It is also HIGHLY BALANCED: Each number is in exactly 34 combinations.

1. 1 2 3 4 5 9
2. 1 2 3 4 5 9
3. 1 2 3 4 6 7
4. 1 2 3 4 6 8
5. 1 2 3 4 7 8
6. 1 2 3 5 6 8
7. 1 2 3 5 6 9
8. 1 2 3 5 7 8
9. 1 2 3 5 7 9
10. 1 2 3 5 8 9
11. 1 2 3 6 7 9
12. 1 2 3 6 8 9
13. 1 2 4 5 6 7
14. 1 2 4 5 6 8
15. 1 2 4 5 6 9
16. 1 2 4 5 7 9
17. 1 2 4 5 8 9
18. 1 2 4 6 7 9
19. 1 2 4 7 8 9
20. 1 2 5 6 7 8
21. 1 2 6 7 8 9
22. 1 3 4 5 6 7
23. 1 3 4 5 6 9
24. 1 3 4 5 7 8
25. 1 3 4 5 7 9
26. 1 3 4 5 8 9
27. 1 3 4 6 8 9
28. 1 3 4 7 8 9
29. 1 3 5 6 7 8
30. 1 3 6 7 8 9
31. 1 4 5 6 7 8
32. 1 4 6 7 8 9
33. 1 5 6 7 8 9
34. 1 5 6 7 8 9
35. 2 3 4 5 6 7
36. 2 3 4 5 6 8
37. 2 3 4 5 7 8
38. 2 3 4 6 7 8
39. 2 3 4 6 7 8
40. 2 3 4 6 7 9
41. 2 3 4 6 8 9
42. 2 3 4 7 8 9
43. 2 3 5 6 7 9
44. 2 3 5 7 8 9
45. 2 4 5 6 8 9
46. 2 4 5 7 8 9
47. 2 5 6 7 8 9
48. 3 4 5 6 7 9
49. 3 4 5 6 8 9
50. 3 5 6 7 8 9
51. 4 5 6 7 8 9

System # 82: Guaranteed two 5–wins if 5 of the numbers drawn are in your set of 10 numbers ©Copyright 2001

Winning possibilities

Guessed	6	5	4	3	%
6	2	4-8	44-50	32-34	2.85
	1	6-12	38-49	32-38	40.00
	-	16	33	40	0.95
	-	14	36-38	36-40	12.38
	-	12	38-42	36-40	43.82
5	-	6	10-12	58-64	2.38
	-	4	16-21	46-58	9.52
	-	2	20-27	38-52	88.10
4	-	-	10	32	0.95
	-	-	9	32	3.81
	-	-	8	32-36	21.90
	-	-	7	36-40	26.67
	-	-	6	34-40	46.67
3	-	-	-	18	13.33
	-	-	-	16	73.33
	-	-	-	14	13.34

The best single guarantee system (# 3) has 50 combinations. The system presented here gives you twice the guarantee in only 96 combinations. It also guarantees at least six 4-wins if five of your numbers are drawn, and at least fourteen 3-wins if three of your numbers are in the draw. If all of the numbers are guessed correctly, you will either win the jackpot (or even two jackpots!) plus many other prizes, or you will get at least twelve 5-wins and a number of other prizes. This is the second (of three) systems with repeated combinations in the book. Again, the system is the best with the main guarantee. The table below contains information on the balance of the system.

Number(s)	Occurrences
1, 2, 3, 4, 6, 8, 9,10	58
5, 7	56

1. 1 2 3 4 5 9
2. 1 2 3 4 5 10
3. 1 2 3 4 6 7
4. 1 2 3 4 6 9
5. 1 2 3 4 7 8

49. 1 3 6 8 9 10
50. 1 3 7 8 9 10
51. 1 4 5 6 9 10
52. 1 4 5 7 8 9
53. 1 4 5 7 8 10

6.	1	2	3	4	8	9
7.	1	2	3	4	9	10
8.	1	2	3	5	6	9
9.	1	2	3	5	6	10
10.	1	2	3	5	7	8
11.	1	2	3	5	7	8
12.	1	2	3	6	7	8
13.	1	2	3	6	8	10
14.	1	2	3	7	8	9
15.	1	2	3	7	8	10
16.	1	2	3	7	9	10
17.	1	2	4	5	6	7
18.	1	2	4	5	6	8
19.	1	2	4	5	6	9
20.	1	2	4	5	6	10
21.	1	2	4	5	7	9
22.	1	2	4	5	8	9
23.	1	2	4	6	8	10
24.	1	2	4	7	8	10
25.	1	2	4	7	9	10
26.	1	2	5	6	7	10
27.	1	2	5	6	8	10
28.	1	2	5	7	9	10
29.	1	2	5	8	9	10
30.	1	2	6	7	8	9
31.	1	2	6	7	9	10
32.	1	2	6	8	9	10
33.	1	3	4	5	6	7
34.	1	3	4	5	6	8
35.	1	3	4	5	7	10
36.	1	3	4	5	8	10
37.	1	3	4	5	9	10
38.	1	3	4	6	7	8
39.	1	3	4	6	7	9
40.	1	3	4	6	7	10
41.	1	3	4	6	7	10
42.	1	3	4	7	9	10
43.	1	3	4	8	9	10
44.	1	3	5	6	7	9
45.	1	3	5	6	8	9
46.	1	3	5	6	9	10
47.	1	3	5	7	9	10
48.	1	3	5	8	9	10
54.	1	4	6	7	8	9
55.	1	4	6	8	9	10
56.	1	5	6	7	8	9
57.	1	5	6	7	8	10
58.	1	6	7	8	9	10
59.	2	3	4	5	6	8
60.	2	3	4	5	6	8
61.	2	3	4	5	7	9
62.	2	3	4	5	7	10
63.	2	3	4	6	7	9
64.	2	3	4	6	8	9
65.	2	3	4	6	8	10
66.	2	3	4	6	9	10
67.	2	3	4	7	8	10
68.	2	3	5	6	7	9
69.	2	3	5	6	7	10
70.	2	3	5	8	9	10
71.	2	3	5	8	9	10
72.	2	3	6	7	8	9
73.	2	3	6	7	9	10
74.	2	4	5	6	7	8
75.	2	4	5	6	9	10
76.	2	4	5	7	8	10
77.	2	4	5	8	9	10
78.	2	4	6	7	8	9
79.	2	4	6	7	8	10
80.	2	4	6	7	8	10
81.	2	4	7	8	9	10
82.	2	5	6	7	8	9
83.	2	5	6	8	9	10
84.	2	5	7	8	9	10
85.	3	4	5	6	7	8
86.	3	4	5	6	8	9
87.	3	4	5	6	8	10
88.	3	4	5	6	9	10
89.	3	4	5	7	8	9
90.	3	4	7	8	9	10
91.	3	5	6	7	8	10
92.	3	5	7	8	9	10
93.	3	6	7	8	9	10
94.	4	5	6	7	9	10
95.	4	5	6	7	9	10
96.	4	5	6	8	9	10

System # 83: Guaranteed two 5–wins if 5 of the numbers drawn are in your set of 11 numbers ©Copyright 2001

Winning possibilities

Guessed	6	5	4	3	%
6	1	14	48	88	2.38
	1	10	57-62	64-80	26.19
	1	8	61	76	4.76
	1	6	62-66	72-80	4.76
	-	16	49	82	4.76
	-	14	53-56	72-78	9.52
	-	12	54-59	72-82	47.63
5	-	6	19	88	2.38
	-	4	24-25	80-82	9.52
	-	2	25-35	64-82	88.10
4	-	-	11	48	6.67
	-	-	9	50-52	20.00
	-	-	8	52-58	33.33
	-	-	7	52-56	40.00
3	-	-	-	24	13.33
	-	-	-	22	40.00
	-	-	-	20	46.67

The best single guarantee system (# 4) has 100 combinations. The system presented here gives you twice the guarantee in 176 combinations, that is, in only 1.76 times the number of combinations needed for the single guarantee system! The system also guarantees at least seven 4-wins if five of your numbers are drawn, and at least twenty 3-wins if three of your numbers are in the draw. The complete system would require 462 combinations. If all of the numbers drawn are guessed correctly, you will either win the jackpot (plus many other prizes), or you will get at least twelve 5-wins and a number of 3 and 4-wins. The system is HIGHLY BALANCED: Each number is in exactly 96 combinations.

1. 1 2 3 4 5 6
2. 1 2 3 4 5 7
3. 1 2 3 4 5 8
4. 1 2 3 4 5 9
5. 1 2 3 4 5 10
6. 1 2 3 4 5 11
7. 1 2 3 4 6 11
8. 1 2 3 4 7 11

89. 1 5 6 7 8 9
90. 1 5 6 7 10 11
91. 1 5 6 8 9 11
92. 1 5 8 9 10 11
93. 1 6 7 8 9 10
94. 1 6 7 8 10 11
95. 1 6 8 9 10 11
96. 1 7 8 9 10 11

9.	1	2	3	4	8	11
10.	1	2	3	4	9	11
11.	1	2	3	4	10	11
12.	1	2	3	5	6	7
13.	1	2	3	5	8	9
14.	1	2	3	5	10	11
15.	1	2	3	6	7	8
16.	1	2	3	6	7	9
17.	1	2	3	6	7	10
18.	1	2	3	6	8	9
19.	1	2	3	6	10	11
20.	1	2	3	7	8	9
21.	1	2	3	7	10	11
22.	1	2	3	8	9	10
23.	1	2	3	8	10	11
24.	1	2	3	9	10	11
25.	1	2	4	5	6	11
26.	1	2	4	5	7	8
27.	1	2	4	5	9	10
28.	1	2	4	6	7	9
29.	1	2	4	6	7	10
30.	1	2	4	6	8	9
31.	1	2	4	6	8	10
32.	1	2	4	7	8	9
33.	1	2	4	7	8	10
34.	1	2	4	7	8	11
35.	1	2	4	9	10	11
36.	1	2	5	6	7	9
37.	1	2	5	6	7	10
38.	1	2	5	6	7	11
39.	1	2	5	6	8	10
40.	1	2	5	6	8	11
41.	1	2	5	6	9	11
42.	1	2	5	7	8	9
43.	1	2	5	7	8	10
44.	1	2	5	7	8	11
45.	1	2	5	9	10	11
46.	1	2	6	7	8	11
47.	1	2	6	7	9	10
48.	1	2	6	9	10	11
49.	1	2	7	8	9	11
50.	1	2	7	9	10	11
51.	1	2	8	9	10	11
52.	1	3	4	5	6	7
53.	1	3	4	5	8	9
54.	1	3	4	5	10	11

97.	2	3	4	5	6	7
98.	2	3	4	5	6	8
99.	2	3	4	5	6	9
100.	2	3	4	5	6	10
101.	2	3	4	5	6	11
102.	2	3	4	6	7	8
103.	2	3	4	6	9	10
104.	2	3	4	7	8	9
105.	2	3	4	7	8	10
106.	2	3	4	7	8	11
107.	2	3	4	7	9	10
108.	2	3	4	8	9	10
109.	2	3	4	9	10	11
110.	2	3	5	6	8	9
111.	2	3	5	6	10	11
112.	2	3	5	7	8	10
113.	2	3	5	7	8	11
114.	2	3	5	7	9	10
115.	2	3	5	7	9	11
116.	2	3	5	8	9	10
117.	2	3	5	8	9	11
118.	2	3	6	7	8	10
119.	2	3	6	7	8	11
120.	2	3	6	7	9	11
121.	2	3	6	8	9	10
122.	2	3	6	8	9	11
123.	2	3	7	8	10	11
124.	2	4	5	6	7	8
125.	2	4	5	6	9	10
126.	2	4	5	7	9	10
127.	2	4	5	7	9	11
128.	2	4	5	7	10	11
129.	2	4	5	8	9	10
130.	2	4	5	8	9	11
131.	2	4	5	8	10	11
132.	2	4	6	7	9	11
133.	2	4	6	7	10	11
134.	2	4	6	8	9	11
135.	2	4	6	8	10	11
136.	2	5	6	7	8	9
137.	2	5	6	7	10	11
138.	2	5	6	8	10	11
139.	2	5	6	9	10	11
140.	2	6	7	8	9	10
141.	2	7	8	9	10	11
142.	3	4	5	6	7	8

55.	1	3	4	6	7	11
56.	1	3	4	6	8	9
57.	1	3	4	6	8	10
58.	1	3	4	6	9	10
59.	1	3	4	7	8	9
60.	1	3	4	7	8	10
61.	1	3	4	7	9	10
62.	1	3	4	8	9	11
63.	1	3	5	6	8	10
64.	1	3	5	6	8	11
65.	1	3	5	6	9	10
66.	1	3	5	6	9	11
67.	1	3	5	7	8	10
68.	1	3	5	7	8	11
69.	1	3	5	7	9	10
70.	1	3	5	7	9	11
71.	1	3	6	7	8	11
72.	1	3	6	7	9	11
73.	1	3	6	7	10	11
74.	1	3	8	9	10	11
75.	1	4	5	6	7	8
76.	1	4	5	6	8	11
77.	1	4	5	6	9	10
78.	1	4	5	6	9	11
79.	1	4	5	6	10	11
80.	1	4	5	7	9	10
81.	1	4	5	7	9	11
82.	1	4	5	7	10	11
83.	1	4	5	8	9	10
84.	1	4	5	8	10	11
85.	1	4	6	7	8	11
86.	1	4	6	7	9	11
87.	1	4	6	7	10	11
88.	1	4	8	9	10	11

143.	3	4	5	6	7	9
144.	3	4	5	6	7	10
145.	3	4	5	6	7	11
146.	3	4	5	7	8	9
147.	3	4	5	7	10	11
148.	3	4	5	8	9	10
149.	3	4	5	8	9	11
150.	3	4	5	8	10	11
151.	3	4	5	9	10	11
152.	3	4	6	7	9	10
153.	3	4	6	8	9	11
154.	3	4	6	8	10	11
155.	3	4	6	9	10	11
156.	3	4	7	8	9	11
157.	3	4	7	9	10	11
158.	3	5	6	7	8	9
159.	3	5	6	7	10	11
160.	3	5	6	8	10	11
161.	3	5	6	9	10	11
162.	3	6	7	8	9	10
163.	3	7	8	9	10	11
164.	4	5	6	7	8	9
165.	4	5	6	7	8	10
166.	4	5	6	7	8	11
167.	4	5	6	8	9	10
168.	4	5	6	9	10	11
169.	4	5	7	8	10	11
170.	4	6	7	8	9	10
171.	4	7	8	9	10	11
172.	5	6	7	8	9	10
173.	5	6	7	8	9	11
174.	5	6	7	9	10	11
175.	5	7	8	9	10	11
176.	6	7	8	9	10	11

Double Guarantees: Lottery systems with two 5-wins guaranteed if 6 of your numbers are drawn

System # 84: Guaranteed two 5–wins if 6 of the numbers drawn are in your set of 10 numbers

Winning possibilities

Guessed	6	5	4	3	%
6	1	2	5	12	9.52
	-	4	4-8	4-12	14.28
	-	2	9-11	4-8	76.20
5	-	2	4	6	3.97
	-	2	2	10	3.97
	-	1	4	9	15.87
	-	1	3	11	15.87
	-	-	8	6	3.97
	-	-	6	8-10	27.78
	-	-	5	10-11	28.57
4	-	-	4	4	2.38
	-	-	3	4	9.52
	-	-	2	6-8	28.57
	-	-	1	8	47.62
	-	-	-	12	11.91
3	-	-	-	6	8.33
	-	-	-	4	16.67
	-	-	-	3	66.67
	-	-	-	2	8.33

The best single guarantee system (# 10) has 14 combinations, so with the above system you have twice the guarantee in 20 combinations, that is, in only 1.43 times the number of tickets for the single guarantee system! The system also guarantees at least five 4-wins if five of your numbers are drawn, and at least two 3-wins (91.67% chances for three or more 3-wins) if three of your numbers are in the draw. The complete system would require 210 combinations. If all of the numbers drawn are guessed correctly, you will get at least the main guarantee, but you can also win the jackpot (plus many other prizes), or you can get four 5-wins and a number of

3 and 4-wins. The system is HIGHLY BALANCED: Each number is in exactly 12 combinations.

1. 1 2 3 4 7 9
2. 1 2 3 5 6 8
3. 1 2 3 6 8 10
4. 1 2 4 5 7 10
5. 1 2 4 7 8 9
6. 1 2 5 7 9 10
7. 1 3 4 5 6 9
8. 1 3 4 6 9 10
9. 1 3 5 6 7 8
10. 1 3 6 7 8 10
11. 1 4 5 6 8 9
12. 1 4 6 8 9 10
13. 2 3 4 5 8 10
14. 2 3 4 6 7 9
15. 2 3 5 8 9 10
16. 2 4 5 6 7 10
17. 2 4 6 7 8 9
18. 2 5 6 7 9 10
19. 3 4 5 7 8 10
20. 3 5 7 8 9 10

System # 85: Guaranteed two 5–wins if 6 of the numbers drawn are in your set of 11 numbers ©Copyright 2001

Winning possibilities

Guessed	6	5	4	3	%
6	1	3	10	18	0.43
	1	2	10	18-23	0.65
	1	1	8-14	17-27	7.36
	-	6	6	21	0.43
	-	4	8-13	12-21	15.37
	-	3	10-15	12-21	27.71
	-	2	11-17	11-20	48.05
5	-	2	0-4	17-27	4.98
	-	1	3-8	13-23	40.69
	-	-	10	12-14	1.09
	-	-	9	11-15	4.11
	-	-	8	13-18	22.93
	-	-	7	15-19	18.18
	-	-	6	16-21	8.02
4	-	-	4	6	0.30
	-	-	3	7-11	16.67
	-	-	2	8-15	48.48
	-	-	1	11-17	29.09
	-	-	-	14-19	5.46
3	-	-	-	7	1.21
	-	-	-	6	12.73
	-	-	-	5	52.12
	-	-	-	4	25.45
	-	-	-	3	8.49

The best single guarantee system (# 11) has 22 combinations. The above system gives you twice the guarantee in just 39 combinations. The system also guarantees at least six 4-wins if five of your numbers are drawn, and at least three 3-wins (91.51% chances for four or more 3-wins) if three of your numbers are in the draw. There are 94.54% chances that you will get at least one 4-win if four of your numbers are drawn. The complete system would require 462 combinations. If you correctly guess all of the numbers drawn, then you will get at least the main guarantee, but you can also win the jackpot (plus many other prizes), or you can get up to six 5-wins and a number of 3 and 4-wins. The next table gives information on the balance of the system.

Number(s)	Occurrences
4, 5, 6, 7,11	22
1, 3, 9,10	21
2, 8	20

1.	1	2	3	4	7	8
2.	1	2	3	4	8	11
3.	1	2	3	5	7	10
4.	1	2	3	5	9	10
5.	1	2	4	5	6	7
6.	1	2	4	5	6	11
7.	1	2	4	6	9	11
8.	1	2	5	6	8	11
9.	1	2	6	7	8	10
10.	1	2	7	9	10	11
11.	1	3	4	5	6	8
12.	1	3	4	6	9	10
13.	1	3	4	7	9	10
14.	1	3	5	6	7	11
15.	1	3	5	6	8	9
16.	1	3	6	7	9	11
17.	1	3	8	9	10	11
18.	1	4	5	7	8	9
19.	1	4	5	7	10	11
20.	1	4	5	8	10	11
21.	1	5	6	7	9	10
22.	2	3	4	5	6	7
23.	2	3	4	5	9	11
24.	2	3	4	6	10	11
25.	2	3	5	6	10	11
26.	2	3	6	7	8	9
27.	2	3	6	7	8	10
28.	2	4	5	8	9	10
29.	2	4	6	8	9	10
30.	2	4	7	9	10	11
31.	2	5	7	8	9	11
32.	3	4	5	6	9	11
33.	3	4	5	7	8	10
34.	3	5	7	8	10	11
35.	3	6	8	9	10	11
36.	4	5	7	8	9	11
37.	4	6	7	8	9	11
38.	4	6	7	8	10	11
39.	5	6	7	9	10	11

System # 86: Guaranteed two 5–wins if 6 of the numbers drawn are in your set of 12 numbers ©Copyright 2001

Winning possibilities

Guessed	6	5	4	3	%
6	1	2	10-15	26-37	1.41
	1	1	10-15	33-38	5.41
	-	5	6-12	28-38	3.57
	-	4	12-16	21-30	3.35
	-	3	12-19	21-31	33.44
	-	2	14-21	21-31	52.82
5	-	2	0-5	23-38	4.80
	-	1	4-9	19-29	38.13
	-	-	12	12-16	0.65
	-	-	11	13-21	1.00
	-	-	10	13-24	5.56
	-	-	9	20-25	16.04
	-	-	8	21-26	27.02
	-	-	7	23-27	6.80
4	-	-	6	1	0.20
	-	-	5	2-3	1.82
	-	-	4	4-13	1.21
	-	-	3	12-16	9.90
	-	-	2	12-18	59.19
	-	-	1	16-20	27.68
3	-	-	-	8	0.45
	-	-	-	7	12.27
	-	-	-	6	48.64
	-	-	-	5	36.82
	-	-	-	4	1.82

The best single guarantee system (# 11) has 38 combinations. The above system gives you twice the guarantee in just 63 combinations, that is, in 1.66 times the number of combinations of the single guarantee system. The system also guarantees at least seven 4-wins if five of your numbers are drawn, at least four 3-wins (98.18% chances for five or more 3-wins) if three of your numbers are in the draw, and at least one 4-win if four of your numbers are drawn. The complete system would require 924 combinations. If you correctly guess all of the numbers drawn, then you will get at least the main guarantee, but you can also win the jackpot (plus many other prizes), or you can get up to five 5-wins and a number of 3 and 4-wins. The next table gives information on the balance of the system.

Number(s)	Occurrences
5	33
4, 7, 8, 9,11	32
1, 3, 6,10,12	31
2	30

1.	1	2	3	4	5	6
2.	1	2	3	4	10	11
3.	1	2	3	5	6	12
4.	1	2	3	7	8	9
5.	1	2	3	10	11	12
6.	1	2	4	5	8	11
7.	1	2	4	6	8	10
8.	1	2	4	7	9	12
9.	1	2	5	7	9	10
10.	1	2	5	8	11	12
11.	1	2	6	7	9	11
12.	1	2	6	8	10	12
13.	1	2	7	8	9	12
14.	1	3	4	5	9	11
15.	1	3	4	6	9	10
16.	1	3	4	7	8	12
17.	1	3	4	7	11	12
18.	1	3	5	6	7	8
19.	1	3	5	7	8	10
20.	1	3	5	9	11	12
21.	1	3	6	7	8	11
22.	1	3	6	9	10	12
23.	1	4	5	6	8	9
24.	1	4	5	7	9	10
25.	1	4	5	7	10	12
26.	1	4	6	7	11	12
27.	1	4	8	9	10	11
28.	1	5	6	7	9	11
29.	1	5	6	7	10	11
30.	1	5	6	8	9	12
31.	1	8	9	10	11	12
32.	2	3	4	5	7	11
33.	2	3	4	6	7	10
34.	2	3	4	6	11	12
35.	2	3	4	8	9	11
36.	2	3	4	8	9	12
37.	2	3	5	7	11	12
38.	2	3	5	8	9	10
39.	2	3	6	7	10	12
40.	2	3	6	8	9	11
41.	2	4	5	6	7	8
42.	2	4	5	9	10	12
43.	2	4	6	9	11	12
44.	2	4	7	8	10	11
45.	2	5	6	7	8	12
46.	2	5	6	8	10	11
47.	2	5	6	9	10	11
48.	2	7	8	10	11	12
49.	3	4	5	6	7	9
50.	3	4	5	8	10	12
51.	3	4	6	8	11	12
52.	3	4	7	9	10	11
53.	3	5	6	7	9	12
54.	3	5	6	8	10	11
55.	3	5	8	9	10	11
56.	3	7	9	10	11	12
57.	4	5	6	9	10	12
58.	4	5	6	10	11	12
59.	4	5	7	8	9	11
60.	4	5	7	8	10	12
61.	4	6	7	8	9	10
62.	5	7	8	9	11	12
63.	6	7	8	9	10	12

Double Guarantees: Lottery systems with two 4-wins guaranteed if 4 of your numbers are drawn

System # 87: Guaranteed two 4–wins if 4 of the numbers drawn are in your set of 9 numbers

Winning possibilities

Guessed	6	5	4	3	%
6	1	5	10	6	9.52
	1	3	13	5	9.52
	1	2	15	4	4.76
	1	-	17	4	2.38
	-	8	6	8	2.38
	-	6	10-12	4-6	14.29
	-	5	11-13	4-6	52.38
	-	4	12	6	4.77
5	-	4	2	14	9.52
	-	2	6-8	8-12	3.17
	-	1	5-10	6-14	73.02
	-	-	12	8	0.79
	-	-	10	8-10	13.50
4	-	-	5	6	6.35
	-	-	4	8	10.32
	-	-	3	10-11	22.22
	-	-	2	8-14	61.11
3	-	-	-	8	2.38
	-	-	-	6	47.62
	-	-	-	5	19.05
	-	-	-	4	30.95

The best single guarantee system (# 19) has 12 combinations. The system presented here gives you twice the guarantee in just 22 combinations. It also guarantees at least ten 4-wins if five of your numbers are drawn, and at least four 3-wins if three of your numbers are in the draw. The complete system would require 84 combinations. If all of the numbers are guessed correctly, you will either win the jackpot (plus some extra cash!), or you will get anywhere between four and eight 5-wins and a number of smaller prizes. The next table contains balance information.

Number(s)	Occurrences
9	16
2, 4, 6, 8	15
1, 3, 5, 7	14

1. 1 2 3 4 5 9
2. 1 2 3 4 6 8
3. 1 2 3 5 7 8
4. 1 2 3 6 7 9
5. 1 2 4 5 6 9
6. 1 2 4 5 7 9
7. 1 2 4 5 8 9
8. 1 2 4 6 7 8
9. 1 2 5 6 8 9
10. 1 3 4 5 6 7
11. 1 3 4 7 8 9
12. 1 3 5 6 8 9
13. 1 4 5 6 8 9
14. 1 5 6 7 8 9
15. 2 3 4 5 6 8
16. 2 3 4 6 7 9
17. 2 3 4 7 8 9
18. 2 3 5 6 7 9
19. 2 3 6 7 8 9
20. 2 4 5 6 7 8
21. 3 4 5 7 8 9
22. 3 4 6 7 8 9

System # 88: Guaranteed two 4–wins if 4 of the numbers drawn are in your set of 10 numbers ©Copyright 2001

Winning possibilities

Guessed	6	5	4	3	%
6	1	-	18	8	14.29
	-	4	12	12	85.71
5	-	1	6	16	71.43
	-	-	10	10	28.57
4	-	-	3	8	14.29
	-	-	2	12	85.71
3	-	-	-	5	100.00

The best single guarantee system (# 20) has 20 combinations. The system presented here gives you the double guarantee in just 30 combinations. It also guarantees ten 4-wins (plus ten 3-wins) if five of your numbers are drawn, five 3-wins if three of your numbers are in the draw, and four 5-wins plus a number of other prizes if all of the numbers drawn are guessed correctly. Of course, you can also win the jackpot plus some extra cash. The system is EXCEPTIONALLY HIGHLY BALANCED: Each number is in exactly 18 combinations; each pair of numbers is in exactly 10 combinations and each triple is in exactly 5 combinations. It is also MATHEMATICALLY MINIMAL for all of the above mentioned guarantees! This system even has an additional nice property: Every two combinations differ in at least two numbers, that is, the combinations are as 'apart' as possible. The complete system would require 210 combinations.

1. 1 2 3 4 5 10
2. 1 2 3 4 7 8
3. 1 2 3 5 6 8
4. 1 2 3 5 7 9
5. 1 2 3 6 9 10
6. 1 2 4 5 6 9
7. 1 2 4 6 7 10
8. 1 2 4 8 9 10
9. 1 2 5 7 8 10
10. 1 2 6 7 8 9
11. 1 3 4 5 6 7
12. 1 3 4 6 8 9
13. 1 3 4 7 9 10
14. 1 3 5 8 9 10
15. 1 3 6 7 8 10
16. 1 4 5 6 8 10
17. 1 4 5 7 8 9
18. 1 5 6 7 9 10
19. 2 3 4 5 8 9
20. 2 3 4 6 7 9
21. 2 3 4 6 8 10
22. 2 3 5 6 7 10
23. 2 3 7 8 9 10
24. 2 4 5 6 7 8
25. 2 4 5 7 9 10
26. 2 5 6 8 9 10
27. 3 4 5 6 9 10
28. 3 4 5 7 8 10
29. 3 5 6 7 8 9
30. 4 6 7 8 9 10

System # 89: Guaranteed two 4–wins if 4 of the numbers drawn are in your set of 11 numbers ©Copyright 2001

Winning possibilities

Guessed	6	5	4	3	%
6	1	-	24	18	11.90
	-	5	15	25	4.76
	-	5	14	28	23.81
	-	4	18	22	11.90
	-	4	17	25	23.81
	-	3	20	22	23.82
5	-	1	9	22	23.81
	-	1	8	25	23.81
	-	1	7	28	23.81
	-	-	12	18	11.90
	-	-	11	22	11.90
	-	-	10	25	4.77
4	-	-	3	16	16.67
	-	-	3	15	33.33
	-	-	2	18	50.00
3	-	-	-	7	66.67
	-	-	-	6	33.33

The best single guarantee system (# 21) has 32 combinations. The system presented here gives you the double guarantee in 55 combinations, that is, in just 1.72 times the number of the combinations needed for the single guarantee. It also guarantees ten 4-wins if five of your numbers are drawn, six 3-wins if three of your numbers are in the draw, and at least three 5-wins plus a number of other prizes if all of the numbers drawn are guessed correctly. Of course, you can also win the jackpot plus smaller prizes. The system is EXCEPTIONALLY HIGHLY BALANCED: Each number is in exactly 30 combinations and each pair of numbers is in exactly 15 combinations. This system has the same property as the preceding one: Every two combinations differ in at least two numbers, that is, the combinations are as 'apart' as possible. The complete system would require 462 combinations.

1.	1	2	3	4	6	10
2.	1	2	3	4	7	9
3.	1	2	3	5	6	7
4.	1	2	3	5	9	11
5.	1	2	3	6	8	11
6.	1	2	3	8	9	10
7.	1	2	4	5	6	11
8.	1	2	4	5	7	8
28.	1	5	6	8	9	11
29.	1	5	7	8	9	10
30.	1	6	7	8	10	11
31.	2	3	4	5	7	11
32.	2	3	4	5	8	10
33.	2	3	4	6	7	8
34.	2	3	4	9	10	11
35.	2	3	5	6	8	9

9.	1	2	4	5	9	10
10.	1	2	4	6	8	9
11.	1	2	4	8	10	11
12.	1	2	5	6	8	10
13.	1	2	5	7	10	11
14.	1	2	6	7	9	10
15.	1	2	7	8	9	11
16.	1	3	4	5	6	8
17.	1	3	4	5	10	11
18.	1	3	4	6	7	11
19.	1	3	4	7	8	10
20.	1	3	4	8	9	11
21.	1	3	5	6	9	10
22.	1	3	5	7	8	11
23.	1	3	6	7	8	9
24.	1	3	7	9	10	11
25.	1	4	5	6	7	10
26.	1	4	5	7	9	11
27.	1	4	6	9	10	11

36.	2	3	5	6	10	11
37.	2	3	5	7	9	10
38.	2	3	6	7	9	11
39.	2	3	7	8	10	11
40.	2	4	5	6	7	9
41.	2	4	5	8	9	11
42.	2	4	6	7	10	11
43.	2	4	7	8	9	10
44.	2	5	6	7	8	11
45.	2	6	8	9	10	11
46.	3	4	5	6	9	11
47.	3	4	5	7	8	9
48.	3	4	6	7	9	10
49.	3	4	6	8	10	11
50.	3	5	6	7	8	10
51.	3	5	8	9	10	11
52.	4	5	6	8	9	10
53.	4	5	7	8	10	11
54.	4	6	7	8	9	11
55.	5	6	7	9	10	11

SYSTEM # 90: GUARANTEED TWO 4–WINS IF 4 OF THE NUMBERS DRAWN ARE IN YOUR SET OF 12 NUMBERS ©Copyright 2001

Winning possibilities

Guessed	6	5	4	3	%
6	1	4	18-19	32-34	0.76
	1	3	16-20	32-37	0.65
	1	2	15-21	30-40	2.60
	1	1	16-17	42-43	0.22
	1	-	16-25	26-45	4.11
	-	6	17-18	32-34	1.08
	-	5	12-19	31-41	3.57
	-	4	11-20	30-47	28.35
	-	3	15-24	24-41	35.39
	-	2	20-25	24-34	22.84
	-	-	31-33	13-15	0.43
5	-	3	6-7	30-31	0.38
	-	2	5-9	27-32	4.92
	-	1	5-11	25-37	47.35
	-	-	10-13	23-32	47.35
4	-	-	8	1	0.20
	-	-	6-7	10-12	0.81
	-	-	3-5	10-22	16.56
	-	-	2	16-24	82.43
3	-	-	-	10	0.91
	-	-	-	9	7.27
	-	-	-	8	24.55
	-	-	-	7	25.45
	-	-	-	6	41.82

The best single guarantee system (# 22) has 41 combinations. The system presented here gives you the double guarantee in just 77 combinations. It also guarantees ten 4-wins if five of your numbers are drawn and six 3-wins if three of your numbers are in the draw. If all of the numbers drawn are guessed correctly, then there are 99.57% chances that you will get at least two 5-wins plus a number of other prizes. Of course, you can also win the jackpot (plus extra cash). The complete system would require 924 combinations. The next table contains information on the balance of the system.

Number(s)	Occurrences
10,11	40
1, 2, 6, 8, 9,12	39
5	38
3, 7	37
4	36

1.	1	2	3	4	5	7
2.	1	2	3	4	9	12
3.	1	2	3	5	6	8
4.	1	2	3	5	6	9
5.	1	2	3	5	8	11
6.	1	2	3	5	10	12
7.	1	2	3	7	10	11
8.	1	2	4	5	10	11
9.	1	2	4	6	7	8
10.	1	2	4	6	7	9
11.	1	2	4	7	8	11
12.	1	2	4	7	10	12
13.	1	2	5	7	9	12
14.	1	2	6	8	9	10
15.	1	2	6	8	11	12
16.	1	2	6	9	10	11
17.	1	2	6	9	11	12
18.	1	2	8	9	10	12
19.	1	3	4	5	7	8
20.	1	3	4	6	8	10
21.	1	3	4	6	11	12
22.	1	3	4	9	10	11
23.	1	3	5	8	9	10
24.	1	3	5	8	11	12
25.	1	3	6	7	9	11
26.	1	3	6	7	10	12
27.	1	3	7	8	9	12
28.	1	4	5	6	9	11
29.	1	4	5	6	10	12
30.	1	4	5	8	9	12
31.	1	4	7	8	9	10
32.	1	4	7	8	11	12
33.	1	5	6	7	8	10
34.	1	5	6	7	11	12
35.	1	5	7	9	10	11
36.	1	5	8	10	11	12
37.	1	6	8	9	10	11
38.	1	6	8	9	11	12
39.	1	6	9	10	11	12
40.	2	3	4	5	6	7
41.	2	3	4	6	10	11
42.	2	3	4	8	9	11
43.	2	3	4	8	10	12
44.	2	3	5	6	9	10
45.	2	3	5	6	11	12
46.	2	3	5	7	10	11
47.	2	3	6	7	8	12
48.	2	3	7	8	9	10
49.	2	3	7	9	11	12
50.	2	4	5	6	8	12
51.	2	4	5	8	9	10
52.	2	4	5	9	11	12
53.	2	4	6	7	9	10
54.	2	4	6	7	11	12
55.	2	5	6	7	10	11
56.	2	5	7	8	9	11
57.	2	5	7	8	10	12
58.	2	6	8	9	10	12
59.	2	6	8	10	11	12
60.	2	8	9	10	11	12
61.	3	4	5	6	7	9
62.	3	4	5	7	8	11
63.	3	4	5	7	9	10
64.	3	4	5	7	10	12
65.	3	4	5	7	11	12
66.	3	4	6	8	9	12
67.	3	5	6	8	9	11
68.	3	5	6	9	10	12
69.	3	5	8	10	11	12
70.	3	5	9	10	11	12
71.	3	6	7	8	10	11
72.	4	5	6	8	10	11
73.	4	6	7	8	9	11
74.	4	6	7	9	10	12
75.	4	7	8	10	11	12
76.	4	7	9	10	11	12
77.	5	6	7	8	9	12

SYSTEM # 91: GUARANTEED TWO 4–WINS IF 4 OF THE NUMBERS DRAWN ARE IN YOUR SET OF 13 NUMBERS ©Copyright 2001

Winning possibilities

Guessed	6	5	4	3	%
6	1	4	15	59	0.06
	1	3	19-20	52-53	0.12
	1	2	16-23	48-60	0.70
	1	1	19-26	44-57	2.45
	1	-	20-28	43-60	3.67
	-	7	13	57	0.06
	-	6	14-19	45-57	0.58
	-	5	14-22	44-62	4.37
	-	4	15-25	40-62	24.83
	-	3	15-27	38-61	40.50
	-	2	21-30	36-55	20.05
	-	1	25-33	34-48	2.61
5	-	3	5	43	0.08
	-	2	4-10	33-48	2.72
	-	1	5-12	30-51	50.27
	-	-	10-17	26-45	46.93
4	-	-	6	14	0.14
	-	-	5	13-19	1.54
	-	-	4	17-24	10.35
	-	-	3	19-26	25.87
	-	-	2	21-30	62.10
3	-	-	-	11	0.70
	-	-	-	10	11.19
	-	-	-	9	30.07
	-	-	-	8	42.66
	-	-	-	7	15.38

The best single guarantee system (# 23) has 66 combinations. The system presented here gives you the double guarantee in 120 combinations. It also guarantees at least ten 4-wins if five of your numbers are drawn and at least seven 3-wins if three of your numbers are in the draw. If all of the numbers are guessed correctly, you will either win the jackpot (plus additional prizes), or you will get anywhere between one and seven 5-wins (97.39% chances for two or more 5-wins) and a number of other prizes. The complete system would require 1,716 combinations. Information on the balance of the system is given in the next table.

Number(s)	Occurrences
6,12	57
2, 4, 7, 9	56
1, 5, 8,11	55
3,10,13	54

1.	1	2	3	4	5	12
2.	1	2	3	4	6	10
3.	1	2	3	4	7	9
4.	1	2	3	4	8	13
5.	1	2	3	5	6	12
6.	1	2	3	5	11	13
7.	1	2	3	6	7	11
8.	1	2	3	6	9	13
9.	1	2	3	8	10	12
10.	1	2	4	5	9	11
11.	1	2	4	6	7	13
12.	1	2	4	7	11	12
13.	1	2	4	8	10	11
14.	1	2	5	6	8	12
15.	1	2	5	6	9	11
16.	1	2	5	7	8	13
17.	1	2	5	7	10	11
18.	1	2	5	9	10	13
19.	1	2	6	8	9	10
20.	1	2	7	8	9	12
21.	1	2	7	10	12	13
22.	1	2	8	9	11	13
23.	1	2	9	11	12	13
24.	1	3	4	5	7	8
25.	1	3	4	5	9	10
26.	1	3	4	6	8	9
27.	1	3	4	7	11	13
28.	1	3	4	9	11	12
29.	1	3	5	6	7	12
30.	1	3	5	8	10	11
31.	1	3	5	9	12	13
32.	1	3	6	7	10	13
33.	1	3	6	8	11	12
34.	1	3	7	8	9	12
35.	1	3	7	9	10	11
36.	1	3	8	10	12	13
37.	1	4	5	6	10	11
38.	1	4	5	6	12	13
39.	1	4	5	7	8	9
40.	1	4	5	8	9	13

61.	2	3	4	8	9	11
62.	2	3	4	11	12	13
63.	2	3	5	6	8	12
64.	2	3	5	6	10	11
65.	2	3	5	7	8	9
66.	2	3	6	7	8	13
67.	2	3	7	8	11	12
68.	2	3	7	9	12	13
69.	2	3	8	9	10	13
70.	2	3	9	10	11	12
71.	2	4	5	6	7	13
72.	2	4	5	6	8	11
73.	2	4	5	8	10	12
74.	2	4	6	7	11	12
75.	2	4	6	9	10	12
76.	2	4	7	8	9	10
77.	2	4	7	9	11	13
78.	2	4	7	10	11	13
79.	2	4	8	9	12	13
80.	2	5	6	7	10	12
81.	2	5	6	9	12	13
82.	2	5	7	9	11	12
83.	2	5	8	9	10	11
84.	2	5	8	11	12	13
85.	2	6	7	8	9	11
86.	2	6	7	9	10	12
87.	2	6	8	10	11	13
88.	2	6	10	11	12	13
89.	3	4	5	6	7	13
90.	3	4	5	7	11	12
91.	3	4	5	8	9	12
92.	3	4	5	10	11	12
93.	3	4	6	7	8	12
94.	3	4	6	8	10	12
95.	3	4	6	10	11	13
96.	3	4	7	8	9	13
97.	3	4	9	10	12	13
98.	3	5	6	7	9	11
99.	3	5	6	8	9	10
100.	3	5	6	8	12	13

41. 1 4 6 7 10 12
42. 1 4 6 8 9 12
43. 1 4 6 8 11 13
44. 1 4 7 9 10 13
45. 1 4 8 10 12 13
46. 1 5 6 7 8 10
47. 1 5 6 7 9 13
48. 1 5 6 9 10 12
49. 1 5 7 8 11 12
50. 1 5 10 11 12 13
51. 1 6 7 8 9 13
52. 1 6 7 11 12 13
53. 1 6 9 10 11 13
54. 1 7 8 9 10 11
55. 1 7 9 10 11 12
56. 2 3 4 5 6 9
57. 2 3 4 5 7 10
58. 2 3 4 5 10 13
59. 2 3 4 6 8 11
60. 2 3 4 7 8 10

101. 3 5 7 10 12 13
102. 3 5 8 9 11 13
103. 3 6 7 9 10 12
104. 3 6 9 11 12 13
105. 3 7 8 10 11 13
106. 4 5 6 7 8 11
107. 4 5 6 8 10 13
108. 4 5 6 9 11 13
109. 4 5 6 11 12 13
110. 4 5 7 9 10 12
111. 4 6 7 9 10 11
112. 4 6 7 9 12 13
113. 4 7 8 11 12 13
114. 4 8 9 10 11 12
115. 5 6 7 10 11 13
116. 5 6 8 9 11 12
117. 5 7 8 10 12 13
118. 5 7 9 10 11 13
119. 6 7 8 10 11 12
120. 6 8 9 10 12 13

System # 92: Guaranteed two 4–wins if 4 of the numbers drawn are in your set of 16 numbers ©Copyright 2001

Winning possibilities

Guessed	6	5	4	3	%
6	1	-	23	88	1.50
	1	-	21	96	2.00
	-	3	21	86	35.96
	-	2	26	76	3.00
	-	2	25	80	5.99
	-	2	24	84	17.98
	-	2	23	88	17.98
	-	1	28	78	11.99
	-	-	40	40	0.60
	-	-	32	72	3.00
5	-	1	9	54	5.49
	-	1	7	62	32.97
	-	-	14	44	5.49
	-	-	11	56	43.96
	-	-	10	60	12.09
4	-	-	6	16	1.10
	-	-	3	28	26.37
	-	-	2	32	72.53
3	-	-	-	10	100.00

The best single guarantee system (# 26) has 152 combinations. The system presented here gives you the double guarantee in 280 combinations. It also guarantees at least ten 4-wins if five of your numbers are drawn and ten 3-wins if three of your numbers are in the draw. If all of the numbers are guessed correctly, you will either win the jackpot (plus some extra cash), or you will get up to three 5-wins and a number of other prizes. The system is EXCEPTIONALLY HIGHLY BALANCED: Each number is in exactly 105 combinations; each pair of numbers is in exactly 35 combinations and each triple is in exactly 10 combinations. It also has an additional nice property: Every two combinations differ in at least two numbers, that is, the combinations are as 'apart' as possible. The complete system would require 8,008 combinations.

1.	1	2	3	4	5	6
2.	1	2	3	4	13	16
3.	1	2	3	5	14	16
4.	1	2	3	6	15	16
5.	1	2	3	7	8	9
6.	1	2	3	7	12	16
141.	2	4	6	11	12	15
142.	2	4	7	8	9	16
143.	2	4	7	8	12	15
144.	2	4	9	12	15	16
145.	2	4	10	11	13	14
146.	2	4	10	11	15	16

7.	1	2	3	8	10	16
8.	1	2	3	9	11	16
9.	1	2	3	10	11	12
10.	1	2	3	13	14	15
11.	1	2	4	5	8	11
12.	1	2	4	5	9	12
13.	1	2	4	6	10	13
14.	1	2	4	7	9	14
15.	1	2	4	7	10	11
16.	1	2	4	8	13	15
17.	1	2	4	8	14	16
18.	1	2	4	12	14	15
19.	1	2	5	6	7	13
20.	1	2	5	6	8	14
21.	1	2	5	7	9	15
22.	1	2	5	10	13	16
23.	1	2	5	10	14	15
24.	1	2	5	11	12	13
25.	1	2	6	7	8	12
26.	1	2	6	8	10	15
27.	1	2	6	9	10	11
28.	1	2	6	9	12	16
29.	1	2	6	11	12	14
30.	1	2	7	10	12	15
31.	1	2	7	11	13	14
32.	1	2	7	11	15	16
33.	1	2	8	9	11	15
34.	1	2	8	9	12	13
35.	1	2	9	10	13	14
36.	1	3	4	5	7	13
37.	1	3	4	5	9	15
38.	1	3	4	6	7	10
39.	1	3	4	6	8	11
40.	1	3	4	8	9	14
41.	1	3	4	10	11	15
42.	1	3	4	12	13	14
43.	1	3	4	12	15	16
44.	1	3	5	6	12	15
45.	1	3	5	7	9	11
46.	1	3	5	7	12	14
47.	1	3	5	8	10	12
48.	1	3	5	8	11	16
49.	1	3	5	10	11	13
50.	1	3	6	7	13	16
51.	1	3	6	7	14	15
52.	1	3	6	8	9	13
147.	2	4	12	13	14	16
148.	2	5	6	8	9	11
149.	2	5	6	10	11	15
150.	2	5	6	12	13	14
151.	2	5	6	12	15	16
152.	2	5	7	8	10	11
153.	2	5	7	9	10	12
154.	2	5	7	9	11	16
155.	2	5	7	12	14	16
156.	2	5	8	10	12	16
157.	2	5	8	11	13	14
158.	2	5	8	11	15	16
159.	2	6	7	9	13	15
160.	2	6	7	10	12	13
161.	2	6	7	11	13	16
162.	2	6	7	14	15	16
163.	2	6	8	9	13	16
164.	2	6	8	9	14	15
165.	2	6	9	10	14	16
166.	2	7	8	10	13	15
167.	2	7	8	10	14	16
168.	2	7	8	11	12	14
169.	2	8	9	10	12	14
170.	2	8	13	14	15	16
171.	2	9	10	11	14	15
172.	2	9	10	13	15	16
173.	2	9	11	12	13	15
174.	2	9	11	12	14	16
175.	2	10	11	12	13	16
176.	3	4	5	6	11	16
177.	3	4	5	7	8	12
178.	3	4	5	8	14	15
179.	3	4	5	9	10	11
180.	3	4	5	9	12	16
181.	3	4	5	10	12	13
182.	3	4	6	7	9	12
183.	3	4	6	10	13	16
184.	3	4	6	10	14	15
185.	3	4	6	11	12	13
186.	3	4	7	8	13	14
187.	3	4	7	9	13	15
188.	3	4	7	9	14	16
189.	3	4	7	11	15	16
190.	3	4	8	10	11	14
191.	3	4	8	12	14	16
192.	3	4	8	13	15	16

53.	1	3	6	9	10	12
54.	1	3	6	11	13	14
55.	1	3	7	8	10	14
56.	1	3	7	8	11	15
57.	1	3	8	12	13	15
58.	1	3	9	10	13	15
59.	1	3	9	10	14	16
60.	1	3	9	11	12	14
61.	1	4	5	6	12	16
62.	1	4	5	7	8	10
63.	1	4	5	10	12	14
64.	1	4	5	11	13	15
65.	1	4	5	11	14	16
66.	1	4	6	7	8	15
67.	1	4	6	8	12	13
68.	1	4	6	9	13	14
69.	1	4	6	9	15	16
70.	1	4	6	11	14	15
71.	1	4	7	9	10	12
72.	1	4	7	10	13	15
73.	1	4	7	10	14	16
74.	1	4	7	11	12	16
75.	1	4	8	9	10	16
76.	1	4	8	9	11	12
77.	1	4	9	11	13	16
78.	1	5	6	7	10	16
79.	1	5	6	7	11	12
80.	1	5	6	8	9	10
81.	1	5	6	9	13	15
82.	1	5	6	10	11	14
83.	1	5	7	8	13	14
84.	1	5	7	8	15	16
85.	1	5	8	9	14	15
86.	1	5	8	12	13	16
87.	1	5	9	10	15	16
88.	1	5	9	11	12	15
89.	1	5	9	13	14	16
90.	1	6	7	8	9	16
91.	1	6	7	9	11	14
92.	1	6	8	11	14	16
93.	1	6	10	12	13	15
94.	1	6	10	12	14	16
95.	1	6	11	13	15	16
96.	1	7	8	11	12	13
97.	1	7	9	10	11	13
98.	1	7	9	12	13	16
193.	3	5	6	7	9	14
194.	3	5	6	7	11	15
195.	3	5	6	8	13	15
196.	3	5	6	8	14	16
197.	3	5	6	10	13	14
198.	3	5	7	8	9	16
199.	3	5	7	10	13	16
200.	3	5	8	9	10	13
201.	3	5	10	14	15	16
202.	3	5	11	12	13	16
203.	3	5	11	12	14	15
204.	3	6	7	8	10	11
205.	3	6	7	8	12	16
206.	3	6	8	9	11	12
207.	3	6	8	10	15	16
208.	3	6	9	10	11	16
209.	3	6	9	12	13	16
210.	3	6	9	12	14	15
211.	3	7	9	10	11	15
212.	3	7	10	12	13	14
213.	3	7	10	12	15	16
214.	3	7	11	12	13	15
215.	3	7	11	13	14	16
216.	3	8	9	10	12	15
217.	3	8	9	11	13	14
218.	3	8	9	11	15	16
219.	3	9	13	14	15	16
220.	3	10	11	12	14	16
221.	4	5	6	7	8	9
222.	4	5	6	7	15	16
223.	4	5	6	8	13	16
224.	4	5	6	9	14	16
225.	4	5	6	10	11	12
226.	4	5	6	13	14	15
227.	4	5	7	9	10	15
228.	4	5	7	9	11	13
229.	4	5	7	11	12	14
230.	4	5	8	10	13	14
231.	4	5	8	10	15	16
232.	4	5	8	11	12	15
233.	4	6	7	10	11	14
234.	4	6	7	12	13	15
235.	4	6	7	12	14	16
236.	4	6	8	9	10	15
237.	4	6	8	9	12	14
238.	4	6	9	10	11	13

99.	1	7	9	12	14	15
100.	1	7	13	14	15	16
101.	1	8	10	11	13	16
102.	1	8	10	11	14	15
103.	1	8	10	12	13	14
104.	1	8	12	14	15	16
105.	1	10	11	12	15	16
106.	2	3	4	5	11	14
107.	2	3	4	6	8	14
108.	2	3	4	6	9	15
109.	2	3	4	7	10	16
110.	2	3	4	7	11	12
111.	2	3	4	8	9	10
112.	2	3	4	9	11	13
113.	2	3	4	10	12	15
114.	2	3	5	6	7	10
115.	2	3	5	6	9	12
116.	2	3	5	7	8	15
117.	2	3	5	8	11	12
118.	2	3	5	9	13	14
119.	2	3	5	9	15	16
120.	2	3	5	10	13	15
121.	2	3	6	7	8	13
122.	2	3	6	10	12	14
123.	2	3	6	11	13	15
124.	2	3	6	11	14	16
125.	2	3	7	9	10	14
126.	2	3	7	9	12	13
127.	2	3	7	11	14	15
128.	2	3	8	10	11	13
129.	2	3	8	12	13	16
130.	2	3	8	12	14	15
131.	2	4	5	6	10	16
132.	2	4	5	7	13	16
133.	2	4	5	7	14	15
134.	2	4	5	8	9	13
135.	2	4	5	9	10	14
136.	2	4	5	12	13	15
137.	2	4	6	7	9	11
138.	2	4	6	7	13	14
139.	2	4	6	8	10	12
140.	2	4	6	8	11	16
239.	4	7	8	10	12	13
240.	4	7	8	11	13	16
241.	4	7	8	11	14	15
242.	4	8	9	11	13	15
243.	4	8	10	11	12	16
244.	4	9	10	12	13	16
245.	4	9	10	12	14	15
246.	4	9	11	12	13	14
247.	4	9	11	14	15	16
248.	4	10	13	14	15	16
249.	5	6	7	8	11	13
250.	5	6	7	8	12	14
251.	5	6	8	10	12	15
252.	5	6	9	10	12	13
253.	5	6	9	11	13	16
254.	5	6	9	11	14	15
255.	5	7	9	12	13	14
256.	5	7	10	11	13	15
257.	5	7	10	11	14	16
258.	5	7	10	12	14	15
259.	5	7	12	13	15	16
260.	5	8	9	10	11	14
261.	5	8	9	12	13	15
262.	5	8	9	12	14	16
263.	5	9	10	11	12	16
264.	5	11	13	14	15	16
265.	6	7	8	10	14	15
266.	6	7	9	10	13	14
267.	6	7	9	10	15	16
268.	6	7	9	11	12	15
269.	6	7	10	11	12	16
270.	6	8	10	11	13	15
271.	6	8	10	13	14	16
272.	6	8	11	12	13	14
273.	6	8	11	12	15	16
274.	6	12	13	14	15	16
275.	7	8	9	10	11	12
276.	7	8	9	10	13	16
277.	7	8	9	11	14	16
278.	7	8	9	12	15	16
279.	7	8	9	13	14	15
280.	10	11	12	13	14	15

DOUBLE GUARANTEES: LOTTERY SYSTEMS WITH TWO 4-WINS GUARANTEED IF 5 OF YOUR NUMBERS ARE DRAWN

You will notice that there is no system with 12 numbers in this section. However, there is a good reason for that: A better system on 12 numbers is included earlier in the book: System # 19 (12 numbers) has 22 combinations (much less than 28, which is twice the number of combinations needed for the single guarantee) and guarantees you not two but three(!) 4-wins if 5 of your numbers are drawn.

SYSTEM # 93: GUARANTEED TWO 4–WINS IF 5 OF THE NUMBERS DRAWN ARE IN YOUR SET OF 10 NUMBERS ©Copyright 2001

Winning possibilities

Guessed	**6**	**5**	**4**	**3**	%
6	1	4	-	-	4.76
	-	2	3	4	47.62
	-	-	6	4	47.62
5	-	5	-	-	0.79
	-	1	4	-	19.84
	-	-	2	6	79.37
4	-	-	5	-	4.76
	-	-	1	4	47.62
	-	-	-	4	47.62
3	-	-	-	5	16.67
	-	-	-	1	83.33

This system has the same basic guarantees as system # 65, namely, two 4-wins if 5 numbers are guessed correctly, and also a 3-win if three of your numbers are drawn. However, in spite of the identical main guarantees, the two systems have different structure, and therefore, different tables of wins. For example, the above system can bring you five 4-wins if 5 of your numbers are drawn, or five 3-wins if three of your numbers are drawn, which is not the case with system # 65. However, system # 65 can bring you two or three 4-wins if 5 of your numbers are drawn in a number of cases where the above system will only bring you one 4-win. Similar situation occurs with the 3 if 3 guarantee. Some further differences can be established by comparing the tables of wins. This system is HIGHLY BALANCED: Each number is in exactly

6 combinations. You can choose one of the two systems according to your personal preferences. The single 4 on 5 guarantee can be achieved in 7 combinations (system # 31). The complete system would require 210 combinations.

1.	1	2	3	5	7	9	6.	1	3	5	7	9	10
2.	1	2	4	6	8	10	7.	2	3	4	6	8	10
3.	1	3	4	5	7	9	8.	2	4	5	6	8	10
4.	1	3	5	6	7	9	9.	2	4	6	7	8	10
5.	1	3	5	7	8	9	10.	2	4	6	8	9	10

System # 94: Guaranteed two 4–wins if 5 of the numbers drawn are in your set of 11 numbers ©Copyright 2001

Winning possibilities

Guessed	6	5	4	3	%
6	1	1	1	12	0.43
	1	-	3-6	6-11	3.25
	-	3	3-4	5-8	1.52
	-	2	2-6	4-11	27.11
	-	1	4-8	3-10	50.00
	-	-	7-10	3-8	17.09
5	-	2	-	6	0.22
	-	1	1-3	4-10	21.64
	-	-	5	3-6	5.84
	-	-	4	3-7	19.26
	-	-	3	6-9	31.17
	-	-	2	8-12	21.87
4	-	-	3	2	0.30
	-	-	2	1-5	11.21
	-	-	1	3-7	53.94
	-	-	-	5-8	34.55
3	-	-	-	5	0.61
	-	-	-	3	27.27
	-	-	-	2	50.30
	-	-	-	1	20.61
	-	-	-	-	1.21

The best single guarantee system (# 32) has 10 combinations. The system presented here gives you the double guarantee in just 17 combinations, that is, in only 1.7 times the number of the combinations needed for the single guarantee system. The complete system would require 462 combinations. If all of the numbers are guessed correctly, you will either win the jackpot (plus some extra cash!), or you will get up to three 5-wins and a number of other prizes. The system is well balanced: Each number is in either 9 or 10 combinations as seen from the table below.

Number(s)	Occurrences
3, 4, 7	10
1, 2, 5, 6, 8, 9,10,11	9

1. 1 2 3 5 8 10
2. 1 2 4 5 10 11

9. 1 5 6 7 9 10
10. 2 3 4 5 7 8

3. 1 2 6 7 8 11
4. 1 2 7 8 9 11
5. 1 3 4 6 7 8
6. 1 3 4 7 9 11
7. 1 3 5 6 9 11
8. 1 4 6 8 9 10

11. 2 3 4 6 7 9
12. 2 3 4 7 10 11
13. 2 3 6 8 9 10
14. 2 4 5 6 9 11
15. 3 4 5 8 10 11
16. 3 5 6 7 10 11
17. 4 5 7 8 9 10

System # 95: Guaranteed two 4–wins if 5 of the numbers drawn are in your set of 13 numbers ©Copyright 2001

Winning possibilities

Guessed	6	5	4	3	%
6	1	-	-	18	1.52
	-	1	5	8	9.09
	-	1	4	11	36.36
	-	1	3	14	9.09
	-	1	3	13	9.09
	-	-	7	8	22.73
	-	-	6	11	12.12
5	-	1	-	9	12.12
	-	-	4	4	3.03
	-	-	3	7	24.24
	-	-	3	6	6.06
	-	-	2	10	30.30
	-	-	2	9	24.25
4	-	-	1	4	32.73
	-	-	1	3	21.82
	-	-	-	8	5.45
	-	-	-	7	29.09
	-	-	-	6	10.91
3	-	-	-	2	81.82
	-	-	-	1	18.18

This system gives a considerable improvement over the single guarantee system (# 34, 21 combinations). Here you get the double guarantee in just 26 combinations, that is, in only 1.24 times the number of the combinations needed for the best single guarantee system. You are also guaranteed to have at least one 3-win if three of your numbers are drawn. The complete system would require 1,716 combinations. If all of the numbers drawn are guessed correctly, you will either win the jackpot (plus some extra cash!), or you will get a 5-win and a number of other prizes, or at least six 4-wins and a number of 3-wins. The system is EXCEPTIONALLY HIGHLY BALANCED: Each number is in exactly 12 combinations and each pair of numbers is in exactly 5 combinations. Also, the combinations of the system are maximally 'apart': Every two combinations differ in at least three numbers.

1.	1	2	3	4	5	13
2.	1	2	3	8	9	11
3.	1	2	4	6	10	11
4.	1	2	5	9	10	12
5.	1	2	6	7	8	13
14.	2	3	6	11	12	13
15.	2	3	7	8	10	12
16.	2	4	5	7	11	12
17.	2	4	6	8	9	12
18.	2	4	7	9	10	13

6.	1	3	4	6	7	12
7.	1	3	5	7	10	11
8.	1	3	6	9	10	13
9.	1	4	5	7	8	9
10.	1	4	8	10	12	13
11.	1	5	6	8	11	12
12.	1	7	9	11	12	13
13.	2	3	5	6	7	9
19.	2	5	8	10	11	13
20.	3	4	5	6	8	10
21.	3	4	7	8	11	13
22.	3	4	9	10	11	12
23.	3	5	8	9	12	13
24.	4	5	6	9	11	13
25.	5	6	7	10	12	13
26.	6	7	8	9	10	11

SYSTEM # 96: GUARANTEED TWO 4–WINS IF 5 OF THE NUMBERS DRAWN ARE IN YOUR SET OF 14 NUMBERS

Winning possibilities

Guessed	6	5	4	3	%
6	1	-	2-5	21-27	1.63
	-	2	1-7	14-25	10.26
	-	1	4-9	12-25	57.81
	-	-	12	12	0.47
	-	-	11	11-12	0.94
	-	-	10	13-16	3.74
	-	-	9	15-19	12.60
	-	-	8	17-20	11.20
	-	-	7	20-21	1.35
5	-	1	2	12-14	4.20
	-	1	1	12-16	6.99
	-	1	-	15-17	3.50
	-	-	6	8	0.70
	-	-	5	8-11	4.90
	-	-	4	10-14	25.17
	-	-	3	12-17	39.86
	-	-	2	14-18	14.68
4	-	-	2	4-6	7.69
	-	-	1	5-9	58.04
	-	-	-	8-12	34.27
3	-	-	-	4	7.69
	-	-	-	3	53.85
	-	-	-	2	38.46

The best single guarantee system (# 35) has 31 combinations. The above system gives you the double guarantee in just 49 combinations, that is, in only 1.58 times the number of combinations needed for the single guarantee system. The complete system would require 3,003 combinations. Aside from the main guarantee, the system also guarantees at least two 3-wins if 3 of your numbers are drawn. If all of the numbers are guessed correctly, you will either win the jackpot (plus some extra cash!), or you will get up to two 5-wins and a number of other prizes. Every two combinations of the system differ in at least two numbers. The system is also HIGHLY BALANCED: Each number is in exactly 21 combinations.

1.	1	2	3	4	5	9
2.	1	2	3	4	8	14
3.	1	2	3	6	7	9
4.	1	2	3	7	13	14
25.	2	3	6	8	9	12
26.	2	3	6	10	11	14
27.	2	4	5	8	12	13
28.	2	4	6	9	11	13

5.	1	2	4	10	11	12
6.	1	2	5	6	8	14
7.	1	2	5	7	8	11
8.	1	2	5	9	10	13
9.	1	2	6	12	13	14
10.	1	3	4	7	11	12
11.	1	3	5	8	10	12
12.	1	3	6	8	10	13
13.	1	3	9	10	11	14
14.	1	4	5	7	13	14
15.	1	4	6	7	10	14
16.	1	4	6	8	11	13
17.	1	4	8	9	12	14
18.	1	5	6	9	11	12
19.	1	5	11	12	13	14
20.	1	7	8	9	10	11
21.	1	7	8	9	12	13
22.	2	3	4	5	6	10
23.	2	3	4	7	8	10
24.	2	3	5	11	12	13

29.	2	4	7	9	11	14
30.	2	5	7	9	12	14
31.	2	6	7	10	12	13
32.	2	8	9	10	11	12
33.	2	8	9	10	13	14
34.	3	4	5	6	7	11
35.	3	4	5	8	9	11
36.	3	4	6	12	13	14
37.	3	4	7	9	10	13
38.	3	5	6	9	13	14
39.	3	5	7	10	12	14
40.	3	7	8	11	13	14
41.	3	9	10	11	12	13
42.	4	5	6	7	8	12
43.	4	5	6	9	10	12
44.	4	5	8	10	11	14
45.	4	10	11	12	13	14
46.	5	6	7	8	9	13
47.	5	6	7	10	11	13
48.	6	7	8	9	10	14
49.	6	7	8	11	12	14

System # 97: Guaranteed two 4–wins if 5 of the numbers drawn are in your set of 15 numbers ©Copyright 2001

Winning possibilities

Guessed	6	5	4	3	%
6	1	1	2-7	22-26	0.16
	1	-	3-10	16-30	1.28
	-	3	2-9	14-31	1.04
	-	2	1-10	16-34	14.31
	-	1	3-12	13-34	45.79
	-	-	6-15	12-33	37.42
5	-	2	0-2	12-15	0.13
	-	1	1-5	10-22	14.12
	-	-	6-7	9-16	2.62
	-	-	5	10-19	10.92
	-	-	4	12-22	25.46
	-	-	3	14-23	29.39
	-	-	2	17-24	17.36
4	-	-	3	3-6	0.81
	-	-	2	3-11	14.07
	-	-	1	5-14	48.57
	-	-	-	8-16	36.55
3	-	-	-	5-6	5.93
	-	-	-	2-4	92.30
	-	-	-	1	1.77

The best single guarantee system (# 36) has 41 combinations. The above system gives you the double guarantee in just 72 combinations, that is, in 1.76 times the number of combinations needed for the single guarantee. The complete system would require 5,005 combinations. If all of the numbers are guessed correctly, you will either win the jackpot (plus some extra cash!), or you will get up to three 5-wins and a number of other prizes. Information on the balance of the system is given in the table below.

Number(s)	Occurrences
5, 9,12	30
2, 3, 6, 7, 8,14	29
1, 4,10,11,13,15	28

1. 1 2 3 4 6 15
2. 1 2 3 5 6 9

37. 2 4 7 9 10 15
38. 2 4 8 9 11 13

3.	1	2	3	9	11	12	39.	2	5	6	8	11	14
4.	1	2	3	10	14	15	40.	2	5	6	9	13	14
5.	1	2	4	7	8	13	41.	2	5	12	13	14	15
6.	1	2	4	8	9	14	42.	2	6	7	8	9	15
7.	1	2	5	7	10	11	43.	2	6	7	11	12	14
8.	1	2	5	7	13	14	44.	2	6	8	10	11	13
9.	1	2	5	8	10	12	45.	2	6	9	10	11	13
10.	1	2	5	11	12	15	46.	2	8	10	12	13	14
11.	1	2	7	11	14	15	47.	3	4	5	6	8	14
12.	1	3	4	5	7	14	48.	3	4	5	10	12	13
13.	1	3	4	6	7	11	49.	3	4	6	9	10	11
14.	1	3	4	7	9	12	50.	3	4	9	12	14	15
15.	1	3	4	10	13	15	51.	3	5	6	7	10	12
16.	1	3	5	11	13	14	52.	3	5	6	9	10	14
17.	1	3	7	8	11	12	53.	3	5	7	11	13	15
18.	1	4	5	9	12	14	54.	3	5	9	11	12	15
19.	1	4	6	11	12	13	55.	3	6	7	8	10	13
20.	1	4	8	9	10	11	56.	3	6	8	11	13	15
21.	1	5	6	8	9	12	57.	3	6	8	12	14	15
22.	1	5	6	8	10	15	58.	3	7	8	9	10	14
23.	1	5	8	9	13	15	59.	3	7	9	10	12	13
24.	1	6	7	10	13	14	60.	4	5	6	7	9	12
25.	1	6	9	12	13	15	61.	4	5	6	8	9	13
26.	1	6	10	12	14	15	62.	4	5	7	10	11	15
27.	1	7	9	10	13	15	63.	4	6	7	8	13	14
28.	1	8	9	11	13	14	64.	4	7	8	12	14	15
29.	2	3	4	5	8	11	65.	4	8	10	11	12	15
30.	2	3	4	8	12	13	66.	4	9	11	13	14	15
31.	2	3	5	10	11	14	67.	4	10	11	12	13	14
32.	2	3	7	8	9	15	68.	5	6	7	12	13	15
33.	2	3	7	12	13	14	69.	5	7	8	9	11	12
34.	2	3	9	12	14	15	70.	5	7	8	10	14	15
35.	2	4	5	6	10	15	71.	5	8	9	10	11	12
36.	2	4	6	7	10	12	72.	6	7	9	11	14	15

Double Guarantees: Lottery systems with two 4-wins guaranteed if 6 of your numbers are drawn

System # 98: Guaranteed two 4–wins if 6 of the numbers drawn are in your set of 11 numbers ©Copyright 2001

Winning possibilities

Guessed	**6**	**5**	**4**	**3**	%
6	1	1	-	3-4	0.43
	1	-	1-2	2-4	1.08
	-	2	0-2	0-3	4.55
	-	1	1-4	0-5	35.93
	-	-	4-5	0-2	7.15
	-	-	2-3	2-5	50.86
5	-	2	-	2	0.22
	-	1	1	0-3	4.76
	-	1	-	2-4	3.90
	-	-	4	-	0.43
	-	-	3	0-2	5.41
	-	-	2	0-3	23.38
	-	-	1	2-4	44.16
	-	-	-	4-5	17.74
4	-	-	2	0-2	2.42
	-	-	1	0-3	26.97
	-	-	-	1-4	70.61
3	-	-	-	3	1.82
	-	-	-	2	15.15
	-	-	-	1	49.09
	-	-	-	-	33.94

The best single guarantee system (# 47) has 5 combinations. The system presented here gives you twice the guarantee in just 7 combinations, that is, in only 1.4 times the number of combinations needed for the single guarantee system! If all of the numbers are guessed correctly, you can also win the jackpot (plus some extra cash!), or up to two 5-wins and a number of other prizes. The complete system would require 462 combinations. The system is well balanced: Each number is in either 3 or 4 combinations as seen from the table below.

Number(s)	Occurrences
1, 3, 4, 5, 6, 7, 8,10,11	4
2, 9	3

1.	1	2	6	8	9	10
2.	1	3	4	5	7	10
3.	1	4	6	7	8	11
4.	1	4	7	8	9	11
5.	2	3	4	5	7	11
6.	2	3	5	6	9	10
7.	3	5	6	8	10	11

System # 99: Guaranteed two 4–wins if 6 of the numbers drawn are in your set of 12 numbers ©Copyright 2001

Winning possibilities

Guessed	**6**	**5**	**4**	**3**	%
6	1	1	-	3	0.87
	1	-	1	4	0.22
	-	2	0-2	1-4	4.76
	-	1	1-4	1-6	28.57
	-	-	5	2-3	1.30
	-	-	4	2-4	19.26
	-	-	3	4-5	17.31
	-	-	2	6	27.71
5	-	2	-	1-2	0.51
	-	1	1	0-4	5.56
	-	1	-	3-4	1.01
	-	-	4	-	0.63
	-	-	3	0-3	4.80
	-	-	2	2-5	20.20
	-	-	1	3-6	50.76
	-	-	-	5-8	16.53
4	-	-	2	0-2	4.24
	-	-	1	0-4	21.82
	-	-	-	2-5	73.94
3	-	-	-	3-4	1.36
	-	-	-	1-2	64.55
	-	-	-	-	34.09

The best single guarantee system (# 48) has 6 combinations. The above system gives you twice the guarantee in only 10 combinations. The complete system would require 924 combinations. If all of the numbers are guessed correctly, you can also win the jackpot (plus some extra cash!), or up to two 5-wins and a number of other prizes. The system is HIGHLY BALANCED: Each number is in exactly 5 combinations.

1. 1 2 5 8 9 10
2. 1 2 8 9 10 12
3. 1 3 4 5 11 12
4. 1 3 6 7 9 11
5. 1 4 6 7 9 11
6. 2 3 4 6 8 10
7. 2 3 4 7 8 10
8. 2 5 6 7 11 12
9. 3 4 5 9 11 12
10. 5 6 7 8 10 12

System # 100: Guaranteed two 4–wins if 6 of the numbers drawn are in your set of 13 numbers ©Copyright 2001

Winning possibilities

Guessed	6	5	4	3	%
6	1	-	-	6	0.76
	-	1	2	4-5	11.36
	-	1	1	5-7	18.18
	-	1	-	7	2.27
	-	-	5	1	2.27
	-	-	4	3-4	13.64
	-	-	3	4-7	28.79
	-	-	2	6-8	22.73
5	-	1	-	2-4	6.06
	-	-	2	2-4	27.27
	-	-	1	3-5	51.52
	-	-	-	6-8	15.15
4	-	-	1	2	16.36
	-	-	1	-	10.91
	-	-	-	4	14.55
	-	-	-	3	47.27
	-	-	-	2	10.91
3	-	-	-	3	4.55
	-	-	-	1	77.27
	-	-	-	-	18.18

This system presents a considerable improvement over the single guarantee system (# 49, 10 combinations). Here you get the double guarantee in just 13 combinations, that is, in only 1.3 times the number of combinations needed for the best single guarantee system. If all of the numbers are guessed correctly, you can also win the jackpot (plus some extra cash!), or a 5-win and a number of other prizes. The system is HIGHLY BALANCED: Each number is in exactly 6 combinations. In addition, the combinations of the system are maximally 'apart': Every two combinations differ in at least three numbers. The complete system would require 1,716 combinations.

1.	1	2	3	5	6	9
2.	1	2	4	5	8	13
3.	1	2	5	10	11	12
4.	1	3	4	7	12	13
5.	1	4	9	10	11	13
6.	1	6	7	8	10	11
7.	2	3	4	6	7	10
8.	2	3	6	11	12	13
9.	2	7	8	9	11	12
10.	3	4	5	7	8	11
11.	3	8	9	10	12	13
12.	4	5	6	8	9	12
13.	5	6	7	9	10	13

System # 101: Guaranteed two 4–wins if 6 of the numbers drawn are in your set of 14 numbers ©Copyright 2001

Winning possibilities

Guessed	6	5	4	3	%
6	1	-	-	8-10	0.70
	-	1	4	6	0.47
	-	1	3	5-7	5.59
	-	1	2	6-9	13.52
	-	1	1	9-10	13.05
	-	1	-	11-12	0.93
	-	-	6	3	1.40
	-	-	5	4-6	6.99
	-	-	4	5-8	25.64
	-	-	3	8-10	25.64
	-	-	2	10-12	6.07
5	-	1	-	4-7	6.29
	-	-	3	2-5	4.20
	-	-	2	3-7	31.47
	-	-	1	5-8	50.35
	-	-	-	8-10	7.69
4	-	-	1	0-4	31.47
	-	-	-	2-6	68.53
3	-	-	-	3	3.85
	-	-	-	2	15.38
	-	-	-	1	73.08
	-	-	-	-	7.69

This system gives a considerable improvement over the single guarantee system (# 50, 14 combinations). Here you get the double guarantee in just 21 combinations, that is, in only 1.5 times the number of combinations needed for the best single guarantee system. If all of the numbers are guessed correctly, you can also win the jackpot (plus some extra cash!), or a 5-win and a number of other prizes. The system is HIGHLY BALANCED: Each number is in exactly 9 combinations. In addition, the combinations of the system are maximally 'apart': Every two combinations differ in at least three numbers. The complete system would require 3,003 combinations.

1. 1 2 4 6 7 12
2. 1 2 4 8 9 11
3. 1 2 7 10 11 13
4. 1 3 4 9 12 13
5. 1 3 5 6 11 14
6. 1 3 7 8 10 14

11. 2 3 5 9 10 12
12. 2 3 8 11 12 14
13. 2 4 5 10 13 14
14. 2 5 6 8 10 11
15. 2 6 7 9 13 14
16. 3 4 6 8 9 14

7.	1	4	5	7	9	10
8.	1	5	6	8	12	13
9.	1	6	9	10	12	14
10.	2	3	5	7	8	13

17.	3	4	6	10	11	13
18.	3	6	7	9	11	12
19.	4	5	7	11	12	14
20.	4	7	8	10	12	13
21.	5	8	9	11	13	14

System # 102: Guaranteed two 4–wins if 6 of the numbers drawn are in your set of 15 numbers ©Copyright 2001

Winning possibilities

Guessed	6	5	4	3	%
6	1	-	-	12-14	0.60
	-	1	4	4-7	1.50
	-	1	3	6-10	8.09
	-	1	2	8-12	17.08
	-	1	1	11-14	5.69
	-	-	6	4-9	1.70
	-	-	5	5-10	13.19
	-	-	4	8-11	28.17
	-	-	3	10-14	16.78
	-	-	2	13-15	7.20
5	-	1	-	5-8	5.99
	-	-	5	-	0.10
	-	-	3	2-5	6.49
	-	-	2	3-9	37.96
	-	-	1	6-11	38.96
	-	-	-	9-12	10.50
4	-	-	1	1-4	32.97
	-	-	-	3-6	67.03
3	-	-	-	3	1.10
	-	-	-	2	39.56
	-	-	-	1	49.45
	-	-	-	-	9.89

The best single guarantee system (# 51) has 19 combinations. The system presented here gives you twice the guarantee in just 30 combinations, that is, in only 1.58 times the number of combinations needed for the single guarantee system. If all of the numbers are guessed correctly, you can also win the jackpot (plus some extra cash!), or a 5-win and a number of other prizes. The system is HIGHLY BALANCED: Each number is in exactly 12 combinations. In addition, the combinations of the system are maximally 'apart': Every two combinations differ in at least three numbers. The complete system would require 5,005 combinations.

1.	1	2	3	5	6	10
2.	1	2	4	5	9	15
3.	1	2	4	7	10	12
4.	1	2	6	12	13	14
5.	1	3	4	8	14	15
6.	1	3	6	9	11	15
16.	2	4	8	9	11	14
17.	2	5	7	11	12	14
18.	2	5	8	10	14	15
19.	2	6	7	9	12	15
20.	2	8	9	10	12	13
21.	3	4	5	7	8	12

7.	1	3	7	8	10	13
8.	1	4	6	10	11	13
9.	1	4	7	9	13	14
10.	1	5	6	8	11	14
11.	1	5	11	12	13	15
12.	1	7	8	9	11	12
13.	2	3	4	6	7	11
14.	2	3	5	8	11	13
15.	2	3	7	13	14	15

22.	3	4	6	9	12	14
23.	3	5	9	10	12	15
24.	3	6	8	12	13	15
25.	3	9	10	11	13	14
26.	4	5	6	8	9	13
27.	4	5	7	10	13	15
28.	4	10	11	12	14	15
29.	5	6	7	9	10	14
30.	6	7	8	10	11	15

Double Guarantees: Lottery systems with two 3-wins guaranteed if 3 of your numbers are drawn

System # 103: Guaranteed two 3–wins if 3 of the numbers drawn are in your set of 8 numbers ©Copyright 2001

Winning possibilities

Guessed	6	5	4	3	%
6	1	2	4	-	21.43
	1	-	6	-	3.57
	-	4	3	-	32.14
	-	3	4	-	42.86
5	-	3	-	4	3.57
	-	1	4	2	32.14
	-	1	3	3	21.43
	-	1	2	4	10.71
	-	-	5	2	32.15
4	-	-	3	2	8.57
	-	-	3	1	5.71
	-	-	2	4	12.86
	-	-	2	2	8.57
	-	-	1	5	51.43
	-	-	1	4	12.86
3	-	-	-	4	14.29
	-	-	-	3	21.43
	-	-	-	2	64.28

The best single guarantee system (# 64) has 4 combinations. The system presented here gives you the double guarantee in 7 combinations. The complete system would require 28 combinations. If all of the numbers drawn are guessed correctly, you are guaranteed at least three 5-wins (plus a number of smaller prizes) but you can also win the jackpot and some extra cash! You are also guaranteed at least five 4-wins if five of your numbers are drawn. The system is MATHEMATICALLY MINIMAL with respect to the main guarantee and also with respect to the guarantee of a 4-win if four of your numbers are drawn. It is also well balanced: Each number of the system is in either 5 or 6 combinations as seen from the next table.

Number(s)	Occurrences
4, 6	6
1, 2, 3, 5, 7, 8	5

1. 1 2 3 4 5 8
2. 1 2 3 4 6 7
3. 1 2 3 5 6 7
4. 1 2 3 6 7 8
5. 1 4 5 6 7 8
6. 2 4 5 6 7 8
7. 3 4 5 6 7 8

SYSTEM # 104: GUARANTEED TWO 3–WINS IF 3 OF THE NUMBERS DRAWN ARE IN YOUR SET OF 9 NUMBERS ©Copyright 2001

Winning possibilities

Guessed	6	5	4	3	%
6	1	2	5	3	1.19
	1	1	6-7	2-3	4.76
	1	-	6-8	2-4	7.14
	-	5	2	4	1.19
	-	4	3-4	3-4	7.14
	-	3	4-6	2-4	39.29
	-	2	6-7	2-3	36.90
	-	1	8	2	2.39
5	-	2	1-3	4-7	2.37
	-	1	1-5	3-8	47.63
	-	-	7	2	1.59
	-	-	6	2-4	8.73
	-	-	5	4-5	27.78
	-	-	4	6	11.90
4	-	-	3	2-4	3.97
	-	-	2	2-6	30.95
	-	-	1	4-8	57.14
	-	-	-	8	7.94
3	-	-	-	4	13.10
	-	-	-	3	35.71
	-	-	-	2	51.19

The best single guarantee system (# 64) has 7 combinations. The system presented here gives you twice the guarantee in just 11 combinations, that is, in only 1.57 times the number of combinations needed for the single guarantee system! The complete system would require 84 combinations. If all of the numbers drawn are guessed correctly, you are guaranteed at least one 5-win (plus a number of smaller prizes) but you can also win the jackpot (plus some extra cash!), or up to five 5-wins and a number of other prizes. You are also guaranteed at least four 4-wins if five of your numbers are drawn. This system is MATHEMATICALLY MINIMAL with respect to the main guarantee. In addition, it is well balanced: Each number of the system is in either 7 or 8 combinations as seen from the table below.

Number(s)	Occurrences
5, 8, 9	8
1, 2, 3, 4, 6, 7	7

1. 1 2 3 4 6 7
2. 1 2 3 5 6 9
3. 1 2 4 5 8 9
4. 1 2 6 7 8 9
5. 1 3 4 7 8 9
6. 1 3 5 6 7 8
7. 1 4 5 6 7 9
8. 2 3 4 5 7 8
9. 2 3 5 7 8 9
10. 2 4 5 6 8 9
11. 3 4 5 6 8 9

System # 105: Guaranteed two 3–wins if 3 of the numbers drawn are in your set of 10 numbers ©Copyright 2001

Winning possibilities

Guessed	6	5	4	3	%
6	1	-	6	8	7.14
	-	2	6	6	85.71
	-	-	12	-	7.15
5	-	1	2	8	35.71
	-	-	5	5	28.57
	-	-	4	8	35.72
4	-	-	3	-	7.14
	-	-	1	6	85.71
	-	-	-	8	7.15
3	-	-	-	3	50.00
	-	-	-	2	50.00

This system presents a considerable improvement over the single guarantee system (# 65, 10 combinations). Here you get the double guarantee in just 15 combinations, that is, in only 1.5 times the number of combinations needed for the best single guarantee system. The complete system would require 210 combinations. If all of the numbers drawn are guessed correctly, you are guaranteed at least twelve 4-wins (plus a number of smaller prizes) but you can also win the jackpot (plus some extra cash!), or two 5-wins and a number of other prizes. You are also guaranteed at least four 4-wins if five of your numbers are drawn. This system is EXCEPTIONALLY HIGHLY BALANCED: Each number is in exactly 9 combinations and each pair of numbers is in exactly 5 combinations. It is also MATHEMATICALLY MINIMAL with respect to the main guarantee. Finally, every two combinations of the system differ in at least two numbers.

1. 1 2 3 4 6 8
2. 1 2 3 7 9 10
3. 1 2 4 5 6 10
4. 1 2 4 6 7 9
5. 1 2 5 7 8 9
6. 1 3 4 5 9 10
7. 1 3 5 6 7 8
8. 1 3 6 8 9 10
9. 1 4 5 7 8 10
10. 2 3 4 5 8 9
11. 2 3 4 7 8 10
12. 2 3 5 6 7 10
13. 2 5 6 8 9 10
14. 3 4 5 6 7 9
15. 4 6 7 8 9 10

System # 106: Guaranteed two 3–wins if 3 of the numbers drawn are in your set of 11 numbers ©Copyright 2001

Winning possibilities

Guessed	6	5	4	3	%
6	1	-	5-6	10-11	4.33
	-	3	2-4	9-13	4.33
	-	2	4-8	4-12	34.63
	-	1	6-9	5-11	47.62
	-	-	10	5-7	4.75
	-	-	9	7-8	4.34
5	-	1	3	6-8	4.33
	-	1	2	7-9	12.99
	-	1	1	10-11	8.66
	-	-	6	4-5	3.25
	-	-	5	5-6	4.76
	-	-	4	7-9	38.96
	-	-	3	9-11	23.81
	-	-	2	12-13	3.24
4	-	-	2	3-6	16.67
	-	-	1	4-7	57.58
	-	-	-	9	6.05
	-	-	-	8	19.70
3	-	-	-	4	12.12
	-	-	-	3	18.18
	-	-	-	2	69.70

The best single guarantee system (# 66) has 11 combinations. The system presented here gives you twice the guarantee in just 20 combinations. If all of the numbers drawn are guessed correctly, you are guaranteed at least nine 4-wins (plus a number of smaller prizes) but you can also win the jackpot (plus some extra cash!), or up to three 5-wins and a number of other prizes. You are also guaranteed at least two 4-wins if five of your numbers are drawn. The system is well balanced: The number 7 is in 10 combinations; each of the remaining numbers participates in exactly 11 combinations. The complete system would require 462 combinations.

1.	1	2	3	4	8	10	11.	1	6	7	8	9	11
2.	1	2	3	5	10	11	12.	2	3	4	7	8	9
3.	1	2	4	5	6	9	13.	2	3	5	6	7	11
4.	1	2	5	6	8	11	14.	2	3	6	8	9	11
5.	1	2	5	7	8	10	15.	2	4	5	7	9	11
6.	1	2	6	7	9	10	16.	2	4	6	9	10	11
7.	1	3	4	5	6	7	17.	3	4	5	6	8	10

8. 1 3 4 7 10 11
9. 1 3 4 8 9 11
10. 1 3 5 6 9 10

18. 3 5 7 8 9 10
19. 4 5 8 9 10 11
20. 4 6 7 8 10 11

System # 107: Guaranteed two 3–wins if 3 of the numbers drawn are in your set of 12 numbers ©Copyright 2001

Winning possibilities

Guessed	6	5	4	3	%
6	1	-	-	20	2.38
	-	1	5	10	85.71
	-	-	9	4	11.91
5	-	1	-	10	16.67
	-	-	3	8	83.33
4	-	-	1	4	66.67
	-	-	-	8	33.33
3	-	-	-	2	100.00

This system presents a considerable improvement over the single guarantee system (# 67, 15 combinations). Here you get the double guarantee in just 22 combinations, that is, in only 1.47 times the number of combinations needed for the best single guarantee system. The complete system would require 924 combinations. If all of the numbers drawn are guessed correctly, you are guaranteed at least nine 4-wins (plus a number of smaller prizes) but you can also win the jackpot (plus some extra cash!), or a 5-win and a number of other prizes. You are also guaranteed at least three 4-wins if five of your numbers are drawn. This system is EXCEPTIONALLY HIGHLY BALANCED: Each number is in exactly 11 combinations; each pair of numbers is in exactly 5 combinations and each triple is in exactly two combinations. It is also MATHEMATICALLY MINIMAL with respect to both the main guarantee and the guarantee three 4-wins on five numbers guessed correctly. Finally, the combinations of the system are maximally 'apart': Every two combinations differ in at least three numbers.

1.	1	2	3	5	6	8	12.	2	3	4	6	7	9
2.	1	2	3	7	10	12	13.	2	3	4	8	11	12
3.	1	2	4	5	7	11	14.	2	3	5	9	10	11
4.	1	2	4	8	9	10	15.	2	4	5	6	10	12
5.	1	2	6	9	11	12	16.	2	5	7	8	9	12
6.	1	3	4	5	9	12	17.	2	6	7	8	10	11
7.	1	3	4	6	10	11	18.	3	4	5	7	8	10
8.	1	3	7	8	9	11	19.	3	5	6	7	11	12
9.	1	4	6	7	8	12	20.	3	6	8	9	10	12
10.	1	5	6	7	9	10	21.	4	5	6	8	9	11
11.	1	5	8	10	11	12	22.	4	7	9	10	11	12

System # 108: Guaranteed two 3–wins if 3 of the numbers drawn are in your set of 13 numbers ©Copyright 2001

Winning possibilities

Guessed	6	5	4	3	%
6	1	-	0-7	12-24	1.98
	-	3	1-4	12-19	0.41
	-	2	2-8	8-20	10.20
	-	1	3-10	7-20	61.60
	-	-	6-11	7-17	25.81
5	-	1	0-4	7-16	15.86
	-	-	5-7	5-12	3.26
	-	-	2-4	6-16	80.27
	-	-	1	16-18	0.61
4	-	-	4	1	0.14
	-	-	3	2-5	0.42
	-	-	2	2-7	4.76
	-	-	1	4-10	60.00
	-	-	-	8-11	34.68
3	-	-	-	5	0.70
	-	-	-	4	6.29
	-	-	-	3	23.08
	-	-	-	2	69.93

The best single guarantee system (# 68) has 21 combinations. The system presented here gives you twice the guarantee in just 34 combinations, that is, in only 1.62 times the number of combinations needed for the single guarantee system! The complete system would require 1,716 combinations. If all of the numbers drawn are guessed correctly, you are guaranteed at least six 4-wins (plus a number of smaller prizes) but you can also win the jackpot (plus some extra cash!), or up to three 5-wins and a number of other prizes. The system also guarantees at least one 4-win if five of your numbers are drawn. Every two combinations of the system differ in at least two numbers. The next table gives information on the balance of the system.

Number(s)	Occurrences
3,12,13	17
4, 5, 7	16
1, 2, 6, 8, 9,10,11	15

1. 1 2 3 4 12 13
2. 1 2 3 5 9 10

18. 2 3 5 6 12 13
19. 2 3 7 10 11 13

3.	1	2	4	7	10	11
4.	1	2	5	8	11	13
5.	1	2	6	7	8	9
6.	1	2	6	10	12	13
7.	1	3	4	5	6	7
8.	1	3	4	8	9	12
9.	1	3	6	8	10	11
10.	1	3	7	11	12	13
11.	1	4	5	6	12	13
12.	1	4	5	9	11	12
13.	1	4	8	9	10	13
14.	1	5	7	8	10	12
15.	1	6	7	9	11	13
16.	2	3	4	6	9	11
17.	2	3	4	7	8	12
20.	2	3	8	9	12	13
21.	2	4	5	6	8	10
22.	2	4	5	7	9	13
23.	2	5	6	7	11	12
24.	2	8	9	10	11	12
25.	3	4	5	7	10	13
26.	3	4	5	10	11	12
27.	3	5	6	8	9	12
28.	3	5	7	8	9	11
29.	3	6	7	8	10	13
30.	3	7	9	10	12	13
31.	4	5	7	8	11	13
32.	4	6	7	9	10	12
33.	4	6	8	11	12	13
34.	5	6	9	10	11	13

SYSTEM # 109: GUARANTEED TWO 3–WINS IF 3 OF THE NUMBERS DRAWN ARE IN YOUR SET OF 14 NUMBERS ©Copyright 2001

Winning possibilities

Guessed	6	5	4	3	%
6	1	-	2	20	1.40
	-	2	3	17	5.59
	-	1	4-6	14-19	55.94
	-	-	12	-	0.23
	-	-	6-10	8-18	36.84
5	-	1	2	8	4.20
	-	1	-	13	8.39
	-	-	4	8	6.29
	-	-	3	9-12	55.94
	-	-	2	13-15	25.18
4	-	-	3	-	1.40
	-	-	1	4-6	58.74
	-	-	-	9	33.57
	-	-	-	8	6.29
3	-	-	-	3	30.77
	-	-	-	2	69.23

The best single guarantee system (# 69) has 25 combinations. The system presented here gives you twice the guarantee in just 42 combinations, that is, in only 1.68 times the number of combinations needed for the single guarantee system! The complete system would require 3,003 combinations. If all of the numbers drawn are guessed correctly, you are guaranteed at least six 4-wins (plus a number of smaller prizes) but you can also win the jackpot (plus some extra cash!), or up to two 5-wins and a number of other prizes. You are also guaranteed at least two 4-wins if five of your numbers are drawn. Every two combinations of the system differ in at least two numbers. The system is also HIGHLY BALANCED: Each number is in exactly 18 combinations.

1. 1 2 3 6 7 9
2. 1 2 3 8 11 13
3. 1 2 4 5 9 13
4. 1 2 4 10 11 12
5. 1 2 5 6 8 14
6. 1 2 6 10 12 13
7. 1 2 7 10 12 14
8. 1 3 4 5 10 13
9. 1 3 4 6 7 11
10. 1 3 4 8 12 14
22. 2 3 5 11 12 13
23. 2 3 7 11 13 14
24. 2 4 5 6 11 14
25. 2 4 5 7 8 12
26. 2 4 6 7 8 13
27. 2 5 7 9 10 11
28. 2 6 8 9 11 12
29. 2 8 9 10 13 14
30. 3 4 5 8 9 11
31. 3 4 6 12 13 14

11.	1	3	5	6	7	12
12.	1	3	9	10	11	14
13.	1	4	5	7	13	14
14.	1	4	6	8	9	10
15.	1	5	7	8	10	11
16.	1	5	9	11	12	14
17.	1	6	9	11	13	14
18.	1	7	8	9	12	13
19.	2	3	4	7	8	10
20.	2	3	4	9	12	14
21.	2	3	5	6	10	14
32.	3	5	6	8	9	13
33.	3	5	7	8	9	14
34.	3	6	8	10	11	12
35.	3	7	9	10	12	13
36.	4	5	6	9	10	12
37.	4	6	7	9	10	14
38.	4	7	9	11	12	13
39.	4	8	10	11	13	14
40.	5	6	7	10	11	13
41.	5	8	10	12	13	14
42.	6	7	8	11	12	14

System # 110: Guaranteed two 3–wins if 3 of the numbers drawn are in your set of 15 numbers ©Copyright 2001

Winning possibilities

Guessed	6	5	4	3	%
6	1	-	3-4	16-24	1.10
	-	2	2-5	15-22	7.19
	-	1	3-7	13-23	44.96
	-	-	12	6	1.20
	-	-	10	12	0.60
	-	-	5-9	14-23	44.95
5	-	1	3	7	0.50
	-	1	2	10	1.00
	-	1	1	11-15	8.49
	-	1	-	12	1.00
	-	-	5	0-9	2.10
	-	-	4	7-12	16.98
	-	-	3	10-14	22.98
	-	-	2	13-17	40.96
	-	-	1	17-19	5.99
4	-	-	2	0-6	6.60
	-	-	1	4-9	47.26
	-	-	-	10	4.40
	-	-	-	9	21.98
	-	-	-	8	19.76
3	-	-	-	5	3.30
	-	-	-	4	7.69
	-	-	-	3	16.48
	-	-	-	2	72.53

The best single guarantee system (# 70) has 31 combinations. The system presented here gives you twice the guarantee in just 55 combinations. The complete system would require 5,005 combinations. If all of the numbers drawn are guessed correctly, you are guaranteed at least five 4-wins (plus a number of smaller prizes) but you can also win the jackpot (plus some extra cash!), or up to two 5-wins and a number of other prizes. The system also guarantees at least one 4-win if five of your numbers are drawn. Every two combinations of the system differ in at least two numbers. The system is HIGHLY BALANCED: Each number is in exactly 22 combinations.

1.	1	2	3	5	6	13
2.	1	2	3	8	10	12
3.	1	2	4	5	12	15
28.	2	3	10	13	14	15
29.	2	4	5	8	9	11
30.	2	4	6	10	11	12

4. 1 2 4 10 12 13
5. 1 2 5 6 8 14
6. 1 2 6 7 11 12
7. 1 2 7 9 11 15
8. 1 2 9 12 13 14
9. 1 3 4 7 8 10
10. 1 3 4 11 14 15
11. 1 3 5 9 10 11
12. 1 3 6 8 11 13
13. 1 3 7 8 9 14
14. 1 3 9 11 12 15
15. 1 4 5 6 8 9
16. 1 4 5 7 13 15
17. 1 4 6 9 11 14
18. 1 5 6 7 12 14
19. 1 5 6 10 11 15
20. 1 6 8 10 14 15
21. 1 7 9 10 13 14
22. 1 8 11 12 13 15
23. 2 3 4 6 7 14
24. 2 3 4 9 11 13
25. 2 3 5 11 13 14
26. 2 3 6 7 9 15
27. 2 3 7 8 12 13

31. 2 4 7 9 12 14
32. 2 4 8 9 10 15
33. 2 5 6 7 9 10
34. 2 5 7 10 12 15
35. 2 6 7 8 13 15
36. 2 8 10 11 14 15
37. 3 4 5 7 8 15
38. 3 4 5 10 12 14
39. 3 4 6 12 14 15
40. 3 4 8 9 13 14
41. 3 5 6 9 10 12
42. 3 5 7 11 12 13
43. 3 5 8 10 13 15
44. 3 6 7 8 10 11
45. 4 5 6 11 13 15
46. 4 5 9 10 14 15
47. 4 6 7 10 11 13
48. 4 6 8 12 13 14
49. 4 7 8 9 11 12
50. 5 7 8 11 12 14
51. 5 7 9 13 14 15
52. 5 8 9 10 12 13
53. 6 8 9 12 13 15
54. 6 9 10 11 13 14
55. 7 10 11 12 14 15

SYSTEM # 111: GUARANTEED TWO 3–WINS IF 3 OF THE NUMBERS DRAWN ARE IN YOUR SET OF 16 NUMBERS ©Copyright 2001

Winning possibilities

Guessed	**6**	**5**	**4**	**3**	%
6	1	-	0-6	17-30	0.86
	-	3	0-1	23-27	0.05
	-	2	0-6	13-30	3.80
	-	1	1-9	11-31	43.96
	-	-	3-11	11-30	51.33
5	-	1	4	6	0.02
	-	1	3	9	0.05
	-	1	2	7-15	1.49
	-	1	1	8-17	4.03
	-	1	-	11-19	3.89
	-	-	5-6	6-14	1.35
	-	-	2-4	7-21	79.81
	-	-	1	16-22	9.00
	-	-	-	20-22	0.36
4	-	-	3	3	0.05
	-	-	2	1-7	4.18
	-	-	1	4-11	48.35
	-	-	-	8-14	47.42
3	-	-	-	5	1.43
	-	-	-	4	6.96
	-	-	-	3	28.21
	-	-	-	2	63.40

The best single guarantee system (# 71) has 38 combinations. The system presented here gives you twice the guarantee in just 69 combinations. The complete system would require 8,008 combinations. If all of the numbers drawn are guessed correctly, you are guaranteed at least three 4-wins (plus a number of smaller prizes) but you can also win the jackpot (plus some extra cash!), or up to three 5-wins and a number of other prizes. Every two combinations of the system differ in at least two numbers. The next table gives information on the balance of the system.

Number(s)	Occurrences
2, 8,15,16	27
1, 3, 7, 9,10,14	26
4, 5, 6,11,12,13	25

1.	1	2	3	4	13	16
2.	1	2	3	5	10	14
3.	1	2	4	8	12	15
4.	1	2	4	8	13	14
5.	1	2	5	7	10	13
6.	1	2	5	9	11	12
7.	1	2	6	9	10	15
8.	1	2	6	11	13	16
9.	1	2	7	8	14	15
10.	1	3	4	7	10	15
11.	1	3	4	8	9	12
12.	1	3	5	6	11	15
13.	1	3	5	7	9	16
14.	1	3	6	7	8	14
15.	1	3	10	11	12	13
16.	1	4	5	6	8	10
17.	1	4	5	7	8	11
18.	1	4	6	9	14	16
19.	1	4	9	11	13	15
20.	1	5	8	13	15	16
21.	1	5	12	14	15	16
22.	1	6	7	9	12	13
23.	1	6	7	10	12	16
24.	1	7	11	13	14	15
25.	1	8	9	10	12	14
26.	1	8	10	11	14	16
27.	2	3	4	5	11	16
28.	2	3	4	6	9	12
29.	2	3	6	7	15	16
30.	2	3	7	8	10	11
31.	2	3	8	9	13	15
32.	2	3	9	13	14	16
33.	2	3	10	12	15	16
34.	2	4	5	6	7	15
35.	2	4	7	9	10	11
36.	2	4	7	10	12	14
37.	2	5	6	8	9	12
38.	2	5	6	8	10	16
39.	2	5	7	9	14	16
40.	2	5	10	11	13	15
41.	2	6	7	11	14	15
42.	2	6	10	13	14	15
43.	2	7	8	12	13	16
44.	2	8	11	12	13	14
45.	3	4	5	7	12	13
46.	3	4	6	8	10	13
47.	3	4	8	11	14	16
48.	3	4	12	14	15	16
49.	3	5	6	12	13	14
50.	3	5	8	9	10	16
51.	3	5	8	9	14	15
52.	3	6	8	12	14	16
53.	3	6	9	10	11	14
54.	3	7	9	11	12	14
55.	3	7	11	13	15	16
56.	4	5	6	7	11	14
57.	4	5	6	9	13	16
58.	4	5	9	10	14	15
59.	4	5	10	11	12	16
60.	4	6	11	12	13	15
61.	4	7	8	9	15	16
62.	4	7	10	13	14	16
63.	5	7	8	10	12	15
64.	5	8	9	11	13	14
65.	6	7	8	9	10	13
66.	6	8	9	11	15	16
67.	6	8	10	11	12	15
68.	7	9	11	12	15	16
69.	9	10	12	13	15	16

System # 112: Guaranteed two 3–wins if 3 of the numbers drawn are in your set of 17 numbers ©Copyright 2001

Winning possibilities

Guessed	6	5	4	3	%
6	1	-	0-5	20-31	0.68
	-	3	1	23	0.01
	-	2	0-6	15-30	2.79
	-	1	1-10	12-34	39.20
	-	-	3-12	12-34	57.32
5	-	1	3	9-11	0.06
	-	1	2	8-15	1.07
	-	1	1	9-18	3.30
	-	1	-	11-20	3.72
	-	-	5-6	6-14	0.77
	-	-	4	7-17	8.03
	-	-	2-3	9-21	69.49
	-	-	1	16-23	12.77
	-	-	-	20-24	0.79
4	-	-	2	1-9	3.66
	-	-	1	4-12	45.63
	-	-	-	8-13	50.71
3	-	-	-	6	0.29
	-	-	-	5	0.74
	-	-	-	4	7.65
	-	-	-	3	28.38
	-	-	-	2	62.94

The best single guarantee system (# 72) has 44 combinations. The system presented here gives you twice the guarantee in just 84 combinations. The complete system would require 12,376 combinations. If all of the numbers drawn are guessed correctly, you are guaranteed at least three 4-wins (plus a number of smaller prizes) but you can also win the jackpot (plus some extra cash!), or up to three 5-wins and a number of other prizes. Every two combinations of the system differ in at least two numbers. Below is given information on the balance of the system.

Number(s)	Occurrences
16	31
1, 2, 3, 4, 6, 7, 9,12,15,17	30
5, 8,10,13,14	29
11	28

1.	1	2	3	4	9	16
2.	1	2	3	5	10	14
3.	1	2	4	5	7	17
4.	1	2	5	11	12	13
5.	1	2	6	9	14	16
6.	1	2	6	10	12	15
7.	1	2	7	8	9	12
8.	1	2	7	10	13	16
9.	1	2	8	14	16	17
10.	1	2	11	14	15	17
11.	1	3	4	8	12	14
12.	1	3	5	8	9	11
13.	1	3	5	10	12	16
14.	1	3	6	7	9	17
15.	1	3	6	14	15	16
16.	1	3	7	11	13	14
17.	1	3	8	13	15	17
18.	1	4	5	10	11	16
19.	1	4	5	13	14	15
20.	1	4	6	9	11	15
21.	1	4	6	10	11	17
22.	1	4	7	8	10	14
23.	1	4	7	11	12	15
24.	1	4	8	9	10	13
25.	1	5	6	7	8	15
26.	1	5	6	9	13	17
27.	1	6	7	8	11	16
28.	1	6	12	13	16	17
29.	1	7	9	12	14	17
30.	1	9	10	15	16	17
31.	2	3	4	6	8	15
32.	2	3	4	6	11	13
33.	2	3	4	7	8	12
34.	2	3	5	9	15	17
35.	2	3	7	12	15	16
36.	2	3	8	10	11	15
37.	2	3	12	13	14	17
38.	2	4	5	8	10	16
39.	2	4	7	9	11	14
40.	2	4	9	10	12	13
41.	2	4	10	14	15	17
42.	2	5	6	9	10	15
43.	2	5	6	11	12	14
44.	2	5	7	8	13	14
45.	2	5	12	15	16	17
46.	2	6	7	10	11	16
47.	2	6	7	13	15	17
48.	2	6	8	9	10	17
49.	2	6	8	11	13	15
50.	2	9	11	13	16	17
51.	3	4	5	6	7	10
52.	3	4	5	8	9	14
53.	3	4	5	10	13	15
54.	3	4	9	10	12	17
55.	3	4	11	14	16	17
56.	3	5	6	8	13	16
57.	3	5	6	11	12	17
58.	3	5	7	11	14	15
59.	3	6	7	9	12	13
60.	3	6	7	10	12	14
61.	3	7	8	10	16	17
62.	3	8	9	13	15	16
63.	3	9	10	11	13	14
64.	3	9	11	12	15	16
65.	4	5	6	9	12	16
66.	4	5	8	11	12	17
67.	4	6	7	13	14	16
68.	4	6	8	12	14	15
69.	4	6	9	15	16	17
70.	4	7	8	9	15	16
71.	4	7	8	11	13	17
72.	4	7	12	13	16	17
73.	5	6	10	13	14	17
74.	5	7	9	10	11	12
75.	5	7	9	13	14	16
76.	5	7	12	14	16	17
77.	5	8	10	12	15	17
78.	5	11	12	13	15	16
79.	6	8	9	11	14	17
80.	6	8	10	12	13	16
81.	7	9	10	14	15	16
82.	7	10	11	13	15	17
83.	8	9	12	13	14	15
84.	8	10	11	12	14	16

System # 113: Guaranteed two 3–wins if 3 of the numbers drawn are in your set of 18 numbers ©Copyright 2001

Winning possibilities

Guessed	6	5	4	3	%
6	2	-	-	32	0.11
	1	-	-	20	0.26
	-	2	6	28	5.17
	-	2	-	20	2.59
	-	1	3	18	15.51
	-	1	-	30	3.10
	-	-	13	20	3.88
	-	-	12	24	0.65
	-	-	9	4	0.86
	-	-	6	16	4.52
	-	-	5	20	46.54
	-	-	4	24	15.51
	-	-	3	28	1.30
5	-	2	-	24	0.93
	-	2	-	-	0.47
	-	1	-	10	3.36
	-	-	6	20	5.60
	-	-	3	8	11.20
	-	-	2	12	42.02
	-	-	1	16	33.61
	-	-	-	20	2.81
4	-	-	2	16	3.92
	-	-	2	-	5.88
	-	-	1	4	23.53
	-	-	-	8	66.67
3	-	-	-	10	1.96
	-	-	-	2	98.04

The best single guarantee system (# 73) has 48 combinations. The system presented here gives you twice the guarantee in just 88 combinations. The complete system would require 18,564 combinations. If all of the numbers drawn are guessed correctly, you are guaranteed at least three 4-wins (plus a number of smaller prizes) but you can also win the jackpot (or even two jackpots!), or up to two 5-wins and a number of other prizes. This system has repeated combinations and is the last (of three) such systems in the book. Information on the balance of the system: The numbers 17 and 18 are each in 40 combinations; the remaining numbers are each in 28 combinations.

1. 1 2 3 16 17 18
2. 1 2 3 16 17 18
3. 1 2 4 5 13 14
4. 1 2 4 6 8 9
5. 1 2 5 6 10 12
6. 1 2 7 8 14 15
7. 1 2 7 9 11 12
8. 1 2 10 11 13 15
9. 1 3 4 5 11 12
10. 1 3 4 6 13 15
11. 1 3 5 6 7 8
12. 1 3 7 9 13 14
13. 1 3 8 9 10 11
14. 1 3 10 12 14 15
15. 1 4 7 10 17 18
16. 1 4 7 10 17 18
17. 1 4 8 11 15 16
18. 1 4 9 12 14 16
19. 1 5 7 11 13 16
20. 1 5 8 10 14 16
21. 1 5 9 15 17 18
22. 1 5 9 15 17 18
23. 1 6 7 12 15 16
24. 1 6 9 10 13 16
25. 1 6 11 14 17 18
26. 1 6 11 14 17 18
27. 1 8 12 13 17 18
28. 1 8 12 13 17 18
29. 2 3 4 5 7 9
30. 2 3 4 6 10 11
31. 2 3 5 6 14 15
32. 2 3 7 8 10 12
33. 2 3 8 9 13 15
34. 2 3 11 12 13 14
35. 2 4 7 11 14 16
36. 2 4 8 10 13 16
37. 2 4 12 15 17 18
38. 2 4 12 15 17 18
39. 2 5 7 10 15 16
40. 2 5 8 11 17 18
41. 2 5 8 11 17 18
42. 2 5 9 12 13 16
43. 2 6 7 13 17 18
44. 2 6 7 13 17 18
45. 2 6 8 12 14 16
46. 2 6 9 11 15 16
47. 2 9 10 14 17 18
48. 2 9 10 14 17 18
49. 3 4 7 12 13 16
50. 3 4 8 14 17 18
51. 3 4 8 14 17 18
52. 3 4 9 10 15 16
53. 3 5 8 12 15 16
54. 3 5 9 11 14 16
55. 3 5 10 13 17 18
56. 3 5 10 13 17 18
57. 3 6 7 10 14 16
58. 3 6 8 11 13 16
59. 3 6 9 12 17 18
60. 3 6 9 12 17 18
61. 3 7 11 15 17 18
62. 3 7 11 15 17 18
63. 4 5 6 16 17 18
64. 4 5 6 16 17 18
65. 4 5 7 8 13 15
66. 4 5 8 9 10 12
67. 4 5 10 11 14 15
68. 4 6 7 8 11 12
69. 4 6 7 9 14 15
70. 4 6 10 12 13 14
71. 4 9 11 13 17 18
72. 4 9 11 13 17 18
73. 5 6 7 9 10 11
74. 5 6 8 9 13 14
75. 5 6 11 12 13 15
76. 5 7 12 14 17 18
77. 5 7 12 14 17 18
78. 6 8 10 15 17 18
79. 6 8 10 15 17 18
80. 7 8 9 16 17 18
81. 7 8 9 16 17 18
82. 7 8 10 11 13 14
83. 7 9 10 12 13 15
84. 8 9 11 12 14 15
85. 10 11 12 16 17 18
86. 10 11 12 16 17 18
87. 13 14 15 16 17 18
88. 13 14 15 16 17 18

PART III
LOTTERY SYSTEMS WITH MULTIPLE GUARANTEES

SYSTEM # 114: GUARANTEED SIX 5–WINS IF 6 OF THE NUMBERS DRAWN ARE IN YOUR SET OF 9 NUMBERS ©Copyright 2001

Winning possibilities

Guessed	6	5	4	3	%
6	1	3	15	5	28.57
	-	6	12	6	71.43
5	-	2	6	14	28.57
	-	1	9	11	57.14
	-	-	12	8	14.29
4	-	-	4	8	14.29
	-	-	3	11	57.14
	-	-	2	14	28.57
3	-	-	-	6	71.43
	-	-	-	5	28.57

The system is MATHEMATICALLY MINIMAL with respect to the main guarantee. It also guarantees at least two 4-wins if four of your numbers are drawn and at least five 3-wins if three of your numbers are drawn. If five of the numbers drawn are guessed correctly, then you will win at least twelve 4-wins, or up to two 5-wins plus a number of other prizes. This system is EXCEPTIONALLY HIGHLY BALANCED: Each number is in exactly 16 combinations and each pair of numbers is in exactly 10 combinations. The complete sytem would require 84 combinations.

1.	1	2	3	4	5	7
2.	1	2	3	4	7	8
3.	1	2	3	4	8	9
4.	1	2	3	5	6	8
5.	1	2	3	5	6	9
6.	1	2	3	5	7	9
7.	1	2	4	5	6	9
8.	1	2	4	6	7	9
9.	1	2	5	6	7	8
10.	1	2	6	7	8	9
11.	1	3	4	5	6	7
12.	1	3	4	6	7	8
13.	1	3	4	6	8	9
14.	1	3	5	7	8	9
15.	1	4	5	6	8	9
16.	1	4	5	7	8	9
17.	2	3	4	5	6	8
18.	2	3	4	5	8	9
19.	2	3	4	6	7	9
20.	2	3	6	7	8	9
21.	2	4	5	6	7	8
22.	2	4	5	7	8	9
23.	3	4	5	6	7	9
24.	3	5	6	7	8	9

System # 115: Guaranteed three 4–wins if 6 of the numbers drawn are in your set of 10 numbers

Winning possibilities

Guessed	**6**	**5**	**4**	**3**	%
6	1	-	2	-	2.38
	-	2	-	2	9.52
	-	1	2	1	19.05
	-	1	1	3	19.05
	-	-	4	-	2.38
	-	-	3	2	47.62
5	-	1	1	1	7.94
	-	1	-	2	3.97
	-	-	2	2	3.97
	-	-	2	1	31.75
	-	-	1	3	39.68
	-	-	-	5	12.69
4	-	-	2	-	2.38
	-	-	1	2	9.52
	-	-	1	1	19.05
	-	-	1	-	2.38
	-	-	-	3	19.05
	-	-	-	2	47.62
3	-	-	-	2	16.67
	-	-	-	1	50.00
	-	-	-	-	33.33

The best single guarantee system (# 46) has 3 combinations. The system presented here gives you three times the guarantee in just 5 combinations, that is, in only 1.67 times the number of tickets needed for the single guarantee system! If all of the numbers drawn are guessed correctly, you can also win the jackpot (plus some extra cash!), or up to two 5-wins and a number of other prizes. Every two combinations of the system differ in at least two numbers. The system is also HIGHLY BALANCED: Each number is in exactly 3 combinations. The complete system would require 210 combinations.

1. 1 2 4 6 7 9
2. 1 3 4 6 8 9
3. 1 3 5 6 8 10
4. 2 3 5 7 8 10
5. 2 4 5 7 9 10

SYSTEM # 116: GUARANTEED FOUR 4–WINS IF 4 OF THE NUMBERS DRAWN ARE IN YOUR SET OF 10 NUMBERS ©Copyright 2001

Winning possibilities

Guessed	6	5	4	3	%
6	1	4	30	20	28.57
	-	8	24	24	71.43
5	-	5	-	50	0.79
	-	2	12	32	39.68
	-	1	16	26	59.53
4	-	-	5	20	28.57
	-	-	4	24	71.43
3	-	-	-	10	100.00

The best single guarantee system (# 20) has 20 combinations. The system presented here gives you four times the guarantee in just 60 combinations. It also guarantees a 5-win if five of your numbers are drawn. The system is MATHEMATICALLY MINIMAL with respect to the following guarantees: 1) ten 3-wins if three of your numbers are in the draw; 2) eight 5-wins if six of your numbers are drawn. Of course, you can also win the jackpot plus some extra cash. The system is EXCEPTIONALLY HIGHLY BALANCED: Each number is in exactly 36 combinations; each pair of numbers is in exactly 20 combinations and each triple is in exactly 10 combinations. The complete system would require 210 combinations.

1.	1	2	3	4	5	9
2.	1	2	3	4	6	7
3.	1	2	3	4	6	8
4.	1	2	3	4	8	10
5.	1	2	3	5	6	10
6.	1	2	3	5	7	8
7.	1	2	3	5	7	10
8.	1	2	3	6	7	9
9.	1	2	3	6	8	9
10.	1	2	3	8	9	10
11.	1	2	4	5	6	7
12.	1	2	4	5	6	8
13.	1	2	4	5	8	10
14.	1	2	4	6	9	10
15.	1	2	4	7	8	9
16.	1	2	4	7	9	10
17.	1	2	5	6	9	10
18.	1	2	5	7	8	9
19.	1	2	5	7	9	10
31.	1	4	5	6	7	10
32.	1	4	5	7	8	10
33.	1	4	6	7	8	9
34.	1	4	6	8	9	10
35.	1	5	6	7	8	9
36.	1	5	6	8	9	10
37.	2	3	4	5	6	10
38.	2	3	4	5	7	8
39.	2	3	4	5	7	10
40.	2	3	4	6	9	10
41.	2	3	4	7	8	9
42.	2	3	4	7	9	10
43.	2	3	5	6	7	9
44.	2	3	5	6	8	9
45.	2	3	5	8	9	10
46.	2	3	6	7	8	10
47.	2	4	5	6	7	9
48.	2	4	5	6	8	9
49.	2	4	5	8	9	10

20. 1 2 6 7 8 10
21. 1 3 4 5 6 9
22. 1 3 4 5 7 9
23. 1 3 4 5 8 9
24. 1 3 4 5 9 10
25. 1 3 4 6 7 10
26. 1 3 4 7 8 10
27. 1 3 5 6 7 8
28. 1 3 5 6 8 10
29. 1 3 6 7 9 10
30. 1 3 7 8 9 10

50. 2 4 6 7 8 10
51. 2 5 6 7 8 10
52. 2 6 7 8 9 10
53. 3 4 5 6 7 8
54. 3 4 5 6 8 10
55. 3 4 6 7 8 9
56. 3 4 6 8 9 10
57. 3 5 6 7 9 10
58. 3 5 7 8 9 10
59. 4 5 6 7 9 10
60. 4 5 7 8 9 10

System # 117: Guaranteed three 4–wins if 4 of the numbers drawn are in your set of 11 numbers ©Copyright 2001

Winning possibilities

Guessed	6	5	4	3	%
6	1	-	30	20	14.29
	-	5	20	30	85.71
5	-	1	10	30	85.71
	-	-	15	20	14.29
4	-	-	3	20	100.00
3	-	-	-	8	100.00

The best single guarantee system (# 21) has 32 combinations. The system presented here gives you the triple guarantee in just 66 combinations, that is, in only 2.06 times the number of combinations needed for the single guarantee! It also guarantees at least fifteen 4-wins if five of your numbers are drawn, eight 3-wins if three of your numbers are in the draw, and at least five 5-wins plus a number of other prizes if all of the numbers drawn are guessed correctly. Of course, you can also win the jackpot plus a number of 3 and 4-wins. The system is EXCEPTIONALLY HIGHLY BALANCED: Each number is in exactly 36 combinations; each pair of numbers is in exactly 18 combinations; each triple is in exactly 8 combinations, and each quadruple is in exactly 3 combinations! It is also MATHEMATICALLY MINIMAL with respect to all of the above mentioned guarantees! Every two combinations of the system differ in at least two numbers, that is, the combinations are as 'apart' as possible. The complete system would require 462 combinations.

1.	1	2	3	4	5	10
2.	1	2	3	4	7	8
3.	1	2	3	4	9	11
4.	1	2	3	5	6	8
5.	1	2	3	5	7	9
6.	1	2	3	6	7	11
7.	1	2	3	6	9	10
8.	1	2	3	8	10	11
9.	1	2	4	5	6	9
10.	1	2	4	5	7	11
11.	1	2	4	6	7	10
12.	1	2	4	6	8	11
13.	1	2	4	8	9	10
14.	1	2	5	6	10	11
15.	1	2	5	7	8	10
16.	1	2	5	8	9	11
17.	1	2	6	7	8	9
34.	1	5	6	7	8	11
35.	1	5	6	7	9	10
36.	1	6	8	9	10	11
37.	2	3	4	5	6	11
38.	2	3	4	5	8	9
39.	2	3	4	6	7	9
40.	2	3	4	6	8	10
41.	2	3	4	7	10	11
42.	2	3	5	6	7	10
43.	2	3	5	7	8	11
44.	2	3	5	9	10	11
45.	2	3	6	8	9	11
46.	2	3	7	8	9	10
47.	2	4	5	6	7	8
48.	2	4	5	7	9	10
49.	2	4	5	8	10	11
50.	2	4	6	9	10	11

18. 1 2 7 9 10 11
19. 1 3 4 5 6 7
20. 1 3 4 5 8 11
21. 1 3 4 6 8 9
22. 1 3 4 6 10 11
23. 1 3 4 7 9 10
24. 1 3 5 6 9 11
25. 1 3 5 7 10 11
26. 1 3 5 8 9 10
27. 1 3 6 7 8 10
28. 1 3 7 8 9 11
29. 1 4 5 6 8 10
30. 1 4 5 7 8 9
31. 1 4 5 9 10 11
32. 1 4 6 7 9 11
33. 1 4 7 8 10 11
51. 2 4 7 8 9 11
52. 2 5 6 7 9 11
53. 2 5 6 8 9 10
54. 2 6 7 8 10 11
55. 3 4 5 6 9 10
56. 3 4 5 7 8 10
57. 3 4 5 7 9 11
58. 3 4 6 7 8 11
59. 3 4 8 9 10 11
60. 3 5 6 7 8 9
61. 3 5 6 8 10 11
62. 3 6 7 9 10 11
63. 4 5 6 7 10 11
64. 4 5 6 8 9 11
65. 4 6 7 8 9 10
66. 5 7 8 9 10 11

SYSTEM # 118: GUARANTEED SIX 4–WINS IF 4 OF THE NUMBERS DRAWN ARE IN YOUR SET OF 11 NUMBERS ©Copyright 2001

Winning possibilities

Guessed	6	5	4	3	%
6	1	5	50	50	28.57
	-	10	40	60	71.43
5	-	2	20	60	71.43
	-	1	25	50	28.57
4	-	-	6	40	100.00
3	-	-	-	16	100.00

The best single guarantee system (# 21) has 32 combinations. The system presented here gives you six times the guarantee in just 132 combinations, that is, in only 4.13 times the number of combinations needed for the single guarantee! It also guarantees sixteen 3-wins if three of your numbers are in the draw, and at least ten 5-wins plus a number of other prizes if all of the numbers drawn are guessed correctly. Of course, you can also win the jackpot plus some extra cash. The system is EXCEPTIONALLY HIGHLY BALANCED: Each number is in exactly 72 combinations; each pair of numbers is in exactly 36 combinations; each triple is in exactly 16 combinations, and each quadruple is in exactly 6 combinations! In addition, the system is MATHEMATICALLY MINIMAL with respect to all of the above mentioned guarantees! It also guarantees a 5-win (chances 71.43% for two 5-wins) if five of your numbers are drawn. The complete system would require 462 combinations.

1.	1	2	3	4	5	7
2.	1	2	3	4	5	10
3.	1	2	3	4	6	11
4.	1	2	3	4	7	8
5.	1	2	3	4	8	9
6.	1	2	3	4	9	11
7.	1	2	3	5	6	8
8.	1	2	3	5	6	9
9.	1	2	3	5	7	9
10.	1	2	3	5	10	11
11.	1	2	3	6	7	11
12.	1	2	3	6	8	10
13.	1	2	3	6	9	10
14.	1	2	3	7	8	11
15.	1	2	3	7	9	10
16.	1	2	3	8	10	11
67.	1	5	6	7	8	11
68.	1	5	6	7	9	10
69.	1	5	6	9	10	11
70.	1	5	7	8	10	11
71.	1	6	7	8	9	10
72.	1	6	8	9	10	11
73.	2	3	4	5	6	8
74.	2	3	4	5	6	11
75.	2	3	4	5	8	9
76.	2	3	4	5	9	10
77.	2	3	4	6	7	9
78.	2	3	4	6	7	10
79.	2	3	4	6	8	10
80.	2	3	4	7	9	11
81.	2	3	4	7	10	11
82.	2	3	4	8	10	11

17. 1 2 4 5 6 9
18. 1 2 4 5 6 10
19. 1 2 4 5 7 11
20. 1 2 4 5 8 11
21. 1 2 4 6 7 9
22. 1 2 4 6 7 10
23. 1 2 4 6 8 11
24. 1 2 4 7 8 10
25. 1 2 4 8 9 10
26. 1 2 4 9 10 11
27. 1 2 5 6 7 8
28. 1 2 5 6 10 11
29. 1 2 5 7 8 10
30. 1 2 5 7 9 11
31. 1 2 5 8 9 10
32. 1 2 5 8 9 11
33. 1 2 6 7 8 9
34. 1 2 6 7 10 11
35. 1 2 6 8 9 11
36. 1 2 7 9 10 11
37. 1 3 4 5 6 7
38. 1 3 4 5 8 10
39. 1 3 4 5 8 11
40. 1 3 4 5 9 11
41. 1 3 4 6 7 8
42. 1 3 4 6 8 9
43. 1 3 4 6 9 10
44. 1 3 4 6 10 11
45. 1 3 4 7 9 10
46. 1 3 4 7 10 11
47. 1 3 5 6 7 10
48. 1 3 5 6 8 11
49. 1 3 5 6 9 11
50. 1 3 5 7 8 9
51. 1 3 5 7 10 11
52. 1 3 5 8 9 10
53. 1 3 6 7 8 10
54. 1 3 6 7 9 11
55. 1 3 7 8 9 11
56. 1 3 8 9 10 11
57. 1 4 5 6 7 11
58. 1 4 5 6 8 9
59. 1 4 5 6 8 10
60. 1 4 5 7 8 9
61. 1 4 5 7 9 10
62. 1 4 5 9 10 11
83. 2 3 5 6 7 10
84. 2 3 5 6 7 11
85. 2 3 5 7 8 10
86. 2 3 5 7 8 11
87. 2 3 5 8 9 11
88. 2 3 5 9 10 11
89. 2 3 6 7 8 9
90. 2 3 6 8 9 11
91. 2 3 6 9 10 11
92. 2 3 7 8 9 10
93. 2 4 5 6 7 8
94. 2 4 5 6 9 11
95. 2 4 5 7 8 9
96. 2 4 5 7 9 10
97. 2 4 5 7 10 11
98. 2 4 5 8 10 11
99. 2 4 6 7 8 11
100. 2 4 6 8 9 10
101. 2 4 6 9 10 11
102. 2 4 7 8 9 11
103. 2 5 6 7 9 10
104. 2 5 6 7 9 11
105. 2 5 6 8 9 10
106. 2 5 6 8 10 11
107. 2 6 7 8 10 11
108. 2 7 8 9 10 11
109. 3 4 5 6 7 9
110. 3 4 5 6 9 10
111. 3 4 5 6 10 11
112. 3 4 5 7 8 10
113. 3 4 5 7 8 11
114. 3 4 5 7 9 11
115. 3 4 6 7 8 11
116. 3 4 6 8 9 11
117. 3 4 7 8 9 10
118. 3 4 8 9 10 11
119. 3 5 6 7 8 9
120. 3 5 6 8 9 10
121. 3 5 6 8 10 11
122. 3 5 7 9 10 11
123. 3 6 7 8 10 11
124. 3 6 7 9 10 11
125. 4 5 6 7 8 10
126. 4 5 6 7 10 11
127. 4 5 6 8 9 11
128. 4 5 8 9 10 11

63.	1	4	6	7	9	11
64.	1	4	6	8	10	11
65.	1	4	7	8	9	11
66.	1	4	7	8	10	11
129.	4	6	7	8	9	10
130.	4	6	7	9	10	11
131.	5	6	7	8	9	11
132.	5	7	8	9	10	11

SYSTEM # 119: GUARANTEED SIX 4–WINS IF 5 OF THE NUMBERS DRAWN ARE IN YOUR SET OF 12 NUMBERS ©Copyright 2001

Winning possibilities

Guessed	6	5	4	3	%
6	1	-	9	24	4.76
	-	3	6	26	8.66
	-	2	10	20	59.74
	-	1	14	14	25.97
	-	-	18	8	0.87
5	-	1	3	18	33.33
	-	-	6	16	66.67
4	-	-	4	-	0.61
	-	-	3	4	2.42
	-	-	2	8	29.09
	-	-	1	12	65.45
	-	-	-	16	2.43
3	-	-	-	4	100.00

The best single guarantee system (# 33) has 14 combinations. The system presented here gives you six times the guarantee in just 44 combinations, that is, in only 3.14 times the number of combinations needed for the single guarantee! The system is MATHEMATICALLY MINIMAL with respect to both the main guarantee and the guarantee of four 3-wins if three of your numbers are in the draw. If all of the numbers are guessed correctly, you will either win the jackpot (plus some extra cash!), or you will get up to three 5-wins and a number of other prizes. The system is EXCEPTIONALLY HIGHLY BALANCED: Each number is in exactly 22 combinations; each pair of numbers is in exactly 10 combinations, and each triple is in exactly 4 combinations! Every two combinations of the system differ in at least two numbers. The complete system would require 924 combinations.

1.	1	2	3	4	5	6
2.	1	2	3	4	7	10
3.	1	2	3	4	8	9
4.	1	2	3	5	11	12
5.	1	2	4	6	11	12
6.	1	2	5	6	7	9
7.	1	2	5	6	8	10
8.	1	2	7	8	9	10
9.	1	2	7	8	11	12
10.	1	2	9	10	11	12
11.	1	3	4	7	8	11
12.	1	3	5	7	9	11
23.	2	3	4	9	10	12
24.	2	3	5	7	9	12
25.	2	3	5	8	10	11
26.	2	3	6	7	8	12
27.	2	3	6	7	10	11
28.	2	3	6	8	9	11
29.	2	4	5	7	8	12
30.	2	4	5	7	10	11
31.	2	4	5	8	9	11
32.	2	4	6	7	9	11
33.	2	4	6	8	10	12
34.	2	5	6	9	10	12

13. 1 3 5 8 10 12
14. 1 3 6 7 10 12
15. 1 3 6 8 9 12
16. 1 3 6 9 10 11
17. 1 4 5 7 10 12
18. 1 4 5 8 9 12
19. 1 4 5 9 10 11
20. 1 4 6 7 9 12
21. 1 4 6 8 10 11
22. 1 5 6 7 8 11

35. 3 4 5 6 7 8
36. 3 4 5 6 9 10
37. 3 4 5 6 11 12
38. 3 4 7 9 11 12
39. 3 4 8 10 11 12
40. 3 5 7 8 9 10
41. 4 6 7 8 9 10
42. 5 6 7 10 11 12
43. 5 6 8 9 11 12
44. 7 8 9 10 11 12

System # 120: Guaranteed four 4–wins if 5 of the numbers drawn are in your set of 13 numbers

Winning possibilities

Guessed	6	5	4	3	%
6	1	-	9	20	3.03
	-	2	9	19	18.18
	-	2	8	22	22.73
	-	2	7	25	9.09
	-	2	6	28	4.55
	-	1	9	24	18.18
	-	-	14	16	13.64
	-	-	13	19	9.09
	-	-	12	22	1.51
5	-	1	3	16	24.24
	-	-	6	14	24.24
	-	-	4	19	48.48
	-	-	4	16	3.04
4	-	-	2	8	32.73
	-	-	1	11	21.82
	-	-	1	9	21.82
	-	-	-	14	18.18
	-	-	-	12	5.45
3	-	-	-	5	18.18
	-	-	-	4	27.27
	-	-	-	3	54.55

The best single guarantee system (# 34) has 21 combinations. The system presented here gives you four times the guarantee in just 52 combinations, that is, in only 2.48 times the number of combinations needed for the single guarantee! It also guarantees three 3-wins if three of your numbers are in the draw. If all of the numbers drawn are guessed correctly, you will either win the jackpot (plus some extra cash!), or you will get up to two 5-wins and a number of other prizes. The system is EXCEPTIONALLY HIGHLY BALANCED: Each number is in exactly 24 combinations and each pair of numbers is in exactly 10 combinations. Every two combinations of the system differ in at least two numbers. The complete system would require 1,716 combinations.

1.	1	2	3	4	7	9
2.	1	2	3	5	8	12
3.	1	2	3	7	12	13
4.	1	2	4	7	8	10
5.	1	2	4	8	11	12
27.	2	3	4	6	10	13
28.	2	3	4	8	9	10
29.	2	3	5	6	10	12
30.	2	3	5	9	10	11
31.	2	3	7	10	11	13

6.	1	2	4	9	12	13
7.	1	2	5	6	8	10
8.	1	2	5	6	9	13
9.	1	2	6	7	9	11
10.	1	2	7	10	11	12
11.	1	3	4	5	11	12
12.	1	3	4	6	9	11
13.	1	3	5	7	8	13
14.	1	3	6	8	10	12
15.	1	3	6	8	11	13
16.	1	3	7	8	9	10
17.	1	3	10	11	12	13
18.	1	4	5	6	7	10
19.	1	4	5	6	9	12
20.	1	4	5	10	11	13
21.	1	4	8	9	11	13
22.	1	5	6	7	11	13
23.	1	5	8	9	10	13
24.	1	6	7	9	10	12
25.	2	3	4	5	8	11
26.	2	3	4	6	7	11
32.	2	4	5	6	7	8
33.	2	4	5	6	12	13
34.	2	5	7	8	12	13
35.	2	5	7	9	11	13
36.	2	6	8	9	10	13
37.	2	6	9	10	11	12
38.	2	8	9	11	12	13
39.	3	4	5	10	12	13
40.	3	4	6	8	9	13
41.	3	4	7	9	12	13
42.	3	5	6	7	8	11
43.	3	5	6	9	11	12
44.	3	5	7	9	10	13
45.	3	6	7	8	9	12
46.	4	5	7	9	10	12
47.	4	5	8	9	10	11
48.	4	6	7	8	12	13
49.	4	6	7	10	11	13
50.	4	7	8	10	11	12
51.	5	7	8	9	11	12
52.	6	8	10	11	12	13

System # 121: Guaranteed three 4–wins if 6 of the numbers drawn are in your set of 14 numbers ©Copyright 2001

Winning possibilities

Guessed	6	5	4	3	%
6	1	-	1	12	0.93
	-	2	1	10-12	1.86
	-	1	5	6	0.93
	-	1	4	7-10	8.39
	-	1	3	9-12	18.65
	-	1	2	11-14	8.39
	-	1	1	14-16	4.66
	-	-	7	6-7	0.93
	-	-	6	6-10	14.45
	-	-	5	8-11	20.05
	-	-	4	10-13	17.48
	-	-	3	14-15	3.28
5	-	1	1	4-6	2.80
	-	1	-	6-8	5.59
	-	-	3	4-7	16.08
	-	-	2	6-10	42.66
	-	-	1	8-11	31.47
	-	-	-	11-12	1.40
4	-	-	2	1	1.40
	-	-	1	2-5	39.16
	-	-	-	3-7	59.44
3	-	-	-	3	3.85
	-	-	-	2	50.00
	-	-	-	1	42.31
	-	-	-	-	3.84

The best single guarantee system (# 50) has 14 combinations. The system presented here gives you the triple guarantee in just 28 combinations, that is, in only twice the number of combinations needed for the single guarantee! If all of the numbers drawn are guessed correctly, you can win the jackpot (plus some extra cash!), or you will get up to two 5-wins and a number of other prizes. The system is HIGHLY BALANCED: Each number is in exactly 12 combinations. Every two combinations of the system differ in at least two numbers. The complete system would require 3,003 combinations.

1. 1 2 3 4 7 11
2. 1 2 3 6 10 14
3. 1 2 3 8 11 13

15. 2 4 5 6 11 14
16. 2 4 6 7 8 13
17. 2 5 7 9 10 11

4.	1	2	5	9	13	14
5.	1	2	7	10	12	14
6.	1	3	4	5	10	13
7.	1	3	5	6	7	12
8.	1	4	6	8	9	10
9.	1	4	8	12	13	14
10.	1	5	6	7	8	11
11.	1	5	9	10	11	12
12.	1	6	9	11	13	14
13.	2	3	4	5	8	12
14.	2	3	4	9	12	14
18.	2	6	7	8	9	12
19.	2	6	10	11	12	13
20.	3	4	5	6	9	13
21.	3	5	7	8	9	14
22.	3	6	8	10	11	12
23.	3	7	8	9	10	13
24.	3	7	11	12	13	14
25.	4	5	6	7	10	14
26.	4	7	9	11	12	13
27.	4	8	9	10	11	14
28.	5	8	10	12	13	14

System # 122: Guaranteed six 4–wins if 5 of the numbers drawn are in your set of 14 numbers ©Copyright 2001

Winning possibilities

Guessed	6	5	4	3	%
6	1	-	12	32	3.03
	-	2	11	36	72.73
	-	-	18	28	24.24
5	-	1	4	24	27.27
	-	-	6	26	72.73
4	-	-	2	12	54.55
	-	-	1	16	27.27
	-	-	-	20	18.18
3	-	-	-	5	100.00

The best single guarantee system (# 35) has 31 combinations. The system presented here gives you six times the guarantee in just 91 combinations, that is, in only 2.94 times the number of combinations needed for the single guarantee! It also guarantees five 3-wins if three of your numbers are in the draw. The system is MATHEMATICALLY MINIMAL with respect to both the main guarantee and the guarantee five 3-wins if three of your numbers are drawn. If all of the numbers drawn are guessed correctly, you will either win the jackpot (plus some extra cash!), or you will get two 5-wins and a number of other prizes, or at least eighteen 4-wins and 28 3-wins. This system is EXCEPTIONALLY HIGHLY BALANCED: Each number is in exactly 39 combinations; each pair of numbers is in exactly 15 combinations, and each triple is in exactly 5 combinations. Every two combinations of the system differ in at least two numbers. The complete system would require 3,003 combinations.

1.	1	2	3	5	6	9
2.	1	2	3	5	8	10
3.	1	2	3	7	9	12
4.	1	2	3	7	10	14
5.	1	2	3	8	11	12
6.	1	2	4	5	6	11
7.	1	2	4	5	8	13
8.	1	2	4	6	7	14
9.	1	2	4	7	9	13
10.	1	2	4	8	12	14
11.	1	2	5	10	11	12
12.	1	2	6	8	11	13
13.	1	2	6	9	13	14
14.	1	2	7	10	11	13
15.	1	2	9	10	12	14
46.	2	3	5	7	8	14
47.	2	3	5	9	13	14
48.	2	3	6	11	12	13
49.	2	3	10	11	13	14
50.	2	4	5	6	10	12
51.	2	4	5	7	11	14
52.	2	4	5	12	13	14
53.	2	4	7	9	10	11
54.	2	4	8	9	10	12
55.	2	5	6	8	9	10
56.	2	5	7	8	9	13
57.	2	5	7	11	12	13
58.	2	5	9	10	11	14
59.	2	6	7	8	10	13
60.	2	6	7	8	12	14

16. 1 3 4 5 9 11
17. 1 3 4 5 10 13
18. 1 3 4 6 10 14
19. 1 3 4 7 12 13
20. 1 3 4 11 12 14
21. 1 3 5 6 13 14
22. 1 3 6 8 9 10
23. 1 3 6 8 12 13
24. 1 3 7 8 9 11
25. 1 3 7 11 13 14
26. 1 4 5 7 8 9
27. 1 4 6 7 8 12
28. 1 4 6 10 11 12
29. 1 4 8 9 10 14
30. 1 4 9 10 11 13
31. 1 5 6 7 9 12
32. 1 5 6 7 11 14
33. 1 5 7 8 10 14
34. 1 5 7 10 12 13
35. 1 5 8 12 13 14
36. 1 5 9 11 12 14
37. 1 6 7 8 10 11
38. 1 6 9 10 12 13
39. 1 8 9 11 13 14
40. 2 3 4 6 7 10
41. 2 3 4 6 9 11
42. 2 3 4 8 10 13
43. 2 3 4 8 11 14
44. 2 3 4 9 12 13
45. 2 3 5 6 7 12
61. 2 6 8 9 11 14
62. 2 6 10 12 13 14
63. 2 7 8 9 11 12
64. 3 4 5 7 8 11
65. 3 4 5 7 10 12
66. 3 4 5 9 12 14
67. 3 4 6 7 8 13
68. 3 4 6 8 9 14
69. 3 5 6 7 11 13
70. 3 5 6 8 12 14
71. 3 5 8 10 11 12
72. 3 5 9 10 11 13
73. 3 6 7 9 10 11
74. 3 6 10 11 12 14
75. 3 7 8 9 13 14
76. 3 7 9 10 12 14
77. 3 8 9 10 12 13
78. 4 5 6 8 9 12
79. 4 5 6 8 11 13
80. 4 5 6 10 13 14
81. 4 5 7 9 10 14
82. 4 6 7 9 13 14
83. 4 6 9 11 12 13
84. 4 7 8 10 11 12
85. 4 7 11 12 13 14
86. 4 8 10 11 13 14
87. 5 6 7 9 10 13
88. 5 6 8 10 11 14
89. 5 8 9 11 12 13
90. 6 7 9 11 12 14
91. 7 8 10 12 13 14

System # 123: Guaranteed four 5–wins if 6 of the numbers drawn are in your set of 14 numbers ©Copyright 2001

Winning possibilities

Guessed	6	5	4	3	%
6	1	-	48	88	9.09
	-	6	33	108	36.36
	-	4	40	100	54.55
5	-	1	16	76	81.82
	-	-	18	78	18.18
4	-	-	5	40	27.27
	-	-	4	44	54.55
	-	-	3	48	18.18
3	-	-	-	15	100.00

The best single guarantee system (# 14) has 98 combinations. The system presented here gives you four times the guarantee in 273 combinations, that is, in only 2.79 times the number of combinations needed for the single guarantee! The system is MATHEMATICALLY MINIMAL with both the guarantee fifteen 3-wins on three numbers guessed correctly and eighteen 4-wins if five of your numbers are drawn. If all of the numbers drawn are guessed correctly, you can also win the jackpot (plus some extra cash!), or six 5-wins and a number of other prizes. This system is EXCEPTIONALLY HIGHLY BALANCED: Each number is in exactly 117 combinations; each pair of numbers is in exactly 45 combinations, and each triple is in exactly 15 combinations. Every two combinations of the system differ in at least two numbers, that is, the combinations are as 'apart' as possible. The complete system would require 3,003 combinations.

1.	1	2	3	4	5	13
2.	1	2	3	4	6	8
3.	1	2	3	4	7	9
4.	1	2	3	4	10	12
5.	1	2	3	4	11	14
6.	1	2	3	5	6	11
7.	1	2	3	5	8	12
8.	1	2	3	5	9	14
9.	1	2	3	6	7	10
10.	1	2	3	6	9	12
11.	1	2	3	6	13	14
12.	1	2	3	7	8	14
13.	1	2	3	7	12	13
14.	1	2	3	8	9	11
15.	1	2	3	8	10	13
137.	2	3	6	9	11	14
138.	2	3	6	11	12	13
139.	2	3	7	8	9	13
140.	2	3	7	8	10	12
141.	2	3	7	9	10	14
142.	2	3	7	9	11	12
143.	2	3	7	10	11	13
144.	2	3	8	9	12	14
145.	2	3	8	11	13	14
146.	2	3	9	10	12	13
147.	2	3	10	11	12	14
148.	2	4	5	6	7	8
149.	2	4	5	6	9	10
150.	2	4	5	6	12	13
151.	2	4	5	7	9	14

16. 1 2 4 5 9 11
17. 1 2 4 5 12 14
18. 1 2 4 6 7 14
19. 1 2 4 6 10 11
20. 1 2 4 7 8 10
21. 1 2 4 7 11 13
22. 1 2 4 8 9 14
23. 1 2 4 8 11 12
24. 1 2 4 9 12 13
25. 1 2 4 10 13 14
26. 1 2 5 6 7 12
27. 1 2 5 6 8 10
28. 1 2 5 6 9 13
29. 1 2 5 7 8 11
30. 1 2 5 7 10 13
31. 1 2 5 8 13 14
32. 1 2 5 9 10 12
33. 1 2 5 10 11 14
34. 1 2 5 11 12 13
35. 1 2 6 7 8 13
36. 1 2 6 7 9 11
37. 1 2 6 8 11 14
38. 1 2 6 9 10 14
39. 1 2 6 10 12 13
40. 1 2 7 8 9 12
41. 1 2 7 9 13 14
42. 1 2 7 10 11 12
43. 1 2 8 10 12 14
44. 1 2 9 10 11 13
45. 1 2 9 11 12 14
46. 1 3 4 5 7 14
47. 1 3 4 5 9 10
48. 1 3 4 5 11 12
49. 1 3 4 6 7 12
50. 1 3 4 6 9 11
51. 1 3 4 6 10 14
52. 1 3 4 7 10 13
53. 1 3 4 8 9 12
54. 1 3 4 8 10 11
55. 1 3 4 12 13 14
56. 1 3 5 6 8 9
57. 1 3 5 6 12 13
58. 1 3 5 7 8 13
59. 1 3 5 7 9 12
60. 1 3 5 7 10 11
61. 1 3 5 8 11 14
152. 2 4 5 7 11 12
153. 2 4 5 8 9 13
154. 2 4 5 8 10 12
155. 2 4 5 11 13 14
156. 2 4 6 7 10 12
157. 2 4 6 8 9 12
158. 2 4 6 8 10 14
159. 2 4 6 8 11 13
160. 2 4 6 9 13 14
161. 2 4 6 11 12 14
162. 2 4 7 8 9 11
163. 2 4 7 8 12 14
164. 2 4 7 9 10 13
165. 2 4 7 10 11 14
166. 2 4 9 10 12 14
167. 2 4 10 11 12 13
168. 2 5 6 7 10 11
169. 2 5 6 7 13 14
170. 2 5 6 8 9 11
171. 2 5 6 9 12 14
172. 2 5 7 8 9 10
173. 2 5 7 8 12 13
174. 2 5 7 9 11 13
175. 2 5 7 10 12 14
176. 2 5 8 10 11 13
177. 2 5 8 11 12 14
178. 2 5 9 10 13 14
179. 2 6 7 8 9 14
180. 2 6 7 8 11 12
181. 2 6 7 9 12 13
182. 2 6 8 9 10 13
183. 2 6 8 12 13 14
184. 2 6 9 10 11 12
185. 2 6 10 11 13 14
186. 2 7 8 10 13 14
187. 2 7 11 12 13 14
188. 2 8 9 10 11 14
189. 2 8 9 11 12 13
190. 3 4 5 6 7 13
191. 3 4 5 6 8 10
192. 3 4 5 7 8 12
193. 3 4 5 7 9 11
194. 3 4 5 8 13 14
195. 3 4 5 10 11 14
196. 3 4 5 10 12 13
197. 3 4 6 7 8 14

62.	1	3	5	9	11	13
63.	1	3	5	10	13	14
64.	1	3	6	7	9	14
65.	1	3	6	8	10	12
66.	1	3	6	8	11	13
67.	1	3	6	9	10	13
68.	1	3	6	11	12	14
69.	1	3	7	8	9	10
70.	1	3	7	8	11	12
71.	1	3	7	10	12	14
72.	1	3	7	11	13	14
73.	1	3	8	9	13	14
74.	1	3	9	10	11	14
75.	1	3	10	11	12	13
76.	1	4	5	6	7	10
77.	1	4	5	6	8	13
78.	1	4	5	6	9	12
79.	1	4	5	6	11	14
80.	1	4	5	7	8	9
81.	1	4	5	7	12	13
82.	1	4	5	8	10	14
83.	1	4	5	9	13	14
84.	1	4	5	10	11	13
85.	1	4	6	7	8	11
86.	1	4	6	7	9	13
87.	1	4	6	8	9	10
88.	1	4	6	8	12	14
89.	1	4	6	11	12	13
90.	1	4	7	8	13	14
91.	1	4	7	9	10	11
92.	1	4	7	9	12	14
93.	1	4	8	9	11	13
94.	1	4	8	10	12	13
95.	1	4	10	11	12	14
96.	1	5	6	7	8	14
97.	1	5	6	7	11	13
98.	1	5	6	8	11	12
99.	1	5	6	9	10	11
100.	1	5	6	10	12	14
101.	1	5	7	8	10	12
102.	1	5	7	9	10	14
103.	1	5	7	11	12	14
104.	1	5	8	9	10	13
105.	1	5	8	9	12	14
106.	1	6	7	9	10	12
107.	1	6	7	10	11	14
198.	3	4	6	7	9	10
199.	3	4	6	8	9	13
200.	3	4	6	8	11	12
201.	3	4	6	9	12	14
202.	3	4	6	11	13	14
203.	3	4	7	8	11	13
204.	3	4	7	9	12	13
205.	3	4	7	11	12	14
206.	3	4	8	9	11	14
207.	3	4	8	10	12	14
208.	3	4	9	10	11	12
209.	3	4	9	10	13	14
210.	3	5	6	7	8	11
211.	3	5	6	7	10	14
212.	3	5	6	8	12	14
213.	3	5	6	9	11	12
214.	3	5	6	9	13	14
215.	3	5	6	10	11	13
216.	3	5	7	8	9	14
217.	3	5	7	9	10	13
218.	3	5	7	11	12	13
219.	3	5	8	9	12	13
220.	3	5	8	10	11	12
221.	3	5	9	10	12	14
222.	3	6	7	8	9	12
223.	3	6	7	8	10	13
224.	3	6	7	9	11	13
225.	3	6	7	10	11	12
226.	3	6	8	9	10	14
227.	3	6	10	12	13	14
228.	3	7	8	10	11	14
229.	3	7	8	12	13	14
230.	3	8	9	10	11	13
231.	3	9	11	12	13	14
232.	4	5	6	7	12	14
233.	4	5	6	8	9	14
234.	4	5	6	9	11	13
235.	4	5	6	10	11	12
236.	4	5	6	10	13	14
237.	4	5	7	8	10	13
238.	4	5	7	8	11	14
239.	4	5	7	9	10	12
240.	4	5	8	9	10	11
241.	4	5	8	11	12	13
242.	4	5	9	11	12	14
243.	4	6	7	8	12	13

108. 1 6 7 12 13 14
109. 1 6 8 9 12 13
110. 1 6 8 10 13 14
111. 1 6 9 11 13 14
112. 1 7 8 9 11 14
113. 1 7 8 10 11 13
114. 1 7 9 11 12 13
115. 1 8 9 10 11 12
116. 1 8 11 12 13 14
117. 1 9 10 12 13 14
118. 2 3 4 5 6 14
119. 2 3 4 5 7 10
120. 2 3 4 5 8 11
121. 2 3 4 5 9 12
122. 2 3 4 6 7 11
123. 2 3 4 6 10 13
124. 2 3 4 7 13 14
125. 2 3 4 8 9 10
126. 2 3 4 8 12 13
127. 2 3 4 9 11 13
128. 2 3 5 6 7 9
129. 2 3 5 6 8 13
130. 2 3 5 6 10 12
131. 2 3 5 7 11 14
132. 2 3 5 8 10 14
133. 2 3 5 9 10 11
134. 2 3 5 12 13 14
135. 2 3 6 7 12 14
136. 2 3 6 8 10 11
244. 4 6 7 9 11 12
245. 4 6 7 10 11 13
246. 4 6 9 10 11 14
247. 4 6 9 10 12 13
248. 4 7 8 9 10 14
249. 4 7 8 10 11 12
250. 4 7 9 11 13 14
251. 4 7 10 12 13 14
252. 4 8 9 12 13 14
253. 4 8 10 11 13 14
254. 5 6 7 8 9 13
255. 5 6 7 9 11 14
256. 5 6 7 10 12 13
257. 5 6 8 9 10 12
258. 5 6 8 10 11 14
259. 5 6 11 12 13 14
260. 5 7 8 9 11 12
261. 5 7 9 12 13 14
262. 5 7 10 11 13 14
263. 5 8 9 11 13 14
264. 5 8 10 12 13 14
265. 5 9 10 11 12 13
266. 6 7 8 9 10 11
267. 6 7 8 10 12 14
268. 6 7 8 11 13 14
269. 6 7 9 10 13 14
270. 6 8 9 11 12 14
271. 6 8 10 11 12 13
272. 7 8 9 10 12 13
273. 7 9 10 11 12 14

System # 124: Guaranteed three 4–wins if 6 of the numbers drawn are in your set of 16 numbers ©Copyright 2001

Winning possibilities

Guessed	6	5	4	3	%
6	1	-	-	20	0.60
	-	1	3	14	35.96
	-	-	9	-	2.00
	-	-	6	12	5.99
	-	-	5	14	35.96
	-	-	4	16	4.50
	-	-	3	20	3.00
	-	-	3	18	11.99
5	-	1	-	10	6.59
	-	-	3	6	21.98
	-	-	2	10	32.97
	-	-	1	12	32.97
	-	-	-	12	5.49
4	-	-	1	4	39.56
	-	-	-	8	6.59
	-	-	-	6	52.75
	-	-	-	-	1.10
3	-	-	-	2	85.71
	-	-	-	-	14.29

The best single guarantee system (# 52) has 25 combinations. The system presented here gives you the triple guarantee in just 48 combinations, that is, in only 1.92 times the number of combinations needed for the single guarantee! If all of the numbers drawn are guessed correctly, you can also win the jackpot (plus some extra cash!), or a 5-win and a number of other prizes. The system is EXCEPTIONALLY HIGHLY BALANCED: Each number is in exactly 18 combinations and each pair of numbers is in exactly 6 combinations. Also, the combinations of the system are maximally 'apart': Every two combinations differ in at least three numbers. The complete system would require 8,008 combinations.

1.	1	2	4	5	13	14
2.	1	2	4	6	8	9
3.	1	2	5	6	10	12
4.	1	2	7	8	14	15
5.	1	2	7	9	11	12
6.	1	2	10	11	13	15
7.	1	3	4	5	11	12
8.	1	3	4	6	13	15
25.	2	4	7	11	14	16
26.	2	4	8	10	13	16
27.	2	5	7	10	15	16
28.	2	5	9	12	13	16
29.	2	6	8	12	14	16
30.	2	6	9	11	15	16
31.	3	4	7	12	13	16
32.	3	4	9	10	15	16

9.	1	3	5	6	7	8
10.	1	3	7	9	13	14
11.	1	3	8	9	10	11
12.	1	3	10	12	14	15
13.	1	4	8	11	15	16
14.	1	4	9	12	14	16
15.	1	5	7	11	13	16
16.	1	5	8	10	14	16
17.	1	6	7	12	15	16
18.	1	6	9	10	13	16
19.	2	3	4	5	7	9
20.	2	3	4	6	10	11
21.	2	3	5	6	14	15
22.	2	3	7	8	10	12
23.	2	3	8	9	13	15
24.	2	3	11	12	13	14

33.	3	5	8	12	15	16
34.	3	5	9	11	14	16
35.	3	6	7	10	14	16
36.	3	6	8	11	13	16
37.	4	5	7	8	13	15
38.	4	5	8	9	10	12
39.	4	5	10	11	14	15
40.	4	6	7	8	11	12
41.	4	6	7	9	14	15
42.	4	6	10	12	13	14
43.	5	6	7	9	10	11
44.	5	6	8	9	13	14
45.	5	6	11	12	13	15
46.	7	8	10	11	13	14
47.	7	9	10	12	13	15
48.	8	9	11	12	14	15

System # 125: Guaranteed four 4–wins if 5 of the numbers drawn are in your set of 16 numbers ©Copyright 2001

Winning possibilities

Guessed	6	5	4	3	%
6	1	-	-	60	1.40
	-	1	9	34	83.92
	-	-	15	20	4.20
	-	-	12	32	10.48
5	-	1	-	30	15.38
	-	-	5	20	46.15
	-	-	4	24	38.47
4	-	-	1	12	92.31
	-	-	-	16	7.69
3	-	-	-	4	100.00

The best single guarantee system (# 37) has 54 combinations. The system presented here gives you four times the guarantee in just 112 combinations, that is, in only 2.07 times the number of combinations needed for the single guarantee! The system is MATHEMATICALLY MINIMAL with respect to the guarantee of four 3-wins if three of your numbers are drawn. If all of the numbers drawn are guessed correctly, you can win the jackpot (plus some extra cash!), or a 5-win and a number of other prizes in 85.32% of the cases. The system is EXCEPTIONALLY HIGHLY BALANCED: Each number is in exactly 42 combinations; each pair of numbers is in exactly 14 combinations, and each triple is in exactly 4 combinations. In addition, the combinations of the system are maximally 'apart': Every two combinations differ in at least three numbers. The complete system would require 8,008 combinations.

1.	1	2	3	4	5	10
2.	1	2	3	6	7	12
3.	1	2	3	8	14	15
4.	1	2	3	9	13	16
5.	1	2	4	6	14	16
6.	1	2	4	7	13	15
7.	1	2	4	8	9	11
8.	1	2	5	6	9	15
9.	1	2	5	7	11	14
10.	1	2	5	8	12	13
11.	1	2	6	10	11	13
12.	1	2	7	8	10	16
13.	1	2	9	10	12	14
14.	1	2	11	12	15	16
15.	1	3	4	6	11	15
57.	2	4	7	8	12	14
58.	2	4	10	11	14	15
59.	2	4	10	12	13	16
60.	2	5	6	7	13	16
61.	2	5	6	8	10	14
62.	2	5	7	10	12	15
63.	2	5	9	10	11	16
64.	2	6	7	8	11	15
65.	2	6	8	9	12	16
66.	2	6	12	13	14	15
67.	2	7	9	11	12	13
68.	2	7	9	14	15	16
69.	2	8	9	10	13	15
70.	2	8	11	13	14	16
71.	3	4	5	6	9	16

16. 1 3 4 7 9 14
17. 1 3 4 8 12 16
18. 1 3 5 6 13 14
19. 1 3 5 7 15 16
20. 1 3 5 9 11 12
21. 1 3 6 8 9 10
22. 1 3 7 8 11 13
23. 1 3 10 11 14 16
24. 1 3 10 12 13 15
25. 1 4 5 6 7 8
26. 1 4 5 11 13 16
27. 1 4 5 12 14 15
28. 1 4 6 9 12 13
29. 1 4 7 10 11 12
30. 1 4 8 10 13 14
31. 1 4 9 10 15 16
32. 1 5 6 10 12 16
33. 1 5 7 9 10 13
34. 1 5 8 9 14 16
35. 1 5 8 10 11 15
36. 1 6 7 9 11 16
37. 1 6 7 10 14 15
38. 1 6 8 11 12 14
39. 1 6 8 13 15 16
40. 1 7 8 9 12 15
41. 1 7 12 13 14 16
42. 1 9 11 13 14 15
43. 2 3 4 6 8 13
44. 2 3 4 7 11 16
45. 2 3 4 9 12 15
46. 2 3 5 7 8 9
47. 2 3 5 11 13 15
48. 2 3 5 12 14 16
49. 2 3 6 9 11 14
50. 2 3 6 10 15 16
51. 2 3 7 10 13 14
52. 2 3 8 10 11 12
53. 2 4 5 6 11 12
54. 2 4 5 8 15 16
55. 2 4 5 9 13 14
56. 2 4 6 7 9 10

72. 3 4 5 7 12 13
73. 3 4 5 8 11 14
74. 3 4 6 10 12 14
75. 3 4 7 8 10 15
76. 3 4 9 10 11 13
77. 3 4 13 14 15 16
78. 3 5 6 7 10 11
79. 3 5 6 8 12 15
80. 3 5 8 10 13 16
81. 3 5 9 10 14 15
82. 3 6 7 8 14 16
83. 3 6 7 9 13 15
84. 3 6 11 12 13 16
85. 3 7 9 10 12 16
86. 3 7 11 12 14 15
87. 3 8 9 11 15 16
88. 3 8 9 12 13 14
89. 4 5 6 10 13 15
90. 4 5 7 9 11 15
91. 4 5 7 10 14 16
92. 4 5 8 9 10 12
93. 4 6 7 11 13 14
94. 4 6 7 12 15 16
95. 4 6 8 9 14 15
96. 4 6 8 10 11 16
97. 4 7 8 9 13 16
98. 4 8 11 12 13 15
99. 4 9 11 12 14 16
100. 5 6 7 9 12 14
101. 5 6 8 9 11 13
102. 5 6 11 14 15 16
103. 5 7 8 11 12 16
104. 5 7 8 13 14 15
105. 5 9 12 13 15 16
106. 5 10 11 12 13 14
107. 6 7 8 10 12 13
108. 6 9 10 11 12 15
109. 6 9 10 13 14 16
110. 7 8 9 10 11 14
111. 7 10 11 13 15 16
112. 8 10 12 14 15 16

SYSTEM # 126: GUARANTEED THREE 4–WINS IF 5 OF THE NUMBERS DRAWN ARE IN YOUR SET OF 17 NUMBERS ©Copyright 2001

Winning possibilities

Guessed	6	5	4	3	%
6	1	-	6	36	1.10
	-	2	4-6	36-44	13.18
	-	1	7-10	30-42	46.16
	-	-	10-12	32-40	39.56
5	-	1	2	22	13.19
	-	-	5	20	19.78
	-	-	4	24	36.26
	-	-	3	28	30.77
4	-	-	3	4	5.71
	-	-	1	12	68.57
	-	-	-	16	25.72
3	-	-	-	4	100.00

The best single guarantee system (# 38) has 70 combinations. The system presented here gives you the triple guarantee in just 136 combinations, that is, in only 1.94 times the number of combinations needed for the single guarantee! The system is MATHEMATICALLY MINIMAL with respect to the guarantee of four 3-wins if three of your numbers are drawn. If all of the numbers drawn are guessed correctly you can win the jackpot (plus some extra cash!), or up to two 5-wins and a number of other prizes. The system is EXCEPTIONALLY HIGHLY BALANCED: Each number is in exactly 48 combinations; each pair of numbers is in exactly 15 combinations, and each triple is in exactly 4 combinations. Every two combinations of the system differ in at least two numbers. The complete system would require 12,376 combinations.

1.	1	2	3	4	6	16
2.	1	2	3	5	15	17
3.	1	2	3	8	9	10
4.	1	2	3	11	12	13
5.	1	2	4	5	8	15
6.	1	2	4	9	11	16
7.	1	2	4	14	16	17
8.	1	2	5	10	13	14
9.	1	2	5	12	15	16
10.	1	2	6	7	10	15
11.	1	2	6	7	11	12
12.	1	2	6	7	13	14
13.	1	2	7	8	9	17
69.	2	5	6	10	11	14
70.	2	5	7	11	13	16
71.	2	5	8	10	14	16
72.	2	5	8	11	13	17
73.	2	5	9	11	13	15
74.	2	6	8	10	12	16
75.	2	6	8	11	14	17
76.	2	6	9	13	15	17
77.	2	7	9	10	12	17
78.	2	7	9	14	16	17
79.	2	7	10	11	15	16
80.	2	9	12	13	15	16
81.	2	12	14	15	16	17

14.	1	2	8	9	13	14	82.	3	4	5	10	11	12
15.	1	2	10	11	12	17	83.	3	4	5	13	14	15
16.	1	3	4	5	6	8	84.	3	4	6	7	10	17
17.	1	3	4	6	11	13	85.	3	4	7	12	15	16
18.	1	3	4	7	14	17	86.	3	4	8	9	12	17
19.	1	3	5	7	11	14	87.	3	4	8	9	13	14
20.	1	3	5	9	12	16	88.	3	4	8	9	15	16
21.	1	3	6	9	12	14	89.	3	4	10	11	15	16
22.	1	3	7	9	12	15	90.	3	5	6	7	8	10
23.	1	3	7	10	14	16	91.	3	5	6	8	13	15
24.	1	3	8	10	11	13	92.	3	5	7	9	13	16
25.	1	3	8	10	15	17	93.	3	5	8	11	14	16
26.	1	3	13	15	16	17	94.	3	5	9	11	14	17
27.	1	4	5	7	8	11	95.	3	5	10	12	13	15
28.	1	4	5	9	10	13	96.	3	6	7	9	10	13
29.	1	4	6	10	12	15	97.	3	6	7	11	12	15
30.	1	4	7	9	13	15	98.	3	6	8	12	14	17
31.	1	4	7	10	12	16	99.	3	6	9	11	15	17
32.	1	4	8	10	12	14	100.	3	6	10	12	14	16
33.	1	4	9	12	13	17	101.	3	7	9	11	13	17
34.	1	4	11	14	15	17	102.	3	8	11	12	16	17
35.	1	5	6	9	14	17	103.	3	10	13	14	16	17
36.	1	5	6	10	11	17	104.	4	5	6	11	12	13
37.	1	5	6	12	13	17	105.	4	5	6	14	15	16
38.	1	5	7	9	11	15	106.	4	5	8	13	16	17
39.	1	5	7	10	13	16	107.	4	5	9	10	14	15
40.	1	5	8	12	14	16	108.	4	5	9	10	16	17
41.	1	6	7	8	16	17	109.	4	5	11	12	16	17
42.	1	6	8	9	11	16	110.	4	6	7	8	9	11
43.	1	6	8	13	15	16	111.	4	6	7	9	14	16
44.	1	6	9	10	14	15	112.	4	6	8	10	14	17
45.	1	7	8	12	13	17	113.	4	6	9	12	15	17
46.	1	8	11	12	14	15	114.	4	6	11	13	14	16
47.	1	9	10	11	16	17	115.	4	7	8	10	11	14
48.	1	11	13	14	15	16	116.	4	7	8	12	13	16
49.	2	3	4	5	7	17	117.	4	7	11	13	15	17
50.	2	3	4	9	10	11	118.	5	6	7	12	13	14
51.	2	3	4	12	13	14	119.	5	6	7	15	16	17
52.	2	3	5	6	9	16	120.	5	6	10	11	15	16
53.	2	3	5	10	12	17	121.	5	7	8	9	10	12
54.	2	3	6	11	14	15	122.	5	7	8	10	15	17
55.	2	3	6	13	16	17	123.	5	7	12	14	15	17
56.	2	3	7	8	11	16	124.	5	8	9	11	12	15
57.	2	3	7	8	12	13	125.	5	8	9	13	14	17
58.	2	3	7	8	14	15	126.	6	7	8	13	14	15
59.	2	3	9	10	14	15	127.	6	7	11	12	16	17

60.	2	4	5	6	7	9
61.	2	4	5	7	12	14
62.	2	4	6	8	12	15
63.	2	4	6	10	13	17
64.	2	4	7	10	13	15
65.	2	4	8	10	13	16
66.	2	4	8	11	15	17
67.	2	4	9	11	12	14
68.	2	5	6	8	9	12

128.	6	8	9	10	11	13
129.	6	9	10	12	13	16
130.	7	8	9	14	15	16
131.	7	9	10	11	12	14
132.	7	10	11	13	14	17
133.	8	9	10	15	16	17
134.	8	10	11	12	13	15
135.	9	11	12	13	14	16
136.	10	12	13	14	15	17

System # 127: Guaranteed three 4–wins if 6 of the numbers drawn are in your set of 18 numbers ©Copyright 2001

Winning possibilities

Guessed	6	5	4	3	%
6	1	-	-	16-20	0.37
	-	1	3	16-17	20.69
	-	1	-	16-20	5.69
	-	-	9	2	0.86
	-	-	7	12	3.88
	-	-	6	14-16	3.23
	-	-	5	16-17	17.45
	-	-	4	13-19	15.51
	-	-	3	16-24	32.32
5	-	1	-	0-12	4.76
	-	-	3	7-11	16.81
	-	-	2	11	16.81
	-	-	1	9-14	58.82
	-	-	-	14	2.80
4	-	-	1	0-8	33.33
	-	-	-	8	3.92
	-	-	-	7	31.37
	-	-	-	5	31.38
3	-	-	-	5	1.96
	-	-	-	2	58.82
	-	-	-	1	39.22

The best single guarantee system (# 54) has 42 combinations. The system pre-ented here gives you the triple guarantee in just 68 combinations, that is, in only .62 times the number of combinations needed for the single guarantee! It also guar-ntees at least one 3-win if three of your numbers are drawn. If all of the numbers rawn are guessed correctly, you can also win the jackpot (plus some extra cash!), or 5-win and a number of other prizes. In addition, the combinations of the system re maximally 'apart': Every two combinations differ in at least three numbers. The omplete system would require 18,564 combinations. Information on the balance of he system is given in the table below.

Number(s)	Occurrences
1, 2, 3, 4, 5, 6, 7, 8, 9,10,11,12,13,14,15,16	23
17,18	20

1.	1	2	3	16	17	18	35.	2	5	9	12	13	16
2.	1	2	4	5	13	14	36.	2	6	7	13	17	18
3.	1	2	4	6	8	9	37.	2	6	8	12	14	16
4.	1	2	5	6	10	12	38.	2	6	9	11	15	16
5.	1	2	7	8	14	15	39.	2	9	10	14	17	18
6.	1	2	7	9	11	12	40.	3	4	7	12	13	16
7.	1	2	10	11	13	15	41.	3	4	8	14	17	18
8.	1	3	4	5	11	12	42.	3	4	9	10	15	16
9.	1	3	4	6	13	15	43.	3	5	8	12	15	16
10.	1	3	5	6	7	8	44.	3	5	9	11	14	16
11.	1	3	7	9	13	14	45.	3	5	10	13	17	18
12.	1	3	8	9	10	11	46.	3	6	7	10	14	16
13.	1	3	10	12	14	15	47.	3	6	8	11	13	16
14.	1	4	7	10	17	18	48.	3	6	9	12	17	18
15.	1	4	8	11	15	16	49.	3	7	11	15	17	18
16.	1	4	9	12	14	16	50.	4	5	6	16	17	18
17.	1	5	7	11	13	16	51.	4	5	7	8	13	15
18.	1	5	8	10	14	16	52.	4	5	8	9	10	12
19.	1	5	9	15	17	18	53.	4	5	10	11	14	15
20.	1	6	7	12	15	16	54.	4	6	7	8	11	12
21.	1	6	9	10	13	16	55.	4	6	7	9	14	15
22.	1	6	11	14	17	18	56.	4	6	10	12	13	14
23.	1	8	12	13	17	18	57.	4	9	11	13	17	18
24.	2	3	4	5	7	9	58.	5	6	7	9	10	11
25.	2	3	4	6	10	11	59.	5	6	8	9	13	14
26.	2	3	5	6	14	15	60.	5	6	11	12	13	15
27.	2	3	7	8	10	12	61.	5	7	12	14	17	18
28.	2	3	8	9	13	15	62.	6	8	10	15	17	18
29.	2	3	11	12	13	14	63.	7	8	9	16	17	18
30.	2	4	7	11	14	16	64.	7	8	10	11	13	14
31.	2	4	8	10	13	16	65.	7	9	10	12	13	15
32.	2	4	12	15	17	18	66.	8	9	11	12	14	15
33.	2	5	7	10	15	16	67.	10	11	12	16	17	18
34.	2	5	8	11	17	18	68.	13	14	15	16	17	18

System # 128: Guaranteed four 4–wins if 5 of the numbers drawn are in your set of 18 numbers ©Copyright 2001

Winning possibilities

Guessed	6	5	4	3	%
6	1	-	12	32	1.10
	-	2	8	48	26.37
	-	1	10	50	26.37
	-	-	14	44	6.59
	-	-	13	48	32.97
	-	-	12	52	6.60
5	-	1	4	24	14.29
	-	-	5	30	28.57
	-	-	4	34	57.14
4	-	-	2	12	40.00
	-	-	1	16	20.00
	-	-	-	20	40.00
3	-	-	-	5	100.00

The best single guarantee system (# 38) has 81 combinations. The system presented here gives you four times the guarantee in just 204 combinations, that is, in only 2.52 times the number of combinations needed for the single guarantee! The system is MATHEMATICALLY MINIMAL with respect to the guarantee of five 3-wins if three of your numbers are drawn. If all of the numbers drawn are guessed correctly, you can win the jackpot (plus some extra cash!), or up to two 5-wins and a number of other prizes. The system is EXCEPTIONALLY HIGHLY BALANCED: Each number is in exactly 68 combinations; each pair of numbers is in exactly 20 combinations, and each triple is in exactly 5 combinations. Every two combinations of the system differ in at least two numbers. The complete system would require 18,564 combinations.

1.	1	2	3	4	7	15
2.	1	2	3	4	8	14
3.	1	2	3	6	14	17
4.	1	2	3	6	15	18
5.	1	2	3	7	13	17
6.	1	2	4	5	9	14
7.	1	2	4	7	9	10
8.	1	2	4	8	10	11
9.	1	2	5	6	12	18
10.	1	2	5	9	12	13
11.	1	2	5	13	16	17
12.	1	2	5	14	17	18
103.	2	5	10	13	15	17
104.	2	6	7	8	9	13
105.	2	6	7	9	10	14
106.	2	6	8	9	16	17
107.	2	6	9	10	15	16
108.	2	7	8	13	15	17
109.	2	7	10	12	14	16
110.	2	7	11	12	14	15
111.	2	8	9	12	13	18
112.	2	8	9	15	17	18
113.	2	8	12	13	14	15
114.	2	9	11	14	17	18

13. 1 2 6 11 15 16
14. 1 2 6 12 16 17
15. 1 2 7 8 11 15
16. 1 2 7 9 11 13
17. 1 2 8 10 12 18
18. 1 2 8 14 15 18
19. 1 2 9 10 12 16
20. 1 2 10 11 13 16
21. 1 3 4 8 13 17
22. 1 3 4 11 12 14
23. 1 3 4 12 13 15
24. 1 3 5 7 10 15
25. 1 3 5 7 12 13
26. 1 3 5 8 13 16
27. 1 3 5 10 11 16
28. 1 3 5 11 12 18
29. 1 3 6 8 9 17
30. 1 3 6 9 11 18
31. 1 3 6 11 14 16
32. 1 3 7 9 10 17
33. 1 3 8 9 14 16
34. 1 3 9 10 16 18
35. 1 3 10 12 15 18
36. 1 4 5 6 7 10
37. 1 4 5 6 9 18
38. 1 4 5 10 11 14
39. 1 4 5 11 17 18
40. 1 4 6 7 15 16
41. 1 4 6 8 10 13
42. 1 4 6 13 15 18
43. 1 4 7 9 16 18
44. 1 4 8 11 12 17
45. 1 4 9 12 14 16
46. 1 4 12 15 16 17
47. 1 4 13 16 17 18
48. 1 5 6 7 8 12
49. 1 5 6 8 9 13
50. 1 5 7 8 15 16
51. 1 5 8 9 14 15
52. 1 5 10 14 15 17
53. 1 5 11 15 16 17
54. 1 6 7 10 14 17
55. 1 6 7 12 14 16
56. 1 6 8 10 12 17
57. 1 6 9 11 13 15
58. 1 6 10 11 13 14
115. 2 10 13 14 15 16
116. 2 11 14 15 16 18
117. 3 4 5 6 9 17
118. 3 4 5 6 10 16
119. 3 4 5 8 17 18
120. 3 4 6 7 11 16
121. 3 4 6 9 11 12
122. 3 4 6 10 12 13
123. 3 4 7 8 14 18
124. 3 4 7 11 14 15
125. 3 4 9 10 13 17
126. 3 4 9 11 13 15
127. 3 4 10 12 14 18
128. 3 4 10 16 17 18
129. 3 5 6 13 14 16
130. 3 5 6 14 15 17
131. 3 5 7 9 12 17
132. 3 5 7 9 14 15
133. 3 5 7 13 14 18
134. 3 5 8 11 13 18
135. 3 5 12 14 17 18
136. 3 6 7 8 9 12
137. 3 6 7 8 11 18
138. 3 6 7 12 13 16
139. 3 6 8 10 12 15
140. 3 6 8 15 17 18
141. 3 7 8 9 10 14
142. 3 7 8 10 11 15
143. 3 7 10 11 16 17
144. 3 8 11 13 15 17
145. 3 8 12 13 15 16
146. 3 9 10 13 14 18
147. 3 9 13 14 15 16
148. 3 11 14 15 16 17
149. 3 12 15 16 17 18
150. 4 5 6 7 11 17
151. 4 5 7 8 12 17
152. 4 5 7 10 12 13
153. 4 5 7 11 13 14
154. 4 5 8 9 15 18
155. 4 5 8 12 15 16
156. 4 5 10 12 14 16
157. 4 5 11 13 15 18
158. 4 6 7 14 15 17
159. 4 6 8 10 15 16
160. 4 6 8 14 15 18

59.	1	7	8	11	12	18	161.	4	6	9	12	14	18
60.	1	7	8	14	16	18	162.	4	7	8	9	10	13
61.	1	7	9	11	17	18	163.	4	7	8	9	12	18
62.	1	7	11	12	13	14	164.	4	7	8	13	14	17
63.	1	7	13	14	17	18	165.	4	7	9	11	13	16
64.	1	8	9	11	15	17	166.	4	8	9	10	11	15
65.	1	8	10	13	16	18	167.	4	8	9	11	12	16
66.	1	9	10	12	15	17	168.	4	9	13	14	16	17
67.	1	9	12	13	14	15	169.	4	10	11	14	15	18
68.	1	10	13	14	15	18	170.	4	10	14	15	16	17
69.	2	3	4	5	8	16	171.	5	6	8	11	13	14
70.	2	3	4	5	9	15	172.	5	6	8	12	14	15
71.	2	3	4	7	16	18	173.	5	6	9	10	16	18
72.	2	3	5	6	10	15	174.	5	6	9	13	16	17
73.	2	3	5	8	10	11	175.	5	6	11	13	15	17
74.	2	3	5	9	11	12	176.	5	6	12	14	16	18
75.	2	3	6	7	13	18	177.	5	7	9	11	16	17
76.	2	3	6	10	13	14	178.	5	7	9	15	16	18
77.	2	3	7	12	16	17	179.	5	7	10	13	15	18
78.	2	3	8	9	12	16	180.	5	8	9	10	11	14
79.	2	3	8	10	12	14	181.	5	8	9	10	13	18
80.	2	3	9	11	13	18	182.	5	8	10	12	14	17
81.	2	3	9	15	16	18	183.	5	9	10	11	12	16
82.	2	3	10	11	13	17	184.	5	9	10	12	13	17
83.	2	3	11	12	14	17	185.	5	11	12	15	16	18
84.	2	4	5	12	13	15	186.	6	7	9	12	14	15
85.	2	4	5	13	14	16	187.	6	7	9	13	15	16
86.	2	4	6	8	11	16	188.	6	7	10	11	17	18
87.	2	4	6	8	13	14	189.	6	7	13	15	17	18
88.	2	4	6	9	14	17	190.	6	8	10	16	17	18
89.	2	4	6	11	12	17	191.	6	8	11	14	16	18
90.	2	4	6	12	13	18	192.	6	9	10	11	12	15
91.	2	4	7	10	12	18	193.	6	9	10	11	14	18
92.	2	4	7	12	15	17	194.	6	10	11	12	13	17
93.	2	4	9	10	15	17	195.	6	12	13	16	17	18
94.	2	4	10	11	17	18	196.	7	8	10	13	15	16
95.	2	4	11	13	16	18	197.	7	8	10	14	16	17
96.	2	5	6	7	8	11	198.	7	9	12	15	17	18
97.	2	5	6	7	10	18	199.	7	10	11	12	13	16
98.	2	5	6	11	12	15	200.	7	10	11	12	15	18
99.	2	5	7	8	16	17	201.	8	9	11	14	16	17
100.	2	5	7	9	11	14	202.	8	11	12	13	14	17
101.	2	5	7	14	16	18	203.	8	11	12	13	16	18
102.	2	5	8	10	17	18	204.	9	12	13	14	17	18

To order the book in Canada, send a check for \$30.99

[\$ 26.99 (book price) + \$4.00 (shipping and handling)]

to the publisher's address given on the back of this page.

Add \$1.00 S+H for each additional book if more than one ordered.

All applicable taxes are included in the price.

Please see the back of this page for more information on ordering.

The publisher can be contacted at the e-mail address

lotbook@telus.net

The book can be ordered via the web-page

http://www3.telus.net/lotbook/

Ordering Information

All prices below are in US $.

Book price: $17.99

Shipping and handling:

- Add $2.70 if you are in Canada
- Add $4.50 if you are in the USA
- Add $6.00 if you are in Europe
- Add $7.00 if you are elsewhere
- Add $1.00 for each additional book if you order more than one

Please send check or money order to the following address:

Lotbook Publishing
1557 4th Avenue, Suite 1088
Prince George, B.C.
V2L 3K1 Canada

Order Form

Please send..........copies of the book to the following address

Name:...

Address line 1:..

Address line 2:..

Address line 3:..

Address line 4:..

Enclosed is a check (money order) for $................................